"And God said,
Let the waters bring forth abundantly
the moving creature that hath life...
And God created great whales,
and every living creature that moveth,
which the waters brought forth abundantly,
after their kind,...
and God saw that it was good."

Genesis 1:20-21

Children's Bible Activities, Stories, and Poems

Instructions

1. This book is for children ages 4-12 and is to be used along with the *Family Bible Lessons* book, which is written for all ages. There are 13 lessons for 13 weeks.

2. Notice the first page of this book. This is the lesson overview and it will appear at the beginning of each week's lesson. It is divided into four parts. The **top left** corner gives the Bible lesson number, title, references, and a hymn that can be used all through the week while you are studying this lesson. The **top right** corner tells about the nature topic. The **bottom left** states the character quality and its definition. The **bottom right** gives the verse(s) to be memorized.

3. The page after the lesson overview is the record page. There will be one after every lesson overview. This is where the children are to keep a record of each day during the week that they study their lesson and say their memory verse. This helps build a habit of consistent study and Scripture memorization.

4. At the bottom of most of the pages is a little note that says the day in which the activity, story, or poem is to be used. It looks like this: "(Day 1)" The day specified corresponds with the day listed in the *Family Bible Lessons* book. For each day there are usually 2 or more pages for the children. You will notice that some activities are very simple. These are for the young children while the more challenging ones are for those who are older. The stories and poems are for all!

Table of Contents

"He gathereth the waters
of the sea together
as an heap:
he layeth up the depth
in storehouses."

Psalm 33:7

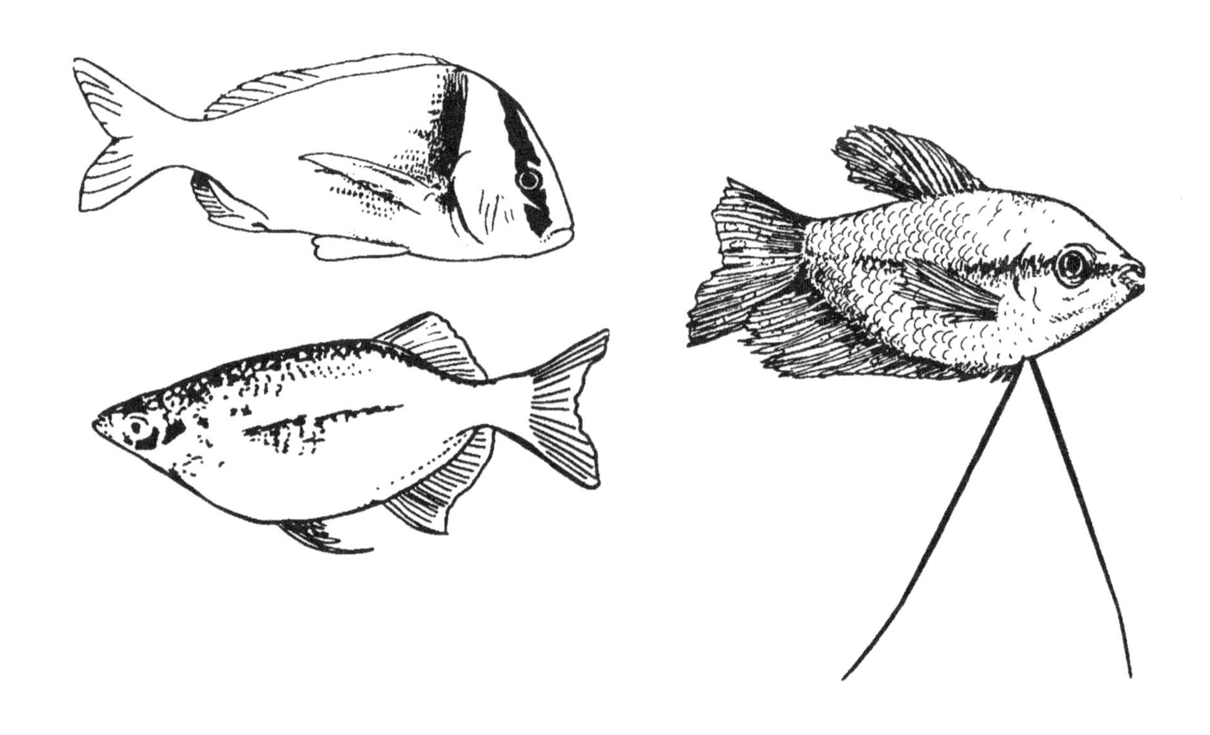

1 – Why Did Jesus Choose to Die?

Bible – Romans 3:23-25; 6:23; Acts 2:38; I John 3:4; Isaiah 53:5-6; John 3:16; Revelation 21:1-4

Song – "I Sing the Mighty Power of God"

Nature – Seas of the World

Character Quality

Unselfishness vs Greediness
Unselfishness is not being unduly attached to one's own interests but rather giving to God first and others second and self last.

Love vs Pride
Love is the foundation for all character qualities. It is giving without any expectation of receiving for self. See I Corinthians 13 and John 3:16.

Memory Verse

*"Beloved, if God so **loved** us, we ought also to **love** one another."*
I John 4:11

Seas of the World

"Ye are the salt of the earth."
God's people are to have a preserving influence
among the seas of people on this planet.
Without the example of their **unselfish love**,
humanity would "freeze up" through selfishness.

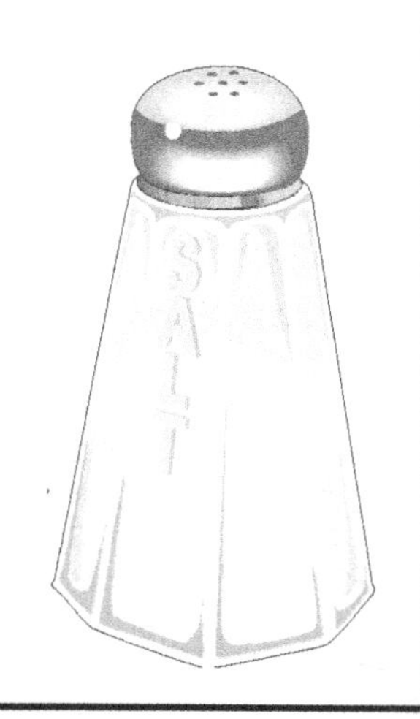

**Draw salt crystals above
for each day this week
you study your lesson,
and say your memory verse.**

"God With Us"

"His name shall be called

_ _ _ _ _ _ _ _...

God With Us."

See Isaiah 7:14; Matthew 1:23; and *The Desire of Ages* 19.

Fill in the blanks and color the letters and picture.

(Day 1)

Seas or Oceans

Read the thoughts below and color the pictures.

Before the Flood

"...The rivers had never yet
passed their boundaries,
but had borne their waters
safely to the sea.
Fixed decrees had kept the waters
from overflowing their banks."

After the Flood

"...The hills and mountains
were surrounded by a vast,
turbid sea."

(Day 1)

Giving

Read and color.

"It was Christ that spread the heavens, and laid the foundations of the earth...It was He that filled the earth with beauty, and the air with song. And upon all things in the earth, and air, and sky, He wrote the message of the Father's **love**...All things Christ received from God, but He took to give...So in the heavenly courts, in His ministry for all created beings: through the beloved Son, the Father's life flows out to all; through the Son it returns, in praise and joyous service, a tide of **love**, to the great Source of all."

Read Psalm 65:6, 95:5, John 8:28, 6:57, 8:50, and 7:18.

(Day 2)

The Ocean Gives

Review ways the ocean gives. Color this picture.

Nellie's Hard Mistress

I paid a visit to a friend's house last summer, and there I found a little slave. Her name was Nelly. She was white, and had blue eyes and golden curls. Nelly had a hard mistress to serve. From morning till night she was trying to please her every way she could think of; but the harder she tried, the worse it was. There was no pleasing her. She was dissatisfied with every thing Nelly did for her. I do not doubt many a night Nelly lay awake, planning something to please her; but it always ended in disappointment; and the worst of it was, she never let Nelly out of her sight. The poor little child was bound to her. "Oh, dear!" you say, "how dreadful!" Yes, it was dreadful, for the little girl never had a happy moment.

Where were her parents? Did she have any! Yes; she had a Father and Mother, and they lived in the same house. It was a fine house, with a great many beautiful things in it. Nelly had twin brothers, too, and a baby sister. They were not slaves. Nobody had this hard mistress but Nelly. She came into the house and took Nelly when she was quite small, so that now Nelly is completely under her. Her Mother grieves over it, and I dare say blames herself for letting it be, in the first place. But the chains are on her, and nobody seems to know how to break them and set the child free.

I ought to tell you at once the name of this cruel mistress, so that if she ever tries to entice you into her service, you may say, "No." Her name is *Self*. Quite likely you have seen her. Serving *"self"* makes Nelly do a great many mean things. While I was there, she took the big orange, leaving the small one to her cousin, two years older than herself.

Nelly has heard of the golden rule, but she never does to others as she would like it to be done to her. She keeps the swing for her *self*, and will only play what she wants to. If her playmates propose something else, Nelly pouts and goes off, or she tries to break up their games.

One day her mother left her little twin brothers in her care. She did not want to be called from her dolls, and therefore came very unwillingly. "Can't Aunt Jane see to them?" said Nelly, with a scowl on her brow. The mother looked very sorry; but Nelly did not mind that. I do not think the little boys were

(Day 2)

happy with her; for, not a great while after, Johnny began to cry, and I heard Charlie indignantly say, "Naughty girl! You bad."

Uncle Charles came. Uncle Charles was fond of the children, and always brought them presents. Almost as soon as he was in the house, Nelly went up to him, "Uncle Charles," she asked, "what have you got for me?" Wasn't that bad manners! I was quite ashamed of her. But *Self*, you know, thinks of nobody but "number one."

You must wait," said Uncle Charles. "Where are the twins?"

They had gone to ride. Uncle Charles, seeing Nelly's impatience, unlocked his trunk and took out a beautiful little workbox for her. It had thimble and scissors, a bodkin and winders, and a cunning knife; altogether it was as pretty a workbox as a little girl could have. Nelly hugged it tight, and looked over the contents all by her<u>self</u>.

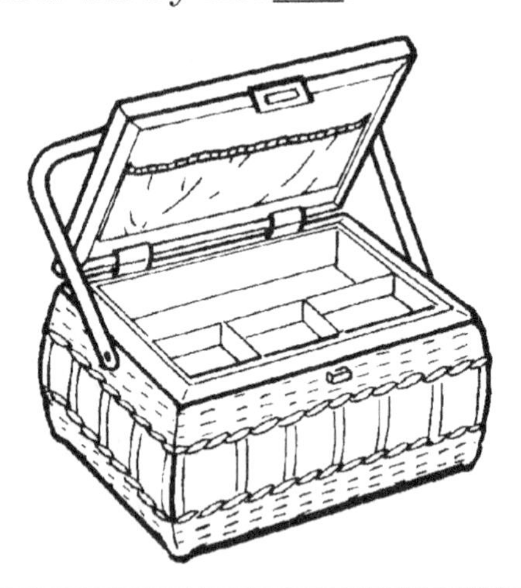

"Have you forgotten to thank kind Uncle Charles, Nelly?" asked her mother.

"Thank you," said Nelly, carelessly.

Pretty soon the twins came home, rosy cheeked, and happy as happy could be. "Let me kiss you, Uncle Charles," cried Charlie, running first. "I kiss too," cried Johnny. "Dear Uncle Charles, I your boy, too."

"What have you brought them?" Asked Nelly.

Uncle Charles went to his trunk and took out two small parcels. What did they contain? A silver cup with Charlie's name on it, and a silver cup with Johnny's name.

The moment Nelly saw the cups she ran out of the room, looking like a much-abused child. "I won't have this common, homely old box!" cried Nelly, as soon as she reached the dining-room. "I don't want it and I won't have it:" so she threw it violently on the floor. "O Nelly! Nelly!"

Her mother was grieved at her conduct, as she had often had cause to be before.

The saddest of all is that Nelly will grow up a stranger to **love**, and especially to her Saviour's precious **love**; for no one can be a follower of the Lord Jesus and a servant of *Self* at the same time. *"No man can serve two masters."*

O my children, *"choose ye this day whom ye will serve."* Not wicked *Self*, who will make you miserable for ever; but the dear Lord Jesus, whose yoke is easy, and whose burden is light, and whose ways are ways of pleasantness and peace.

—Carrier Dove

Color these items which might come from the workbox.

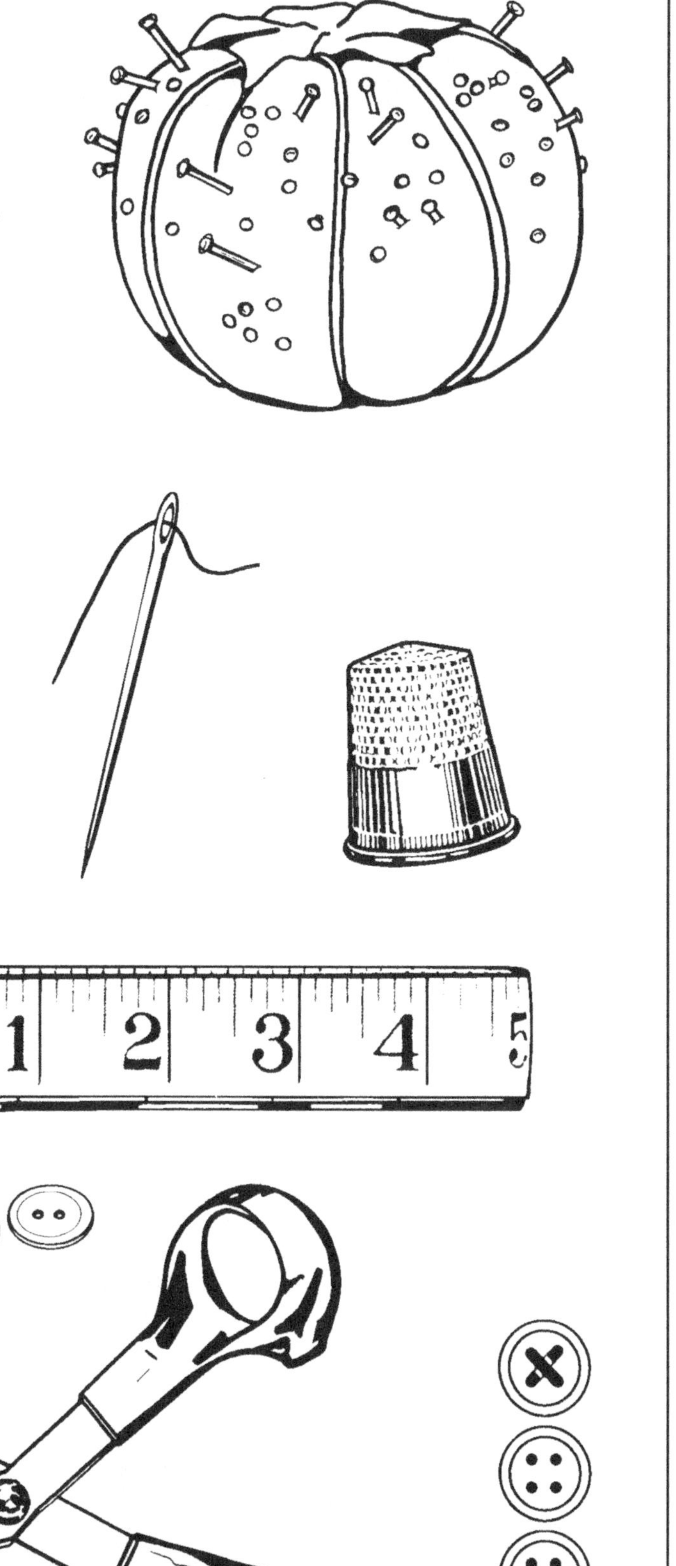

The Ocean's Ministry

Unselfishly the ocean takes
The rain that falls upon its breast;
And low, musical sounds it makes
To give the spirit of man sweet rest.

The ocean waves obey God still.
Their goings and comings are planned,
That they might fulfill His good will
In washing the shores of the land.

—Unknown

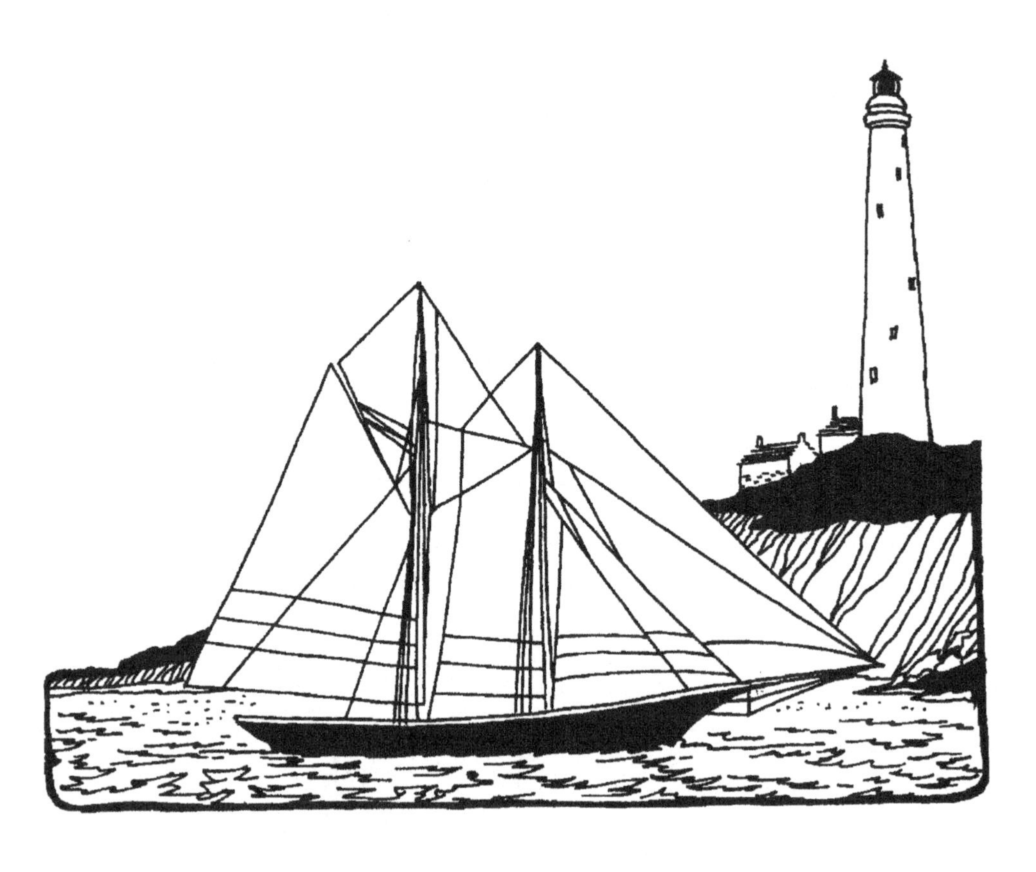

(Day 2)

God's Plan

(Day 3)

World Oceans (or Seas)

1. ______________

____

LATNICTA
CANOE

2. ______________

____

FICAIPC
NEAOC

3. ______________

____

DAINNI
ACNEO

Unscramble the words and write in the names of the three major oceans. What are the 4th & 5th largest oceans? Color the oceans on the world map a blue shade.

4. ______________ 5. ______________

(Day 3)

Law of Love

Answer these questions and fill in the blanks.

1. Who is the Friend of sinners?

2. How does Satan represent God's law?
What is God's law?

3. How does Jesus unveil this deception?

4. What does Hebrews 2:17 tell us?

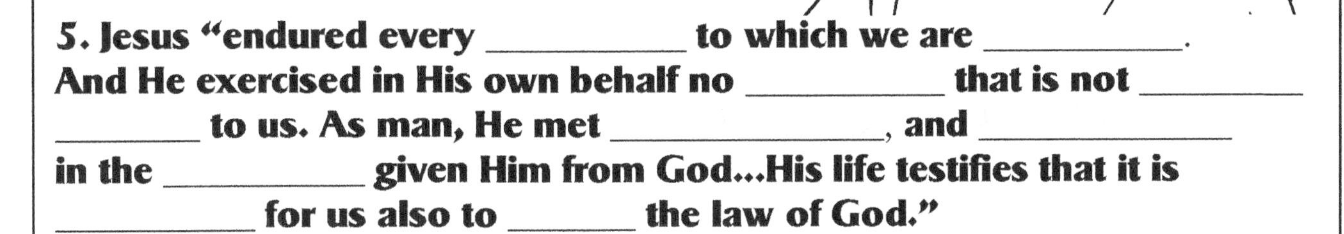

5. Jesus "endured every __________ to which we are __________. And He exercised in His own behalf no __________ that is not __________ __________ to us. As man, He met ______________, and ____________ in the __________ given Him from God...His life testifies that it is __________ for us also to _______ the law of God."

6. What does Psalm 40:8 say?

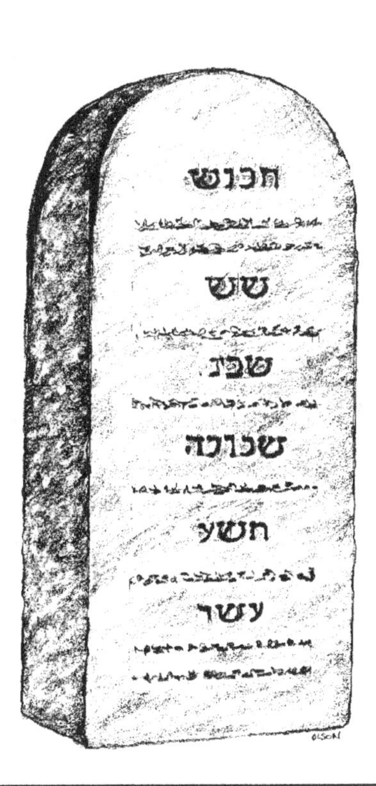

(Day 4)

Ocean Area and Depth

Answer these questions and color the picture.

1. How much of the world's oceans cover the earth's surface?

2. Where does God store water?

3. Who are God's law made for and why?

4. What does the ocean show man? How?
What Bible verse reminds us of this fact?
Is there bounds in your life?

5. Explain the depths of the ocean.

6. What else has great depth to it?

7. What are many islands in the ocean?

1.	5.
	6.
2.	7.
3.	8.
	9.
4.	10.

(Day 4)

Playing Like a Christian

I heard of two little children, a boy and a girl, who used to play a great deal together. They both became converted. One day the boy came to his Mother, and said, “Mother, I know that Emma is a Christian.”

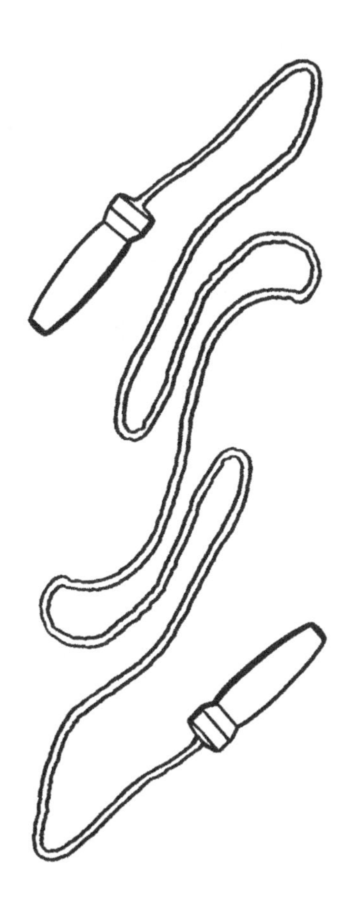

“What makes you think so, my child?”

“Because, Mother, she plays like a Christian.”

“Plays like a Christian?” said the Mother; the expression sounded a little odd.

“Yes,” replied the child,” if you take everything she’s got, she doesn’t get angry. Before, she was selfish; and if she didn’t have everything her own way, she would say, ‘I won’t play with you; you are an ugly little boy.’ ”

(Day 4)

Who Christ Is, And How He Lived on Earth

Jesus! how bright His glories shine!
The great IMMANUEL, all divine;
One with the Father He appears,
And all the Father's honor mirrors;
Yet He, to bring salvation dawn,
Has put our mortal nature on.
He in a humble virgin's tum
A feeble infant did become;
A stable was His lodging said,
And the rude manger was His bed.
Growing in life, He still was seen
Humble, laborious, poor, and keen;
The Son of God, from year to year,
Did as a carpenter appear.
At length, when he to preach was sent,
Through towns and villages He went,
And travell'd with unwearied zeal
God's will and nature to reveal.
To prove the heavenly truths He taught,
Unnumbered miracles were wrought.
The blind beheld Him, and the ear
Which had been deaf, His voice could hear;
Sickness obey's His healing hand,
And devils fled at His command;
The lame for joy around Him leap;
The dead he wakens from their sleep.
Through all His life His doctrine shines,
Drawn in the plainest, fairest lines;
And death at length did he sustain,
Our pardon and our peace to gain;
That sinners, who condemned stood,
Might find salvation in His blood.
All honor then ascribed be,
To Him who lived and died for me!

—Adapted from Unknown Author

(Day 4)

Fashioned as a Man

"And being found in fashion as a man, he humbled himself, and became obedient unto death, even the death of the cross."
Philippians 2:8

Answer these questions

1. What was Satan's purpose in Christ's death? but what happened?

2. Through the eternal ages what happens to our relationship with Christ?

3. What names is Jesus called in Isaiah 9:6?

4. What does Hebrews 7:26 and 2:11 tell us?

5. What happens when we are in Christ?

6. Finish this statement: "Christ __________ is our __________."

"Heaven is enshrined in humanity, and humanity is enfolded in the bosom of Infinite Love."
The Desire of Ages 26

(Day 5)

Opposite Characters

Which words describe

Christ	**or**	**Satan**

love

pride

taking

giving

hate

humbleness

joy

obedience

discord

unselfishness

disobedience

selfishness

"In stooping to take upon himself humanity, Christ revealed a character the opposite of the character of Satan."
The Desire of Ages 25

Use a ruler and draw a line from the words to the right picture that describes either Christ or Satan.

Learn the song on the next 3 pages, *"Beauty for Ashes."*

(Day 5)

Beauty for Ashes

"By His life and His death, Christ has achieved even more than recovery from the ruin wrought through sin. It was Satan's purpose to bring about an eternal separation between God and man; but in Christ we become more closely united to God than if we had never fallen.

In Christ the family of earth and the family of heaven are bound together. Christ glorified is our brother. Heaven is enshrined in humanity, and humanity is enfolded in the bosom of Infinite Love." DA 25, 26

He suf-fered death which was ours, that we might re- ceive the
life which was His. 1.By His life and His death He is bound to us by a
2.(And) in Christ earth & heav-en....are bound to- geth- er and en-
tie that can nev-er be bro-ken."
fold-ed in the bos- om of love."
1
2
"Beau- ty for ash- es, the
oil of joy for mourn- ing, the gar- ment of praise for the
Beauty for Ashes - page 2

spir-it of heav-i-ness; that they might be called trees of right-eous-ness" right-eous-ness."
Coda
(And) in Christ earth & heav-en are bound to-geth-er, and en-fold- ed in the
bos- om of in- fi- nite love........"
Beauty for Ashes - page 3

Ocean Temperatures

Answer these questions using the key below.

1. The oceans cover ____________ percent of the earth's surface.

2. Most of the water is found ______________ of the equator.

3. The ocean is called a storehouse in which Bible text?

4. Which is the largest ocean?

5. The largest ocean contains ______________ of the world's water.

6. What is the average depth of the ocean?

7. Where is the ocean the warmest?

8. Where is the ocean the coldest?

9. At the floor of the ocean the temperature stays between __________.

10. Only Christ can deliver us from the ____________ of sin.

Key

poles	south	70	Psalm 33:7
12,200 feet (3,730 meters)	Pacific Ocean	one half	34°– 39° F. (1°– 4° C.)
equator	depths		

(Day 5)

Work of Redemption

"Sin can never again
enter the universe.
Through eternal ages
all are secure
from apostasy.
By love's self-sacrifice,
the inhabitants
of earth and heaven
are bound to their Creator
in bonds
of indissoluble union."

The Desire of Ages 26

Memorize these thoughts from The Desire of Ages.

(Day 6)

God of Love

Read the message below after filling in the blanks.

"By ______'______ ______—______,

the inhabitants of ______ and ______

are ______ to their Creator in ______

of indissoluble (cannot be broken) ______."

Key

A B C D E F G H I J K L M

N O P Q R S T U V W X Y Z

(Day 6)

Unselfishly Bear One Another's Burdens

How often is the happiness of many a well-meaning couple marred by their forgetfulness of the duty enjoined upon us, to *"bear one another's burdens, and so fulfill the law of Christ!"*

How often, when John comes home from work a little "put out" because things have not gone quite smoothly at the workshop, or Sally is just a wee bit out of temper because the children have been rather more troublesome than usual. How often, we say, in such a case, instead of gentle words to make things pleasant, some such remark as they indulged in: "Why, how cross you are tonight!" This leads to the retort: "I'm not cross a bit; it's you that are always trying to make a body angry."

One word of course brings on another, and a most uncomfortable evening they spend, you may be sure.

Now, we know a couple with whom this difficulty not infrequently occurred, and very wretched for the time it made them. But they were really very fond of one another, and had more common sense than many people we have met with. What wonder, then, that they could put their heads together, and try to find some means by which this state of things could be gotten over with?

They did, and now we will tell you the experiment they tried, and what was the result. It was agreed between them that if things had gone unpleasantly with John during the day, when he came home he was to wear his cap a little on one side, and Sally then must do her very best to make all smooth at home. If, on the contrary, her temper had been ruffled by little household troubles in the day, a corner of her apron was to be tucked up on John's return, and he was then to be more amiable than usual.

"Bear ye one another's burdens, and so fulfill the law of Christ."
Galatians 6:2

(Day 6)

The plan was tried, and answered the need admirably; many a pleasant evening was enjoyed, which otherwise would have been passed in great discomfort. At last they found themselves in this dilemma. One evening John returned with his cap immensely on one side, and what was his dismay on entering the house to find that Sally's apron was also tucked up! Now, what was to be done? Whose duty was it to give way and try and make things pleasant for the other? The difficulty lasted only for a moment. Looking at each other strangely, they both burst out into a hearty laugh. John gave his wife a long and **loving** kiss, and they have since been heard to say it was one of the happiest evenings they ever spent.

More than this, that every night, we have good cause to know, they lifted up their hearts together in thanks to Him to enabled them to overcome the wicked one, and that He would ever keep them steadfast in their **love** to Him, and to each other; and now we are sure that for many miles around there is not a happier couple to be met than John and Sally.

Composition

1. Six main elements of the ocean are:

1. ______________________	LIDROECH
2. ______________________	DUMSIO
3. ______________________	FULURS
4. ______________________	GENSIMUAM
5. ______________________	CILACUM
6. ______________________	TAMUSISOP

2. Which two elements above make up table salt?

1. 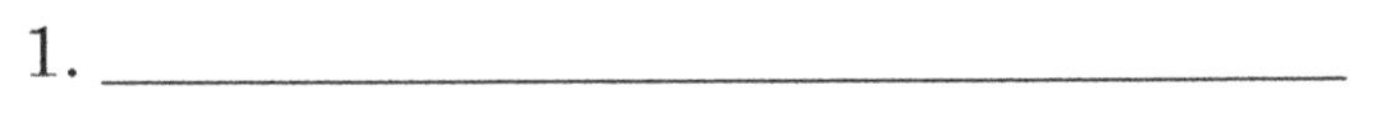

2. 

3. Which two elements make up God's kingdom?

1. 	NESFELSUNSIHS
2. ______________________	VOLE

4. What is the ocean known for? ______________________

Read Matthew 5:13

(Day 6)

Self-sacrificing
Love
Most salts come to the ocean
by the wearing away
of rocks on land.
These can be carried by rivers
to the oceans.
Patient, unselfish, self-sacrificing love
can wear down the resistance
of the hardest heart.
Read and color
this picture of the ocean.
(Day 6)

Unselfish Love

Selfish adults and children always want the best for themselves. They like to fare better than all the rest. At a party they always scramble for the best places; at dinner they always cry out for the biggest serving. If you offer them an apple—they choose the largest on the plate; a toy—they choose the very best one; a book—they choose the most attractive one. They never leave the best for anyone else. Their selfishness makes them try to grab all the good things for themselves. We cannot all have the best things, and we should be willing to give other people a turn.

It is said of Frederick Denison Maurice, who was a preacher and teacher, that his sweet disposition was conspicuous even in his childhood. Generosity seemed as natural to him as selfishness to other children. One day, when he was five ears old, he came into the family room with a biscuit in one hand and a flower in the other. A gentleman who was present said to Frederick's mother, "Now we will see what he likes best; children always give up what they least care for." Then turning to the child, he said, "Frederick, which will you give me—the flower or the biscuit?" "Choose which you like," answered the boy, holding out both his hands. That was a right and **unselfish** spirit. He was willing that another should choose the best. Be a boy or girl after that fashion.

Selfish people always keep their good things to themselves. Sometimes their motto is "Get all you can, and keep all you can." There is a story about a King Alfred. The story tells how often he was in sore straits when pursued by the Danes, and at one time was brought so low that he and the queen had only a single loaf of bread. That day a poor man came and knocked at the door and asked for charity. "We have only got one loaf; it is not enough for ourselves," said the queen. But King Alfred replied, "Give him half of it; he is a Christian." And they gave him half. How much nobler it is to go shares, like the king, then to stick to what you have got. Make it a rule to go shares with your pleasures and comforts and possessions. Do not keep them all to yourselves, but give some of them away. Do not be greedy but **unselfish**.

Selfish people are careless of the needs of others. The Bible text tells us, *"...They all look to their own way, every one for his gain, from his quarter* (Isaiah 56:11). They never put themselves out to help the needy. So, too, selfish men, women, and children are absorbed in their own aims and pursuits, and deaf to the cry, blind to the sorrow, regardless of the needs of their less fortunate brethren. They always say, "Take care of number one" their ruling principle in life. Jesus Christ teaches us to give up our own pleasure, to sacrifice our own ease, to set aside our own desires, and by so doing we can help or bless another. A gentleman was waiting one evening outside the railway station at Leeds, when a raged, dirty boy came up to him with "Buy an evening paper, sir. Please do, good Sir. Only seven left, and they's all my profit." He had a right honest face; but he was ragged and wet, and the gentleman said, "Why, boy, you have no cap on this rainy night. Have you no cap to wear?" Yes, sir," was the reply, "I'se got a cap, but I lent it to my sister." "Where is she?" "Over there, sir, in

(Day 6)

that old doorway, waiting till I sell out." "But she has no cap on, my lad; where is it?" "Oh, sir, she's got no boots or stockings, so I told her to put her feet inside my cap to keep 'em warm, and prevent her ketchin' a cold. Have a paper, sir, please: 'twouldn't hurt you to buy the lot.' You may be sure he did not plead in vain. What a brave, **unselfish**, generous hero he was! He did not think of himself at all; he only thought of his little sister; and he was quite willing to stand bareheaded in the pouring rain so that her feet might be kept cosy and warm. What a happy world this would be if all had this **unselfish love** for others.

Jesus Christ thought not of Himself when He left heaven for earth, and lived, toiled, and died for poor and sinful men. His heart was full of **unselfish love**, and He laid down His life for the sake of others. then let us pray and strive to be like HIM. It is shameful to be a selfish and greedy person. It is Christlike to be **unselfish**, generous, and **loving**: nor could higher praise be given!

Selfishness

"Please, Betty," says young Tommy,
"One little bite for me;
The cake is such a big one,
And full as it can be
Of plums that would taste splendid
To such a boy, you see."

"No, no," says selfish Betty,
"This cake is very nice,
I cannot let you have a bit
Of it at any price.
My mamma knows how much I need,
She gave me all the slice."

"Then eat it," says wise Tommy,
"I know 'twill make you sick,
And I shall be revenged on you
In that way very quick;
For too much cake will punish you
As surely as a stick."

"And, Betty, you will learn at last,
What all learn soon or late,
That only sad unhappiness
On selfishness can wait;
For kindly angels never come
To children through that gate."

—*Unknown*

Discuss this story-poem starting with these questions.

Who all were selfish?
Did both children have some selfish traits?
Should Betty have shared with Tommy?
Would it be wise to eat something that might make you sick?
Could Tommy have shared something more healthful with Betty?

2 – By the Sea

Bible – John 21:1-22

Song – "Jesus Saviour, Pilot Me"

Nature – The Importance of the Sea

Character Quality

Forgiveness vs Condemnation
Forgiveness is the act of pardon of an offender, by which he is considered and treated as not guilty as God **forgives** us.

Memory Verse

"And Jesus came and spake unto them,
saying, All power is given unto me
in heaven and in earth.
Go ye therefore, and teach all nations,
baptizing them in the name
of the Father, and of the Son,
and of the Holy Ghost:
Teaching them to observe all things
whatsoever I have commanded you:
and, lo, I am with you alway,
even unto the end of the world. Amen."
Matthew 28:18-20

OR

*"But there is **forgiveness** with thee,*
that thou mayest be feared."
Psalm 130:4

The Importance of the Sea

Each person born into this world
has to make a voyage over the sea called life.

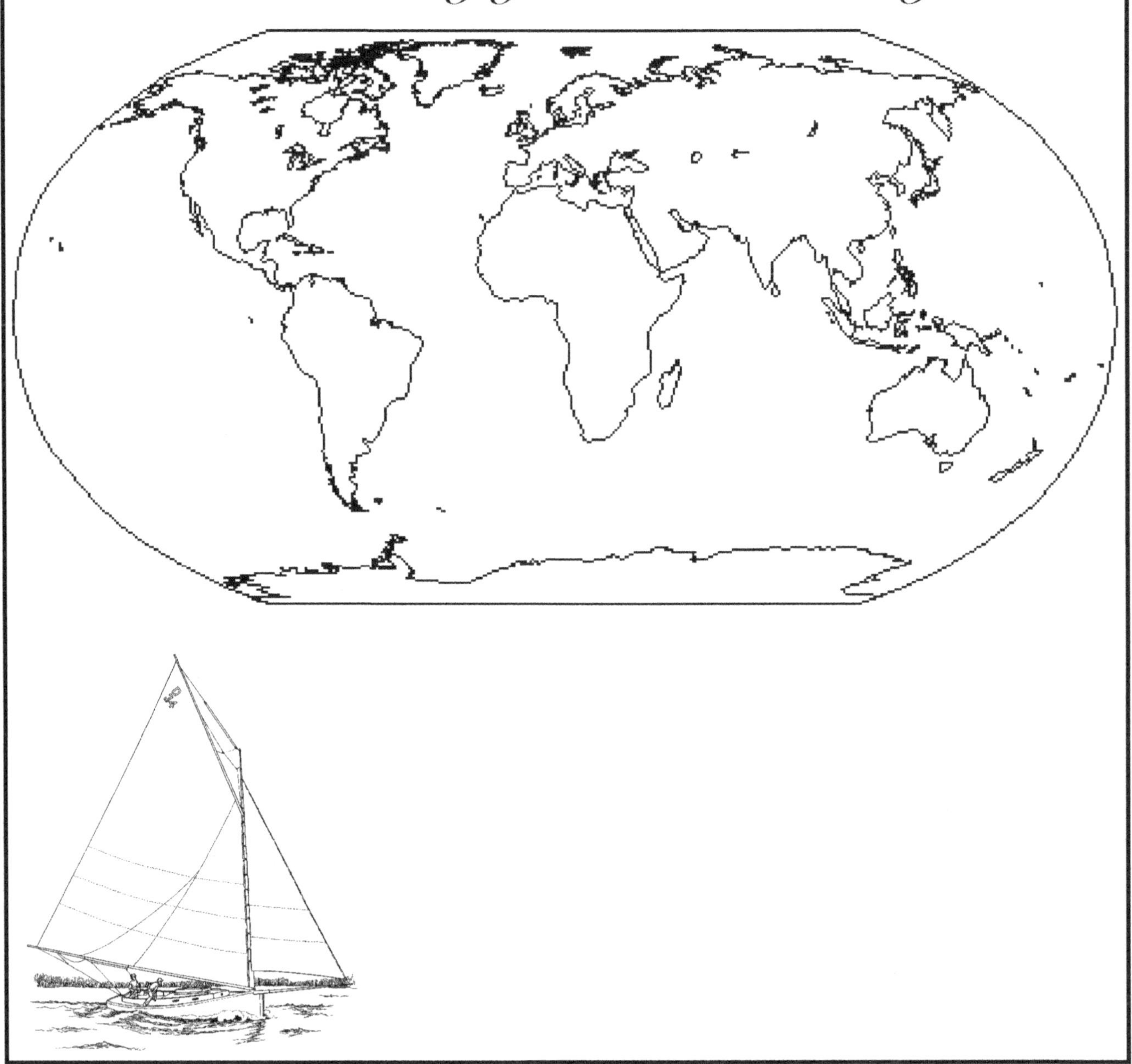

Place a boat seal on the ocean
for each day this week
you study your lesson,
and say your memory verse.

The Sea of Galilee

Answer these questions:

1. Describe the disciples' appearance when going to meet Jesus.

2. The meeting between Jesus and His disciples was to take place at the ____________ of ________________.

3. Can you think of other stories in the Bible that took place at or on the water?

Color this picture by the sea.

(Day 1)

Importance of the Sea

The Sea provides:

1. _ _ _ _

2. _ _ _ _ _ _

3. _ _ _ _ _ _ _

4. influences the _ _ _ _ _ _ _

5. _ _ _ _ _ _ _ _ _ _ _ _ _ _

If you cannot write draw the answers in this space above.

(Day 1)

Fishing

Read and color.

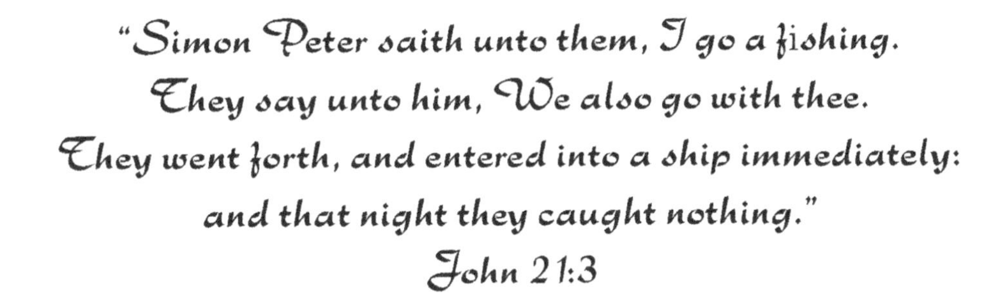

"Simon Peter saith unto them, I go a fishing.
They say unto him, We also go with thee.
They went forth, and entered into a ship immediately:
and that night they caught nothing."
John 21:3

Reread John 21:4-6 from the Bible.

(Day 2)

Ocean Energy

The ocean
has several forms
of energy!

Who is the One
who posses all energy?

They are:

P________________

N____________ ______

P_________ _________

E________________

How did
He demonstrate it
in today's lesson?

What did it symbolize?

Another kind of energy:

J__________'

E_________

(Day 2)

Eva Sundown

Sue was an Indian girl but she love Jesus; and nothing grieved her so much as to displease him.

"Eva," said the teacher one day, "will you sweep the schoolhouse for me tonight?"

"Yes, ma'am" said she very cheerfully; and so Eva was left alone in the deserted schoolroom.

Having occasion to return, what was the teacher's surprise to find the broom lying on the floor and little Eva sobbing violently.

"What is the matter, my dear child?" said she, anxiously.

She hid her face in Miss A's dress, but could not speak. At last she said, "Oh, I have been so wicked!"

"Why, Eva, what have you done?"

"Oh, I don't love Jesus enough," sobbed the child. "I looked mad at some girls today!"

"Did you strike them?"

"No."

"Nor speak unkind words to them?"

"Oh! No, no; but I looked mad. I was very angry in my heart, and I'm afraid Jesus never can **forgive** me.

She could not be comforted until they knelt and asked Jesus to **forgive** His little child her sin.

When they arose from prayer her face was radiant with a sense of pardoned sin.

That Indian girl knew that Jesus looks at the heart even of a little child.

(Day 2)

A Child's Humble Confession and Prayer

A sinner, Lord, behold I stand,
In thought, and word, and deed;
But Jesus sits at Thy right hand,
For such to intercede.

From early infancy, I know,
A rebel I have been,
And daily as I older grow,
I fear I grow in sin;

But God can change this evil heart,
And give a holy mind,
And His own heavenly grace impart,
Which those who seek shall find.

To heaven can reach the softest word—
A child's repenting prayer—
For tears are seen, and sighs are heard,
And thoughts regarded, there.

Then let me all my sins confess,
And pardoning grace implore;
That I may love my follies less,
And love my Saviour more.

—Unknown

(Day 2)

The Voice of the Lord is Upon The Waters

A lonely spot, with nothing more
Than rocks and winds and waves, half-veiled in fog;
The place a might poem, grandly wrought,
In handwriting of God.

Against the rocks upon the shore,
The surging waters of the ocean beat,
While, in unnumbered voices, solemnly,
*"Deep calleth unto deep."**

One Gull, above the lonely waves,
Whose tossing spray his weary efforts mocks,
Dips his white wing beneath the brine, then sinks
To rest upon the rocks.

God's *"voice is..."* on *"the waters"*** dark;
It sounds above the wintry waves, and breathes
Among the pines upon the cliff's proud crest,
And whispers in the breeze.

The roar of billows on the rocks
Voices the power of God; but in reply,
His tender love and mercy echo forth
In the lone sea-gull's cry.

—*Unknown*

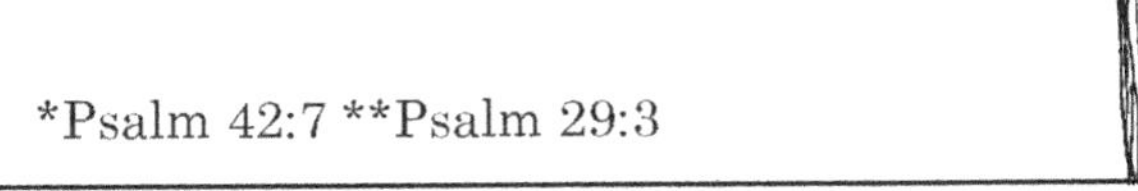

*Psalm 42:7 **Psalm 29:3

(Day 2)

Casting Nets

"Cast your net on the right side of the ship,

the side of faith."

7 Testimonies 213

(Day 2)

Breaking Bread

Fill the net with lots of fish seals or draw them.

"And he said unto them,
Cast the net on the right side of the ship, and ye shall find.
They cast therefore, and now they were not able to draw it
for the multitude of fishes"
John 21:6

(Day 3)

Minerals From the Sea

S______________ and g____________ are mined from the sea

floor and contain v______________ minerals. **F**_________________

is a valuable character quality.

Fill in the words above then use the key to fill in the blanks below. Read the message.

"_____ _____ _____ _____ _____ _____
18 28 29 36 4 27

_____ _____ _____ _____ _____ _____ _____
10 11 12 23 2 37 9

_____. _____ _____ _____ _____ _____ _____ _____
25 17 16 32 19 22 13 30

_____ _____ _____ _____, _____ _____ _____ _____
7 35 34 15 1 31 20 5

_____ _____ _____ _____ _____ _____
33 24 14 38 6 21

_____ _____ _____."
8 26 3

Key

1. and
2. as
3. brethren
4. can
5. cannot
6. creating
7. draws
8. for
9. **forgive**
10. **forgiveness**
11. from
12. God
13. God
14. hearts
15. Him
16. is
17. It
18. Jesus
19. love
20. love
21, love
22. of
23. only
24. others'
25. others
26. our
27. receive
28. teaches
29. that
30. that
31. that
32. the
33. touch
34. unto
35. us
36. we
37. we
38. without

(Day 3)

The Commission ("To Send")

The stories of Jesus' life in the Bible can remind us today how Jesus takes care of us daily that we may become "Fishers of Men."

1. What did these words bring to the disciples' minds?
   "Jesus saith unto them, Come and dine...."

2. Being by the sea once more brought other memories to the disciples which were ______________________________.

3. What other story did the experience in John 21:2-6 remind the disciples about in their earlier experiences with Jesus?

4. What does the word "commission" mean?

(Day 4)

Other Uses of the Ocean

Answer these questions:

1. What are other special things found in the ocean? Color pictures.

2. Fill in the blanks below to answer question number one.

3. Give some examples of spiritual lessons from the answer of question number one.

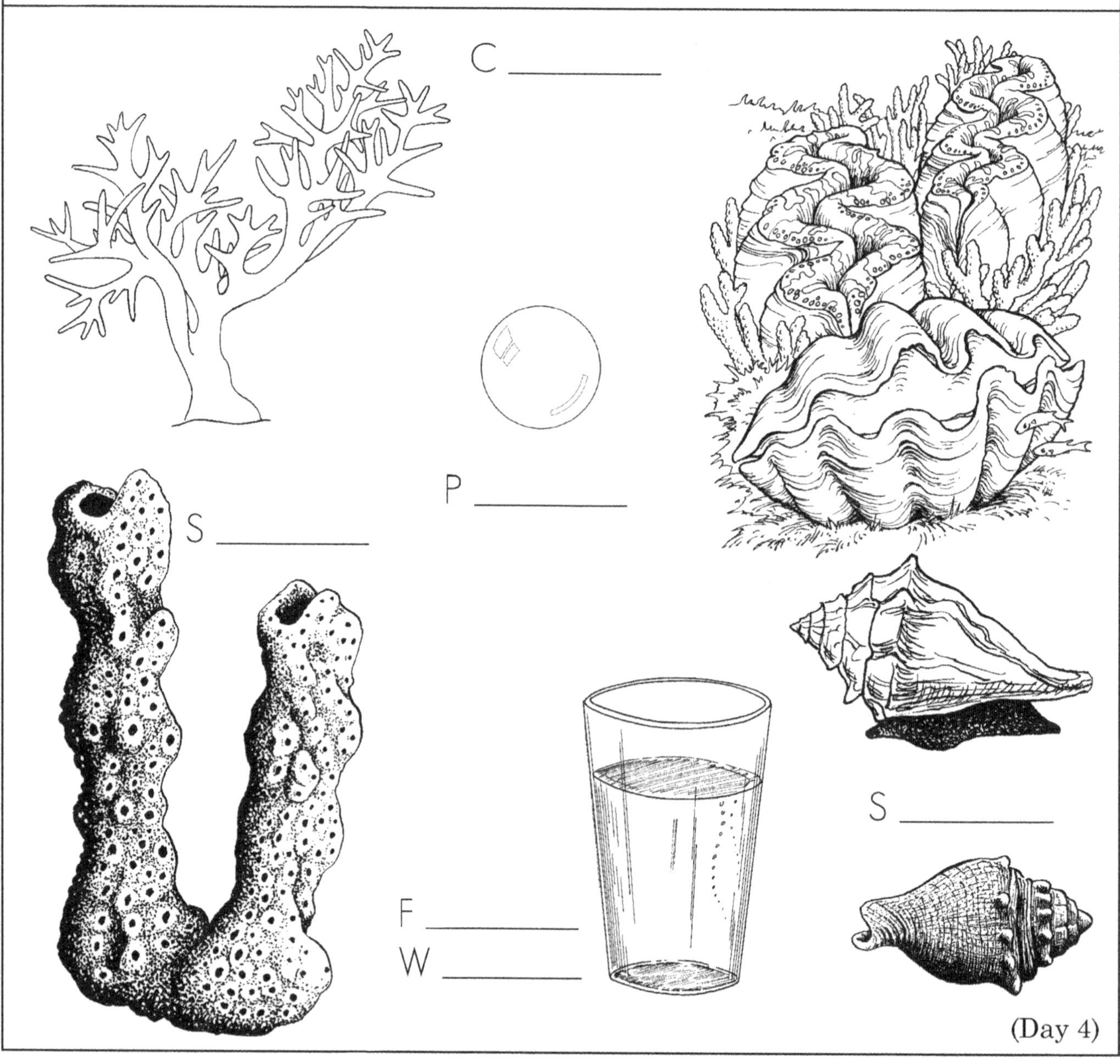

(Day 4)

Forgiving Others

"And forgive us our debts
as we forgive our debtors."
Matthew 6:12

A story is told of a certain nobleman of Alexandria, who complained bitterly to the bishop about his enemies. While in the midst of his tale, the bell sounded for prayers; and the bishop and the nobleman dropped on their knees–the former leading in the Lord's Prayer. When the bishop came to the petition, *"Forgive us our trespasses,"* he stopped suddenly, leaving the other to go on alone. The nobleman attempted to continue; but, startled by the sound of his unaccompanied voice, and recalled by his companion's silence to the significance of the petition, he stammered, ceased praying, and rose from his knees. It is an easy thing to say, *"Forgive us our trespasses,"* but it is difficult sometimes to say it understandingly. If we stop at this petition, when we are repeating the Lord's Prayer, until we have fully entered into the spirit of it, how many of us will always go on?

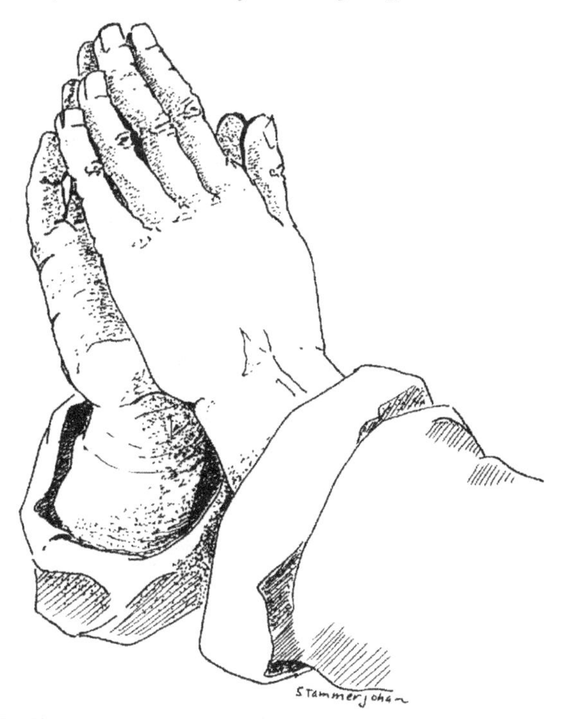

(Day 4)

FORGIVENESS

Lord, I have dar'd to disobey
My friends on earth, and Thee in heav'n'
O help me now to come and pray,
For Jesus sake to be **forgiven**.

I cannot say I did not know,
For I've been taught Thy holy will;
And while my conscience told me so,
And bid me stop, I did it still.

But Thou was there to see my crime,
And write it in Thy judgment book,
O make me fear another time,
A sinful thought, or word, or look.

Forgive me, Lord; **forgive**, I pray,
This naughty thing that I have done;
And take my sinful heart away,
And make me holy like Thy Son.

—Unknown

(Day 4)

Peter's Denial

Read this verse.

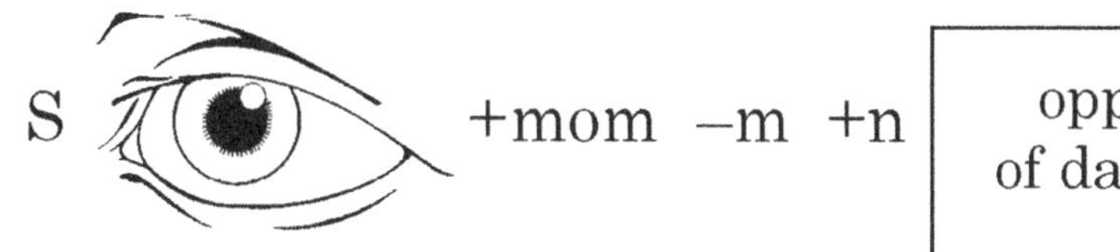

S +mom –m +n opposite of daughter of Jonas,

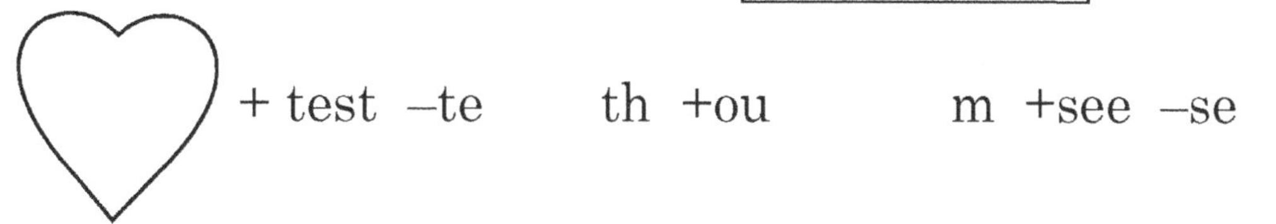

+ test –te th +ou m +see –se

core –c +m th +an the +see –e? . . .

Fee +d m ."

John 21:15

How many times did Jesus ask Peter this question?

____________________ times

(Day 5)

Children are sometimes referred to as lambs.
Color this picture and think about today's lesson.
(Day 5)

The Ocean Influences Our Climate

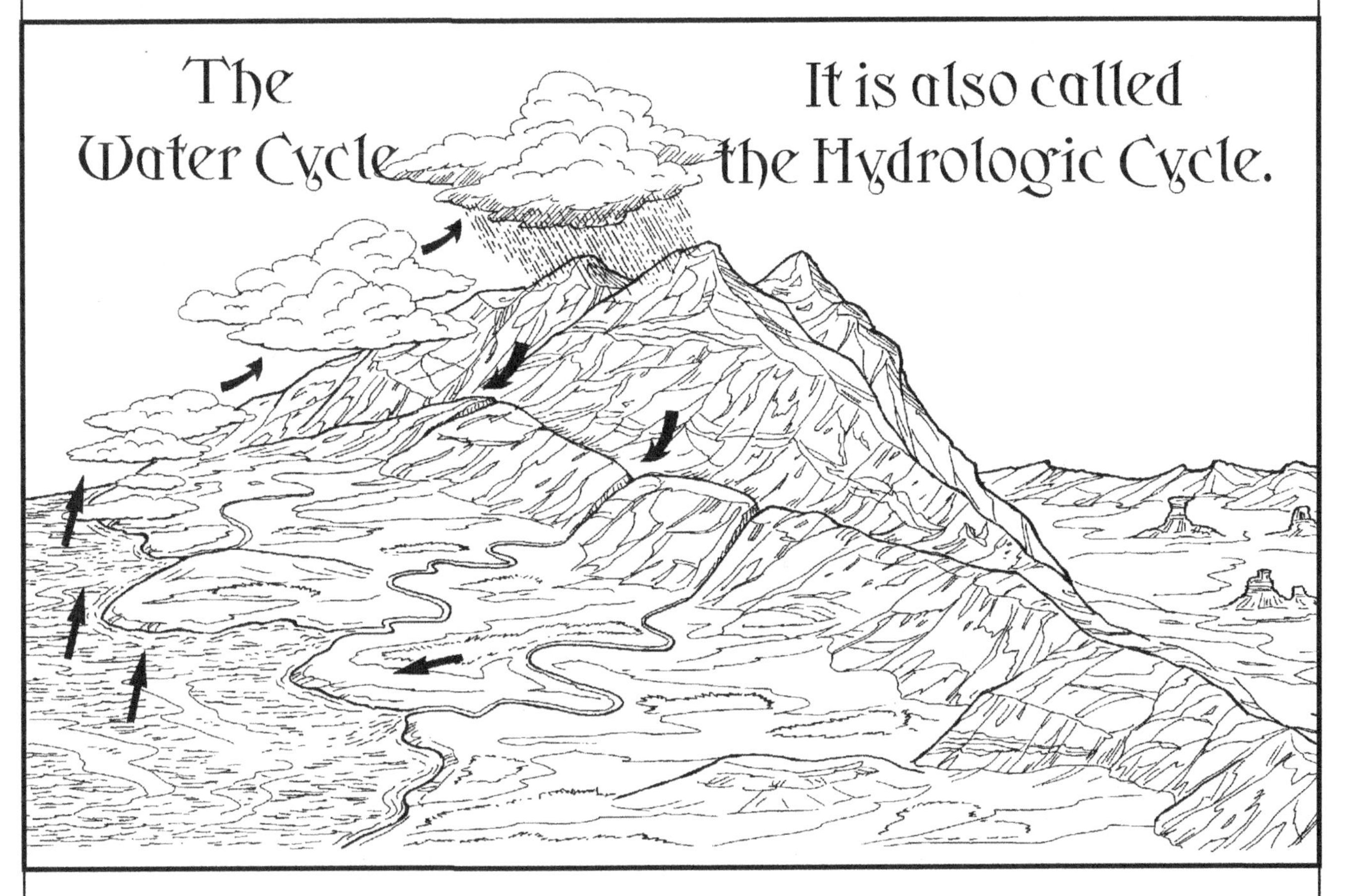

Write out a spiritual lesson using the picture above or tell your teacher in your own words.

(Day 5)

Water
Read then color.
God's forgiveness draws us to Him.
Jesus was drawing Peter closer
to Himself, like water is drawn up
into the air to form clouds.
He had forgiven him.
"I have blotted out as a thick cloud,
thy transgressions, and, as a cloud,
thy sins" (Isaiah 44:22).
Peter, in turn, was to water
the lambs and sheep giving back
what he had received.
(Day 5)

Peter's Future

"Verily, verily, I say unto thee, When thou wast young, thou girdest thyself, and walkedst whither thou wouldest: but when thou shalt be old, thou shalt stretch forth thy hands and another shall gird thee, and carry thee whither thou wouldest not."
John 21:18

What did these words mean that Jesus spake to Peter? End at the cross.

(Day 6)

Transportation

1. Can you identify these ships? List them below in the blanks.

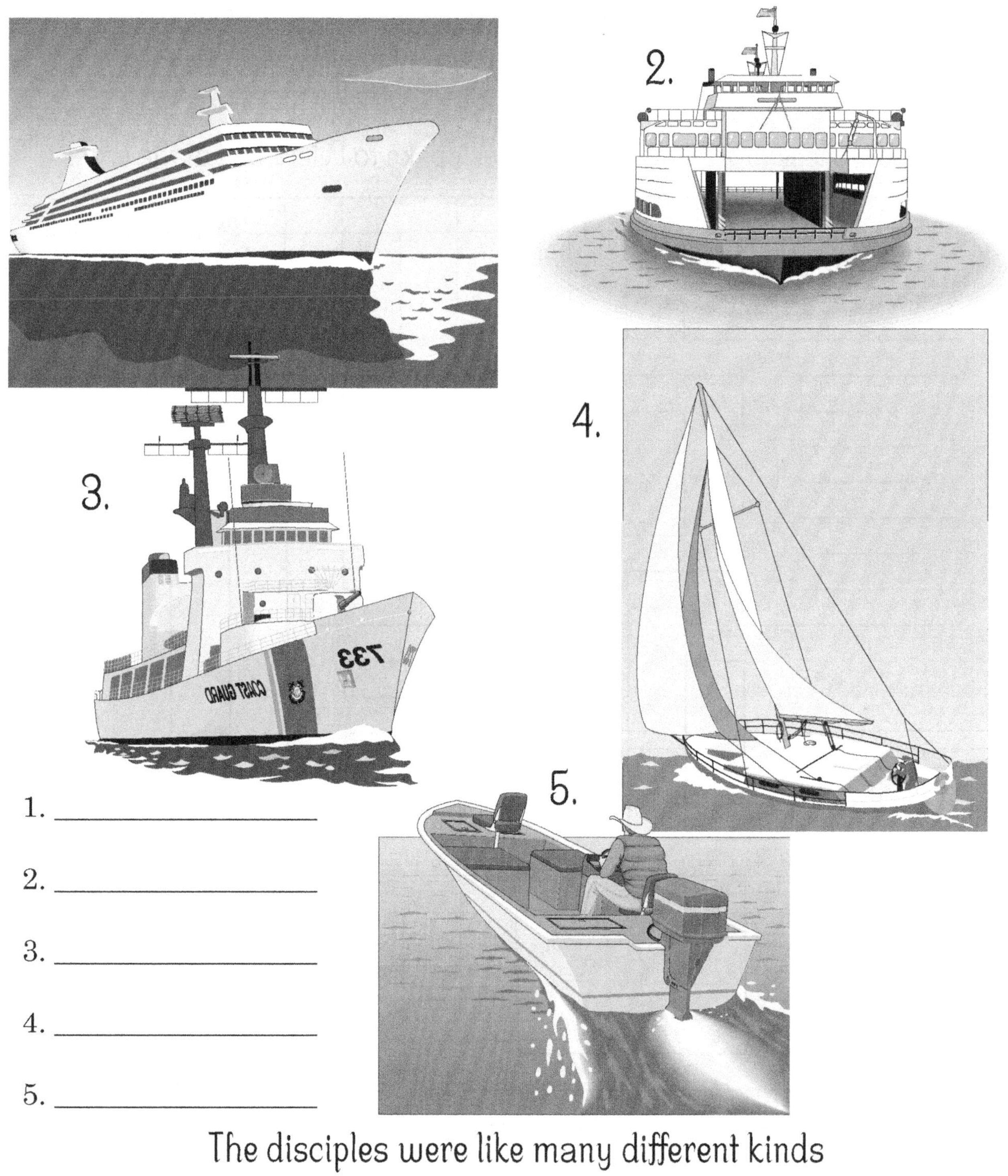

1. ____________________

2. ____________________

3. ____________________

4. ____________________

5. ____________________

The disciples were like many different kinds of ships and boats, each doing a different work.

(Day 6)

The Signal

(Forgiveness)

The young, young man sat alone on the bus and most of the time stared out the window. He was in his mid-twenties, nice looking with a kind face. His dark blue shirt matched the color of his eyes. His hair was short and neat. Occasionally he would look away from the window and the anxiety on his young face touched the heart of the grandmotherly woman sitting across the aisle. The bus was just approaching the outskirts of a small town when she was so drawn to the young man that she scooted across the aisle and asked permission to sit next to him.

After a few moments of small talk about the warm spring weather, he blurted out, "I've been in prison for two years. I just got out this morning and I'm going home." His words tumbled out as he told her he was raised in a poor but proud family and how his crime had brought his family shame and heartbreak. In the whole two years he had not heard from them. He knew they were too poor to travel the distance to where he had been in prison and his parents probably felt too uneducated to write. He had stopped writing them when no answers came.

Three weeks before being released, he desperately wrote one more letter to his family. He told them how sorry he was for disappointing them and asked for their **forgiveness**.

He went on to explain about being released from prison and that he would take the bus to his hometown—the one that goes right by the front yard of the house where he grew up and where his parents still lived. In his letter, he said he would understand if they wouldn't **forgive** him.

He wanted to make it easy for them and so asked them to give him a signal that he could see from the bus. If they had **forgiven** him and wanted him to come back home, they could tie a white ribbon on the old apple tree that stood in the front yard. If the signal wasn't there, he wold stay on the bus, leave town and be out of their lives forever.

As the bus neared his street, the young man became more and more anxious to the point he was afraid to look out the window because he was so sure there would be no ribbon.

(Day 6)

After listening to his story, the woman asked simply, "Would it help if we traded seats and I'll sit near to the window and look for you?" The bus traveled a few more blocks and then she saw the tree. She gently touched the young man's shoulder and choking back tears said, "Look! Oh look! The whole tree is covered with white ribbons."

Forgiving

"Then came Peter to him, and said, Lord,
how oft shall my brother sin against me,
and I forgive him? till seven times?

The Christian way, if one has done us an injury, is to go to him in the spirit of love and talk the matter over with him. Perhaps it is all a misunderstanding, needing only a word of explanation. We are probably as much to blame as the other person is when things go wrong between us and another.

"There is so much bad in the best of us,
And so much good in the worst of us,
That it hardly behooves any of us
To talk about the rest of us."

Our **forgiving** is to be unlimited. The rabbis taught that no one should **forgive** another more than three times. Peter thought he was making the limit great enough when he suggested that the Master's followers should **forgive** seven times. but Jesus swept away all counting of times, and said a Christian should **forgive** seventy times seven times.

How did Jesus show Peter He had **forgiven** him for denying Him?

See The Desire of Ages 811:2-812:2.

"The Saviour's manner
of dealing with Peter
had a lesson for him and
for his brethren.
It taught them to meet
the transgressor
with patience, sympathy,
and forgiving love...."

The Desire of Ages 815:1

3 – Jesus Returns to Heaven

Bible – John 21:1-22; Acts 1; I Corinthians 15:3, 7; Matthew 28:16-20; Luke 24:50-53

Song – "Lift Up the Trumpet"

Nature – Life in the Sea—Plankton

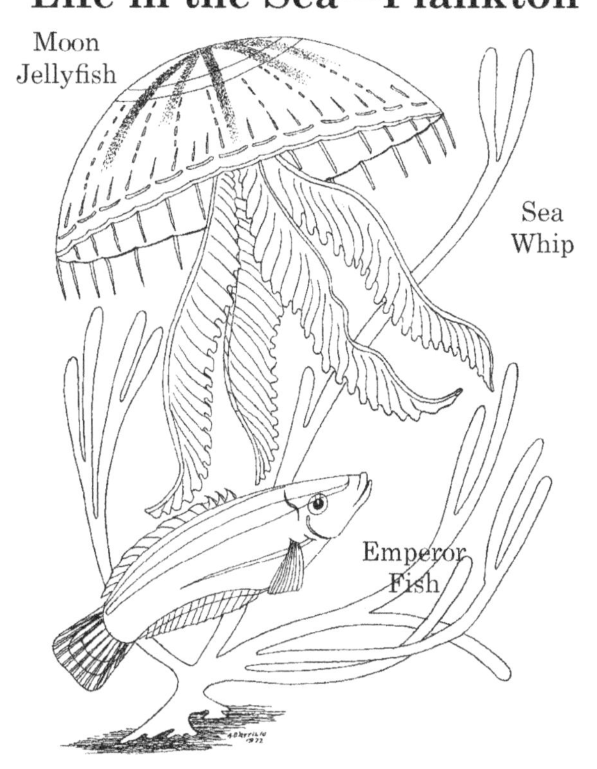

Character Quality

Gladness vs Sadness

Gladness is the bright, cheerful spirit and happy countenance that comes from a full relationship with God.

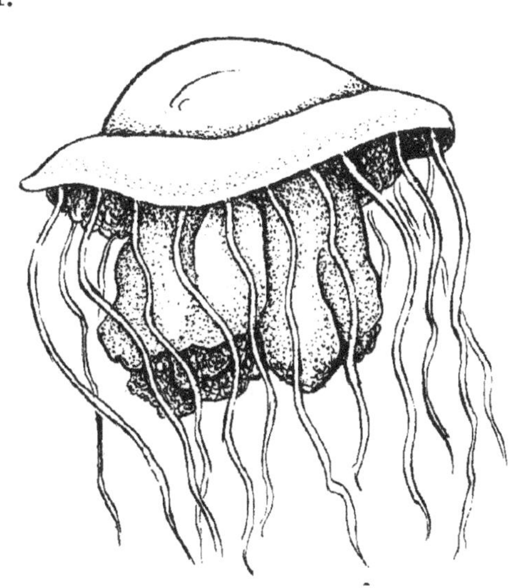

Memory Verse

"Which also said,
Ye men of Galilee,
why stand ye gazing
up into heaven?
this same Jesus, which is taken
up from you into heaven,
shall so come in like manner
as ye have seen him go into heaven."
Acts 1:11

Life in the Sea—Plankton

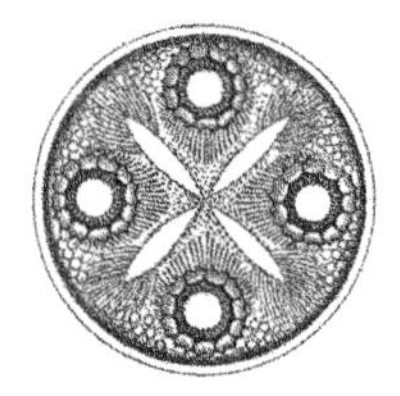

Plankton is the most basic kind of food
that God has provided for the creatures of the sea.

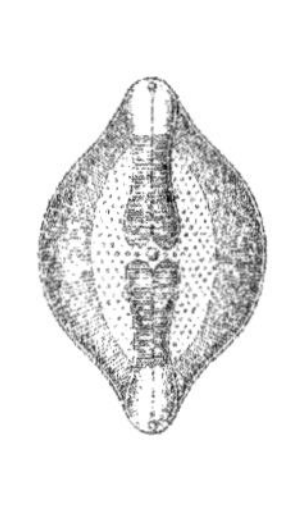

Draw one diatom or plankton above
for each day this week
you study your lesson,
and say your memory verse.

On the Mountainside

Find the following words in the Word-Find.
Which word is in the puzzle more than once?

WORD FIND PUZZLE

GO, TEACH, ALL, NATIONS, BAPTIZING, NAME, FATHER, SON, HOLY-SPIRIT, TEACHING, WITH, YOU, END, WORLD, **GLADNESS**

G	N	I	T	B	H	C	A	E	T
I	I	Z	P	A	T	D	G	A	O
T	E	A	C	H	I	N	G	L	L
N	W	L	G	O	W	E	N	S	N
G	O	L	L	L	S	N	I	S	A
W	R	I	A	Y	O	U	Z	E	T
T	L	T	D	S	N	D	I	N	I
R	D	H	N	P	R	Z	T	D	N
P	I	Y	E	I	E	E	P	A	S
S	U	O	S	R	H	M	A	L	N
Y	E	N	S	I	T	A	B	A	A
S	N	O	I	T	A	N	H	T	M
L	O	H	O	S	F	R	E	A	F

Where are the above words found in the Bible?

____

(Day 1)

Life in the Sea—Plankton 1

Unscramble the names of these sea creatures and color the picture.

____

HEWAL

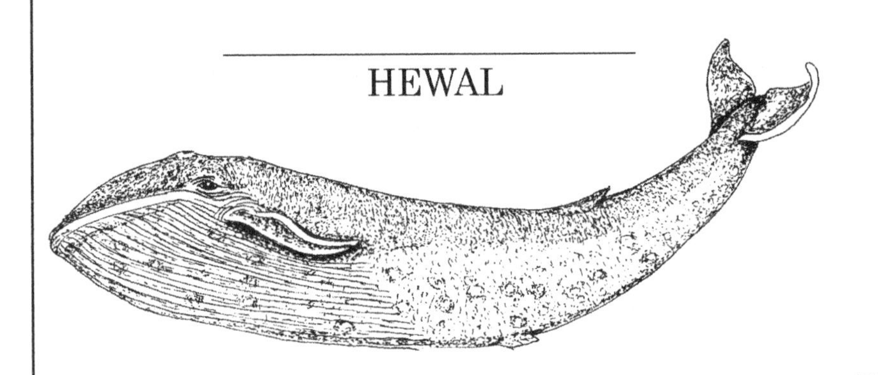

____

SIFH

__________ ______________________

AES MUCBUCRE

____

LEYLISHJF

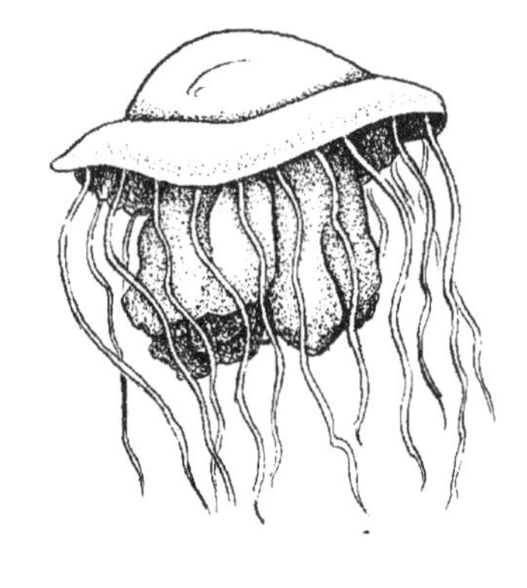

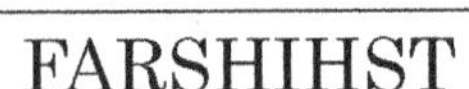

FARSHIHST

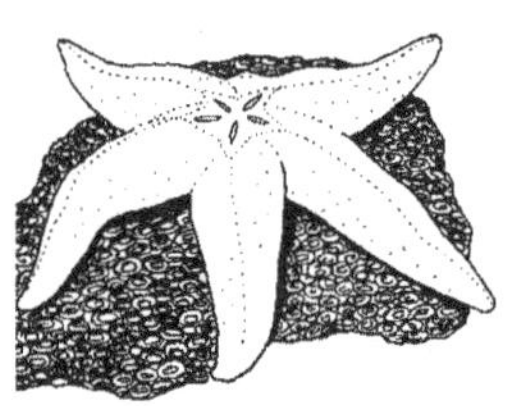

__________ ______________________

EAS NEMONEA

KANLOTPN

____

ESLE

The sea is like another world in our world. The disciples were to go from the Jewish world to *"all the world"* with the gospel.

(Day 1)

Going Home

Color this picture as teacher rereads Acts 1:9-11.
What floated down to the disciples from heaven?

(Day 2)

Plankton 2

Answer these questions.

1. How many cells do most plankton have?

2. Where do plankton live?

3. How do plankton move?

4. What is the purpose of plankton? What spiritual lesson can this share with us?

5. What kind of pigment does the diatom cells contain? What does it do for them? One spiritual lesson can be___________.

6. Describe a diatom. How do they multiply? The spiritual lesson is___________________.

7. What do diatoms have within them and what makes it work?

8.The diatoms going from their resting (seek-like) stage to their "blooming" stage reminds us__________________________.

9. How many species of diatoms are there?

10. Where do diatoms go when they die?

11. How are dead diatoms remains used? How do they look?This can teach us______.

12. Where do the diatoms usually live?

13. What is a dinoflagellate? Where do they live?

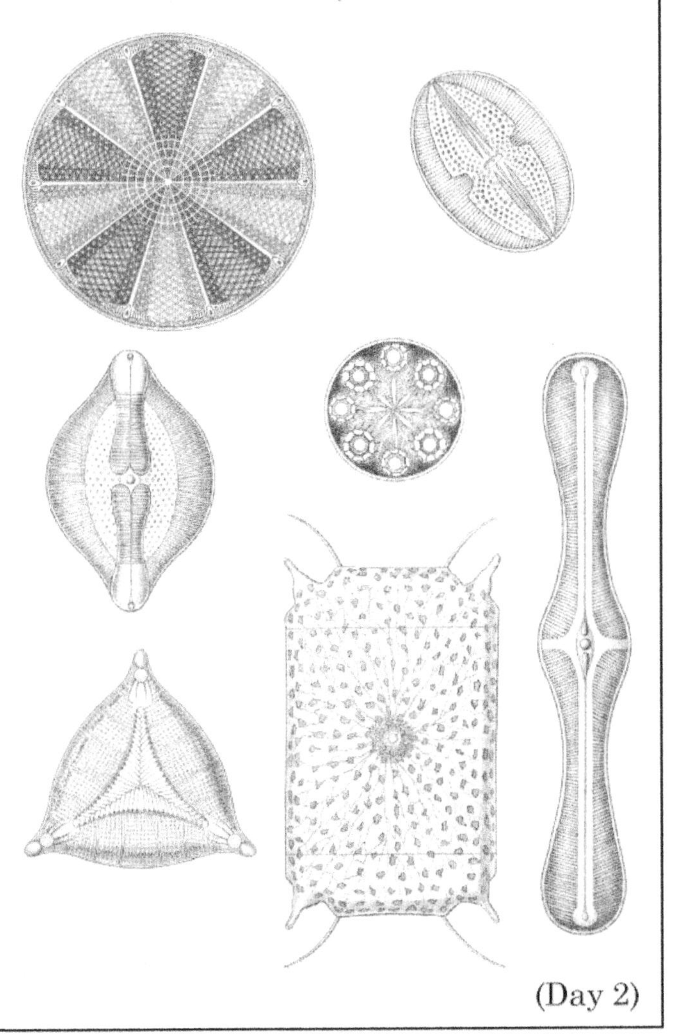

(Day 2)

Gladness of Heart

"Little Annie Wilder has joined the church," said Mrs. Fielding to her friend, Mrs. Brewster. "Joined the church! Well, I must say I don't believe in filling the church with children, and such material, too. I don't believe Annie Wilder knows how to read."

"And her mother is such a low-lived termagant,"* added the first speaker.

"Yes, and that isn't the worst of it; she takes a drop too much, I am told."

"Say a great many drops and you will get nearer the truth," was the reply.

This bit of dialogue took place in Mrs. Fielding's pretty summer parlor, in a certain suburb.

It happened that not long thereafter Annie Wilder came to Mrs. Fielding and asked for work. She was set to washing dishes and cleaning vegetables, and a most efficient little handmaiden she proved to be. She was as happy as a bird, warbling snatches of hymn and song, as she hurried from one task to another with a **glad** heart.

One day Mrs. Fielding said: "Annie, I wonder that you are not more serious since you joined the church. It is a great responsibility to be a church member, and religion is a serious thing."

Annie paused in her work, looked at the lady with her sweet, truthful eyes, and said: "I don't know what you mean, ma'am."

"I feared as much," said Mrs. Fielding. "Child, do you know what it means to join the church?"

"It means being on Jesus' side," said Annie, her **glad** face radiant, "and oh, I love Him so that I can't help singing."

"But," said Mrs. Fielding, "don't you have any fears, any struggles?"

"Why should I, M'am?" asked the child, her clear eyes opening wide.

The lady said no more, but she shook her head ominously as she walked away.

*Violent, quarreling, scolding woman

(Day 2)

The hot weather came on; family trials were onerous;* nobody had an appetite; the children were cross; papa was critical. One morning Mrs. Fielding felt particularly out of condition. The sun, but a little way on his journey, shone with noonday intensity; not a leaf stirred; the breakfast was tasteless; the flies were aggravating. I don't know how it happened, but it only takes a little spark to make an explosion when the circumstances are set. Some unguarded word was spoken, a temper blazed; a child was slapped and sent away from the table; the husband remonstrated; sharp words followed; there were tears, recriminations, a downright quarrel.

"Oh, the trouble of living!" groaned Mrs. Fielding, when her husband and children were out of the house and she was left alone. "I cannot bear it, I cannot bear it," and she gave herself up to hysterical sobbing.

By and by, when the storm was a little cleared away, came Annie, her face serene, her eyes soft and untroubled.

"Please excuse me, ma'am, for being so late," she said, "but mother was bad this morning and wouldn't let me come."

"What is the matter with her?"

The child blushed.

"She has been drinking, I suppose," said Mrs. Fielding.

Annie raised her arm at that minute, and there on the soft, fair flesh was the livid mark of a blow.

"What is that?"

"Please don't ask me, ma'am; it is nothing."

"Your mother has been beating you–and what a face! You look as if you hadn't a trouble in the world. How can you bear such things?"

"I keep saying 'em over, ma'am."

"Saying what over?"

"The charity verses. I said 'em so fast I didn't hear mother very plain."

"What do you mean?"

" '*Love suffereth long and is kind'*—isn't it beautiful, ma'am?" and the child's face glowed. "And then when I started to come here," she continued, "I couldn't help feeling bad and lonesome, and I thought

*Troublesome

of another verse: *'Lo, I am with you alway, even unto the end of the world.'* Always, ma'am, think of that! It means Jesus, ma'am, and oh, I love Him so!" Mrs. Fielding went to her own room, dumb before the wisdom of an ignorant child. Presently Annie's voice came floating out on the stifling air. She was singing: "His loving kindness, oh, how great."

—Mrs. M. F. Butts

Jesus Reigns

Mighty God, while angels bless Thee
May an infant sing Thy praise?
Lord of all in earth and heaven,
Let us now our voices raise.
Hallelujah, Hallelujah,
Praise the Lord.

Rise, ascend, immortal Saviour,
Leave this earth and take thy throne;
In our hearts come reign forever;
Make these children all Thine own.
Hallelujah, Hallelujah,
Praise the Lord.

—Unknown

The Condescending King

Jesus was once despis'd and low,
A stranger and distress'd!
Without a home to which to go,
A pillow where to rest;

Now on a high majestic seat
He reigns above the sky;
And angels worship at His feet;
Or at His bidding fly.

Once He was bound with prickly thorns,
And scoff'd at in His pain;
Now a bright crown His head adorns,
And He is King again.

But what a condescending King!
Who, though He reigns so high,
Is pleas'd when little children sing,
And listens to their cry.

He sees them from His heavenly throne,
He watches all their ways,
And stoops to notice for His own
The youngest child that prays.

—*Unknown*

(Day 2)

Comforting Angels

Answer these questions on the lines below.

1. Who stood by the disciples?

2. What did they look like?

3. What does gazing mean?

4. The angels gave what promise?

1. ______________________________

2. ______________________________

____

3. ______________________________

____

4. ______________________________

____

____

____

(Day 3)

Other Plankton

Can you identify these creatures? Check today's lesson.

1\.

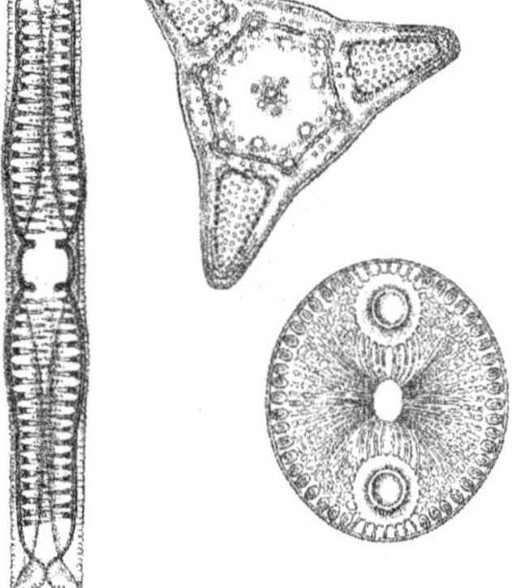

____

2\.

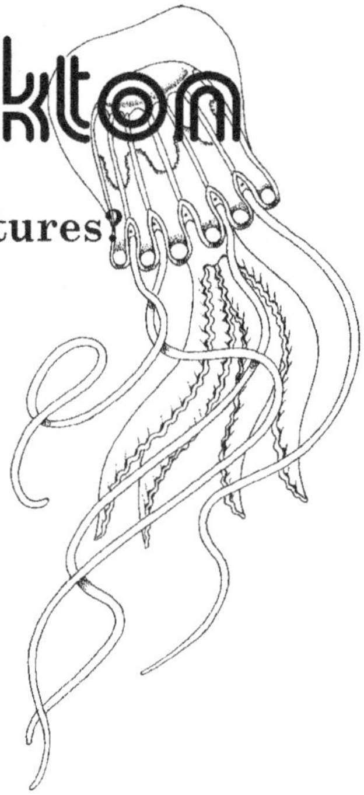

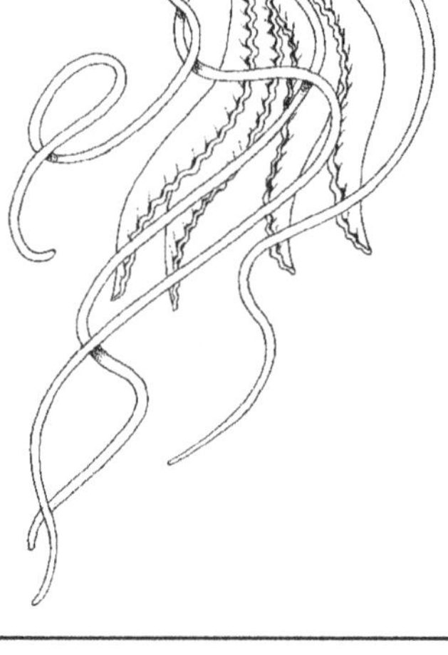

____

3\.

____

4\.

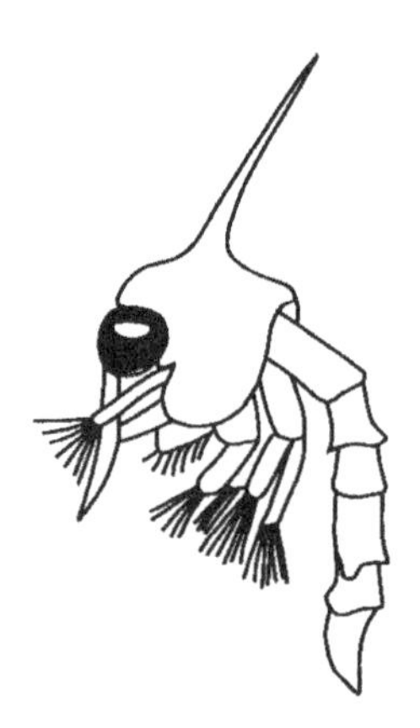

____

5. All in nature ______________ one another.

The angels came to ________________ the disciples

with the **glad** news of Jesus' return in the future.

(Day 3)

Jesus Welcomed Back to Heaven

Psalm 24 is set to poetry in these verses.
Read this as a speaking choir. Females read one line then males the next.

The earth belongeth to the LORD, And all that it contains;
The world that is inhabited And all that there remains.

For He upon the waters vast Did its foundation lay;
He firmly has established it Upon the floods to stay.

Who is the man that shall ascend Into the hill of God?
Or who within His holy place Shall have a firm abode?

Whose hands are clean, whose heart is pure, And unto vanity
Who has not lifted up his soul, Nor sworn deceitfully.

This is the man who shall receive The blessing from the LORD;
The God of his salvation shall Him righteousness accord.

Lo, this the generation is That after Him inquire,
O Jacob, who do seek Thy face With all their heart's desire.

Ye gates, lift up your heads on high; Ye doors that last for aye,
Be lifted up, that so the King Of glory enter may.

But who of glory is the King? The mighty LORD is this;
Ev'n that same LORD that great in might And strong in battle is.

Ye gates, lift up your heads on high, Ye doors that last for aye,
Be lifted up, that so the King Of glory enter may.

But who is He that is the King Of glory? Who is this?
The LORD of Hosts and He alone The King of glory is.

—*Unknown*

(Day 4)

Jellyfish 1

Review today's Nature Lesson as you discuss it and color this picture. See the Answer Key for which colors to use.

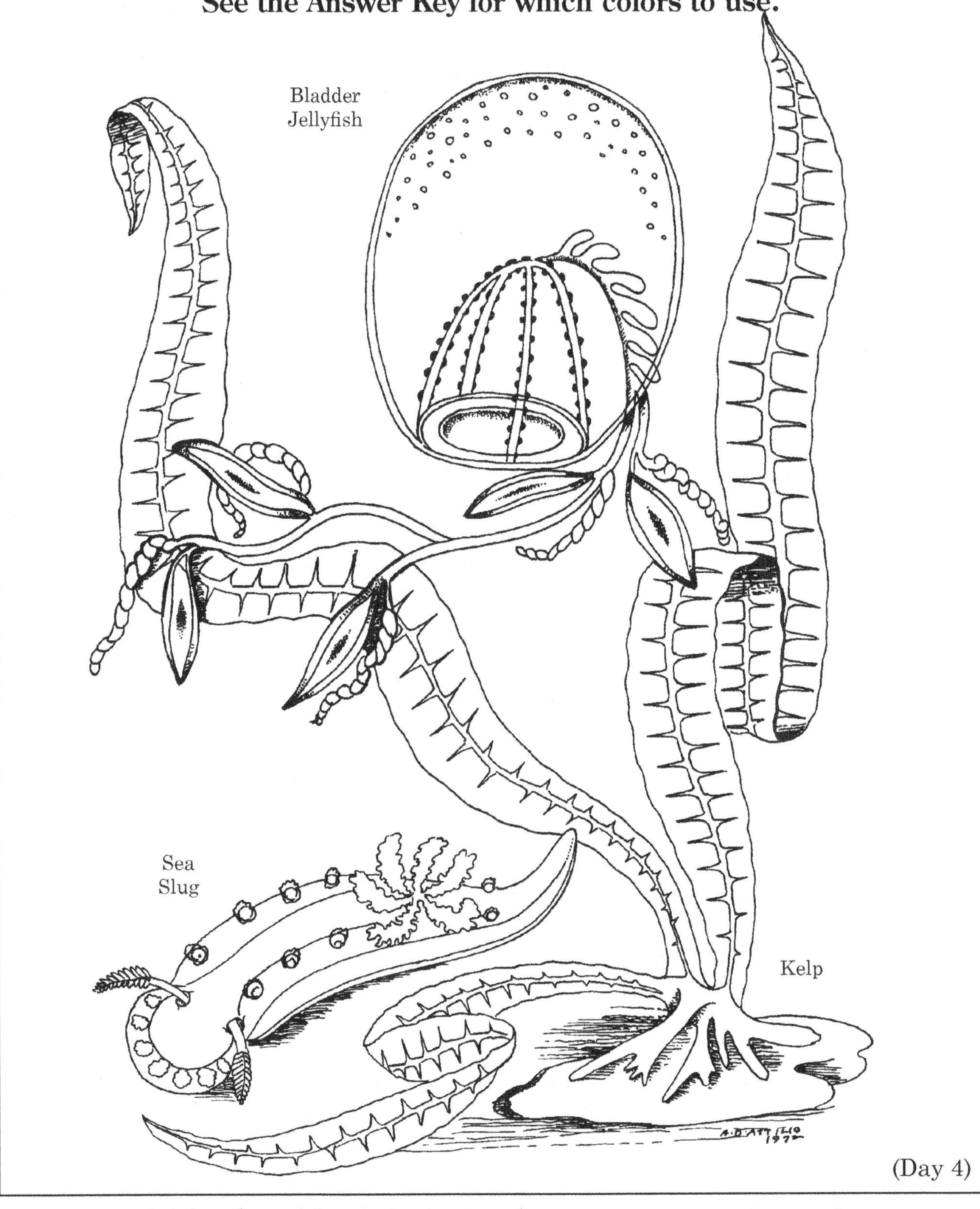

(Day 4)

Patty's Faith

"The young lions do lack, and suffer hunger:
but they that seek the Lord
shall not want any good thing."
Psalm 34:10

Down at the foot of the long, high mountains, in a little bit of a home, lived the Widow Dunn with her three children. But it was a home, however small; it was to them quite a beautiful place. But now there had been such a long winter it seemed dreary enough.

One day in early March came that had a breath of south wind at last, and the three watched the long icicles hanging from the eaves, and saw the water drip with great joy. Then, Mrs. Dunn told Patty she might put on her hood and shawl and go down to Mrs. Brown's for some spearmint, as Freddie did not seem quite well. Patty was a strong girl of ten, and the run of half a mile was pure fun to her, and so was the play of an hour that she had leave to stay; then she put on her things again.

"Here is your spearmint Patty," said good Mrs. Brown; "and here, put these rolls in your pocket. I've just made them, and Bessie and Fred will like them;" for the good neighbor knew how very poor they were at the Widow's house.

"Better hurry up, Patty; there's a storm coming," said Mr. Brown, meeting her at the door; and if Patty had only heeded, all would have been well, but the barn was by the road, and there Patty stopped a long time to watch the "cutest" little calf playing with its mother, so that when she really left, the air was full of scudding snow and the wind roared over the mountains like a hundred lions, poor Patty thought. But, thoroughly frightened, she only thought of home, and ran on and on over the hills, quite blinded by the snow, and falling often, until a gust, more fearful than any before, carried her far out of her way and threw her against a fence. It was growing dark, too, and every minute the wind roared louder. She staggered a little farther, then she was carried on again until she struck against something softer than a stone wall, and she knew nothing more for a long time.

(Day 4)

When at last she roused up, the noise did not seem quite so loud; but when she put out one hand it struck into the soft snow, but the other felt something warm and soft. For a long time Patty was too frightened to think. At last it came to her that her poor little self and a sheep were buried together in the snow, and she put her head on her woolly friend and cried enough tears to have quite melted a small snowbank and sent her to sleep.

When she awoke she was stiff and hungry, though not cold; but she did not cry. Instead, she thought of a verse her mother often said: "*They that seek the Lord shall not want any good thing.*" We will trust Him, won't we, sheepie?" she said, and turning, her hand hit her pocket and the rolls. "He does care for [and help] us, sheepie, He does!" she exclaimed, as she bit into the precious gift.

But, oh, how many times poor Patty had to say over her verse in the long hours after. She slept, said all her chapters, ate another rolls; finally she did not seem to think straight, and her verses ran together strangely, and it would soon have been too late, had not the helpful men out digging for sheep found these two by the little hole their breaths had melted, and taken her home forty hours after she left it; and her mother had thought her safe at Mr. Brown's all through those terrible hours.

"But, mother," said Patty, "I never cried a tear after I thought of your trust verse. I knew the Lord meant poor sheepie and me, and I knew he put the rolls in my pocket on purpose. He always gives us just what we need, doesn't He? I had just enough, and I want to thank Him always."

*"Thou has put **gladness** in my heart..."* (Psalm 4:7).

"Thou has put <u>gladness</u> in my heart [mind], more than in the time that their corn and their wine increased."

Psalm 4:7

Redeemer's Return

Sing This Song

Revelation 5:12; Psalm 24:7-10

Eulene Borton

**Could insert here the hymn "Worthy, Worthy, Is the Lamb"*

(Day 4)

Redeemer's Return 2
10
Lift up your heads, O ye gates; and be ye lift up, ye
13
ev - er - last - ing doors; and the King of glo - ry
15
[King of glo - ry] shall come in. Who is this King of
18
glo - ry? [Who is this King of glo - ry?] The

Redeemer's Return 3
21
1.
Lord strong and might - y, the Lord might - y in
24
bat - tle [the Lord strong and might - y]...
27
2.
Lord of hosts, he is the King of glo - ry [Lord of hosts, he is the
30
King of glo - ry— is the King of glo - ry].

Redeemer's Return 4
33
Wor - thy ___ [wor - thy] is the Lamb that was slain [wor-thy is the Lamb ___ that was
37
slain] ______ to re-ceive pow - er, and rich - es, and wis - dom, and strength, and
40
hon - our, and glo - ry, and bless - ing. [Wor - thy, wor - thy is the Lamb.]
Copyright © 1977 by Eulene Borton
Used by permission
Sing also Hebrews 7:25
which is found
in the song book
"Listen and Learn" #1,
pages 31-32.

Choosing A New Disciple

Matthias means: "________ _____ ____________"

Each letter has a number that takes its place.
To discover the message, match the numbers with the letters.
Write the letters on the lines above the numbers.

CODE

A	B	C	D	E	F	G	H	I	J	K	L	M
1	2	3	4	5	6	7	8	9	10	11	12	13
N	**O**	**P**	**Q**	**R**	**S**	**T**	**U**	**V**	**W**	**X**	**Y**	**Z**
14	15	16	17	18	19	20	21	22	23	24	25	26

"
1 14 4   20 8 5 25   7 1 22 5   6 15 18 20 8

20 8 5 9 18   12 15 20 19;   1 14 4   20 8 5   12 15 20

6 5 12 12   21 16 15 14   13 1 20 20 8 9 1 19;   1 14 4

8 5   23 1 19   14 21 13 2 5 18 5 4   23 9 20 8

20 8 5   5 12 5 22 5 14   1 16 15 19 20 12 5 19."

1 3 20 19   A : B F

(Day 5)

Matthias

Who was matthias?

Read this information.
The disciple was chosen by lot
to fill Judas' place.

He had followed Christ since the days
of His baptism and had been a witness
of Christ's acts and preachings,
although not one
of the 12 intimate disciples.
Nothing more is known of his history.
It is thought he was one of the seventy
sent out by Jesus.

**"After these things
the Lord appointed
other seventy also,
and sent them two and two
before his face
into every city and place,
whither he himself
would come."**

Luke 10:1

(Day 5)

Jellyfish 2

Fill in the blanks—use the *Family Bible Lesson* while reviewing today's Nature Lesson. Do the Dot-to-Dot below.

The jellyfish has other family members which are:
________________, _________ ________________, and ___________

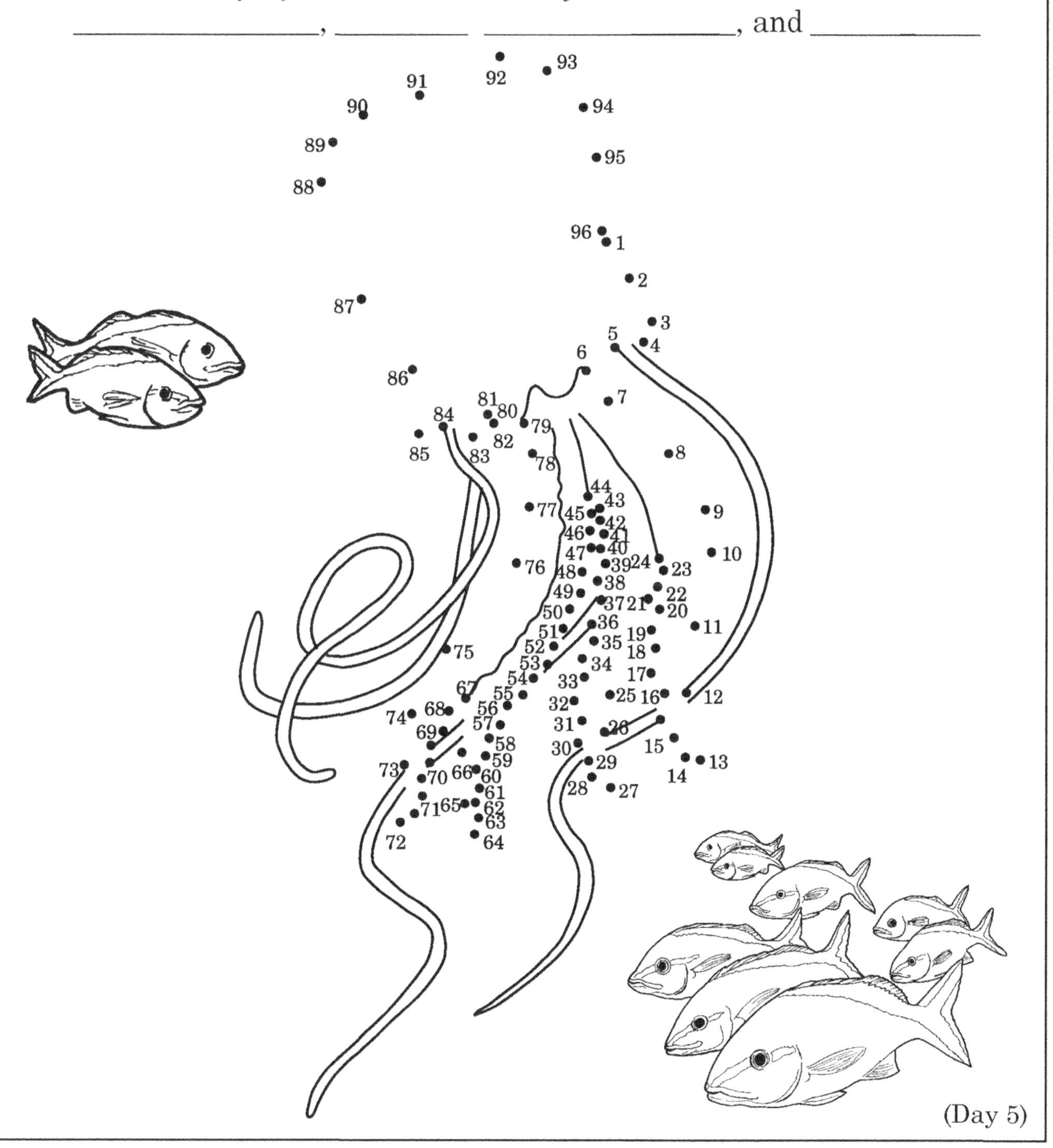

(Day 5)

Box Jellyfish or Sea Wasp

Read then color.

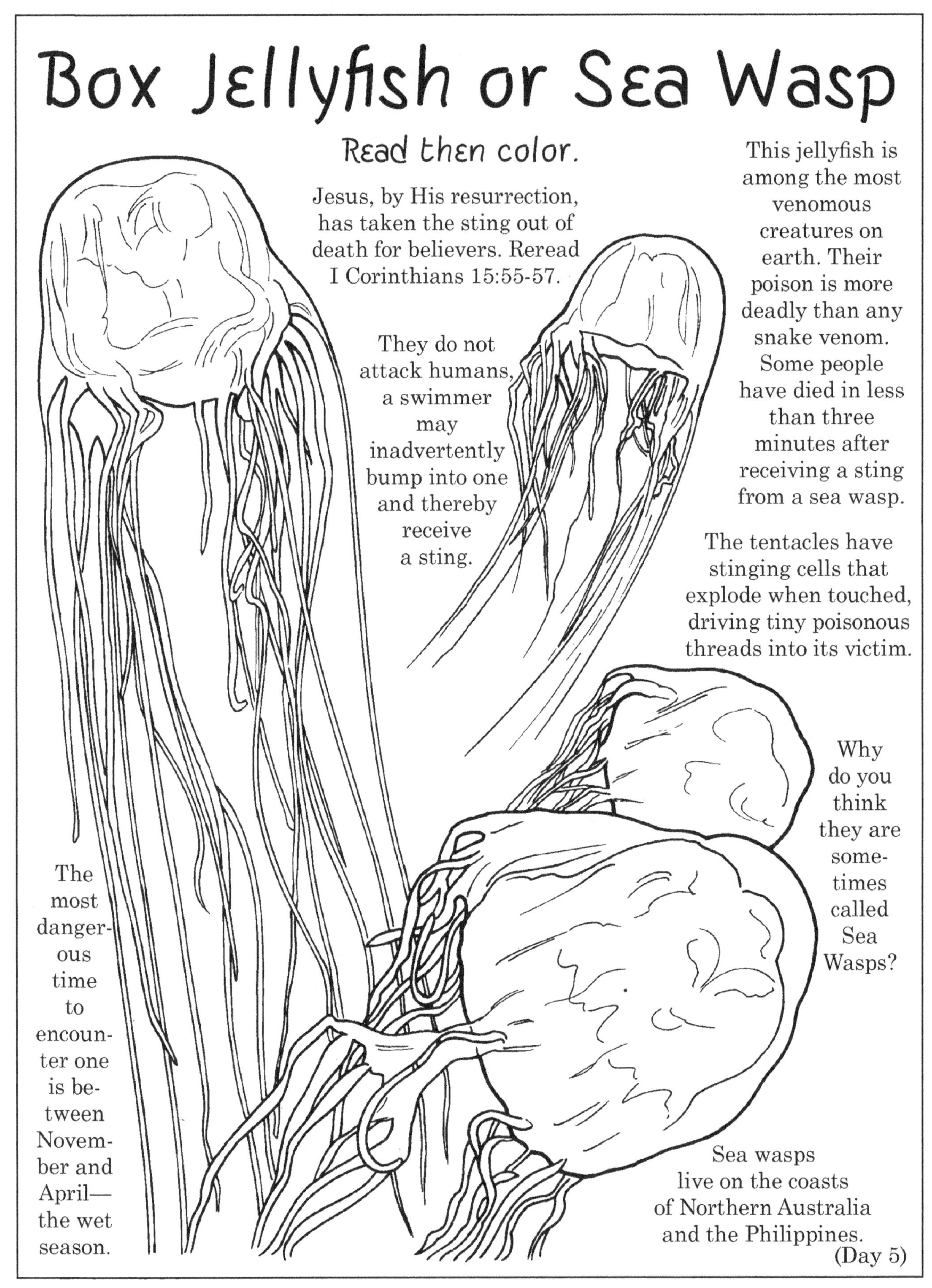

Jesus, by His resurrection, has taken the sting out of death for believers. Reread I Corinthians 15:55-57.

This jellyfish is among the most venomous creatures on earth. Their poison is more deadly than any snake venom. Some people have died in less than three minutes after receiving a sting from a sea wasp.

They do not attack humans, a swimmer may inadvertently bump into one and thereby receive a sting.

The tentacles have stinging cells that explode when touched, driving tiny poisonous threads into its victim.

Why do you think they are sometimes called Sea Wasps?

The most dangerous time to encounter one is between November and April—the wet season.

Sea wasps live on the coasts of Northern Australia and the Philippines.

(Day 5)

Going Forth to Witness

Gospel means: "good tidings," or good news."
Commission: An order or instruction giving authority to perform special duties.
Draw a line from the "disciples" to the "world" going through the maze.

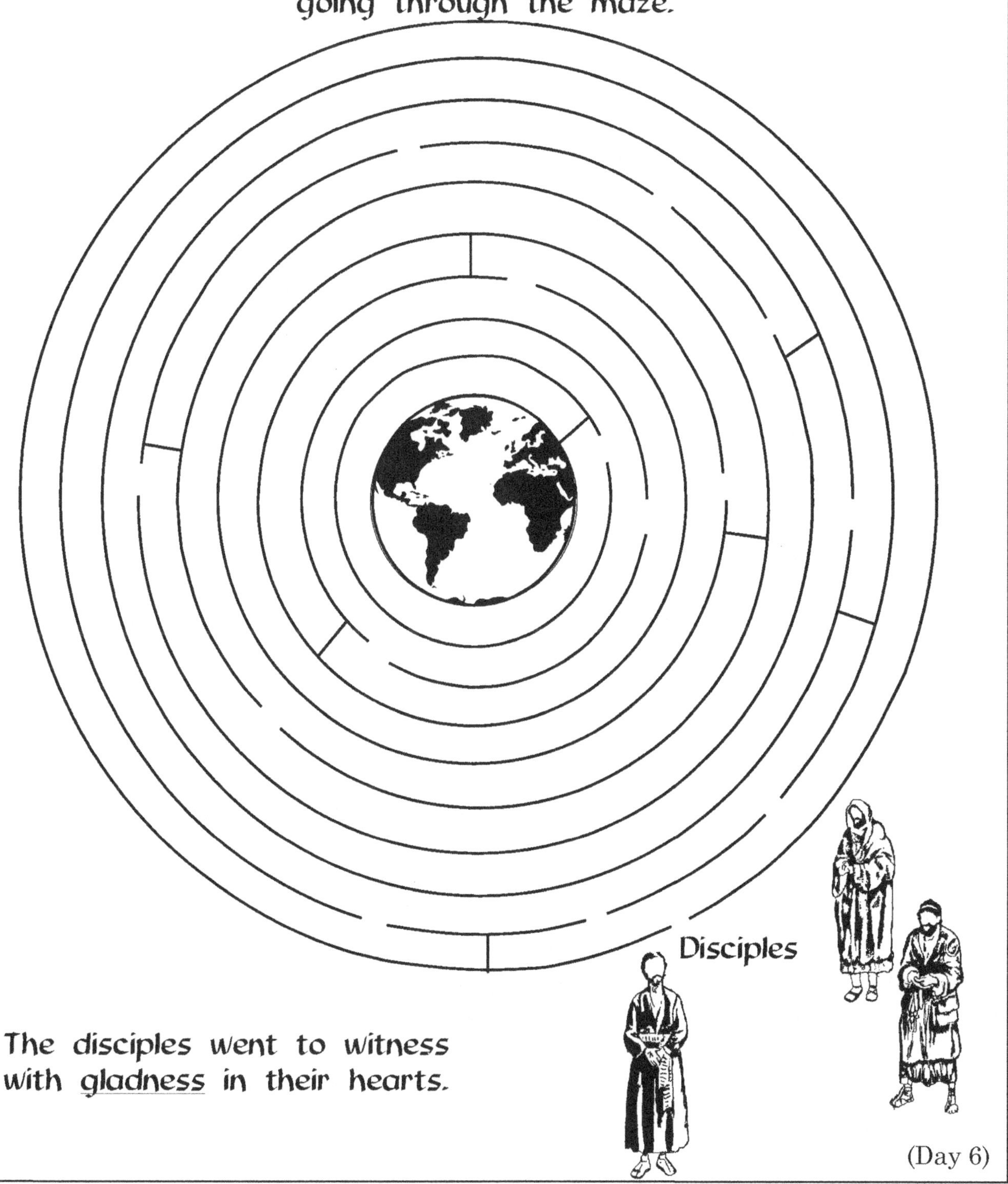

The disciples went to witness with gladness in their hearts.

(Day 6)

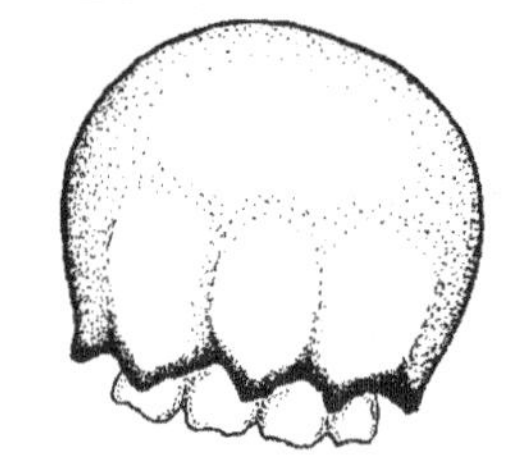

Jellyfish 3

Do You Know?

1. J__ __ __ __ - __ __ __ __
2. __E__
3. __ __ __ __ __ __ __L__ __
4. __ __ __ __ __L__ __
5. __ __ __Y__ __
6. F__ __ __
7. __ __I__ __ __
8. S__ __ __ __ __ __ __ __
9. H__ __ __ __ __

Answer these questions below then fill in the words above to remember facts about the Jellyfish!

1. Jellyfish get their names from their ________________ material between the two layers of cells that make up the creature's body.

2. Some jellyfish are small as a __________ while others are much larger.

3. Each jellyfish has a certain number and length of ______________.

4. The body of the jellyfish looks like a bell or ______________ .

5. ____________ are tubelike bodies where scyphozoan jellyfish eggs develop.

6. The last half of their name.

7. Some jellyfish can cause painful and dangerous ___________ to people.

8. _______ __________ have a poison more deadly than any snake.

9. Another member of the jellyfish family is the ________________ .

(Day 6)

Homecoming

A missionary doctor had spent forty years of his life ministering in the primitive villages of Africa. Finally, he decided to retire. He wired ahead that he would be returning by ship and gave the date and time of his arrival.

As he was crossing the Atlantic, he thought back over all the years he had spent helping to heal the people of Africa, both physically and spiritually. Then his thoughts raced ahead to the grand homecoming he knew awaited him in America because he had not been home in all forty years.

As the ship pulled into port, the old man's heart swelled with pride as he saw the homecoming that had been prepared. A great crowd of people had gathered, and there was a huge banner saying, "Welcome Home." As the man stepped off the ship onto the dock and awaited a great ovation, his heart sank. Suddenly he realized the people had not gathered to pay tribute to him but to a movie star who had been aboard the same ship.

He waited in anguish with his heart breaking. No one had come to welcome him home. As the crowd disbursed, the old man was left waiting alone. Tilting his face heavenward, he spoke these words, "O God, after giving all those years of my life to my fellow man, was it too much to ask that one person—just one person—be here to welcome me home?"

In the quietness of his heart, he seemed to hear the voice of God whisper to him, "You're not home yet. When you come home with me, you will be welcomed." —Michael Broome retold by Alice Gray

Jesus is coming soon to collect all who are His for heaven and then there will be a "Welcome Home" that will be observed by the whole heavenly host with Jesus leading us into the beautiful city of God. **Will you be there?** (Day 6)

Everlasting Life

Memorize this verse and then color the picture
and the words to the verse.

"And every one
that hath forsaken houses,
or brethren or sisters, or father, or mother,
or wife, or children, or lands,
for my name's sake,
shall receive a hundredfold,
and shall inherit everlasting life."

Matthew 19:29

(Day 6)

4 – Baptism of the Holy Spirit

Bible – Acts 2:1-47

Song – "Holy Spirit Faithful Guide"

Nature – Life in the Sea—Nektons

Character Quality

Purity vs Impurity
Purity is living in the visible presence of God daily, and this showing itself by the refinement of thought and manner.

Memory Verse

"Then Peter said unto them, Repent, and be baptized every one of you in the name of Jesus Christ for the remission of sins, and ye shall receive the gift of the Holy Ghost."
Acts 2:38

Nekton—Fish

Fish have bodies that enable them to move quickly through the water as they search for food. The disciples would be like these fish that God designed to move quickly. They would carry the gospel to the world in one generation.

Draw or put a seal of a fish on this picture for each day this week you study your lesson, and say your memory verse.

Days of Preparation

Fill in the Bible verse by answering the questions and then using the key.

Key

1. The third Member of God's family. _ _ _ _ _ _ _ _ _ _
   1 2 3 4 5 6 7 8 7 9

2. Tongues of ____________. _ _ _ _
   10 7 8 11

3. The character quality this week. _ _ _ _ _ _
   6 12 8 7 9 4

4. Luke 24:53 says "continually in the temple ___________ and blessing God." _ _ _ _ _ _ _ _
   6 8 13 7 5 7 14 15

5. "In obedience to Christ's _____________, they waited in Jerusalem for the promise..." (*Acts of the Apostles* 35) _ _ _ _ _ _ _
   16 2 17 17 13 14 18

6. To stay in a place. _ _ _ _
   19 13 7 9

" _ _ _   _ _ _ _   _ _ _   _ _ _   _ _
13 14 18   19 1 11 14   9 1 11   18 13 4   2 10

_ _ _ _ _ _ _ _ _   _ _ _   _ _ _ _ _
6 11 14 9 11 16 2 5 9   19 13 5   10 12 3 3 4

_ _ _ _,   _ _ _ _   _ _ _ _   _ _ _
16 2 17 11   9 1 11 4   19 11 8 11   13 3 3

_ _ _ _   _ _ _   _ _ _ _ _ _   _ _
19 7 9 1   2 14 11   13 16 16 2 8 18   7 14

_ _ _   _ _ _ _ _."
2 14 11   6 3 13 16 11

_ _ _ _ 2:1
13 16 9 5

(Day 1)

Nektons

What is a nekton? ____

Which pictures below are nektons? Answer Yes or No for each picture.

1. ____________________

2. ____________________

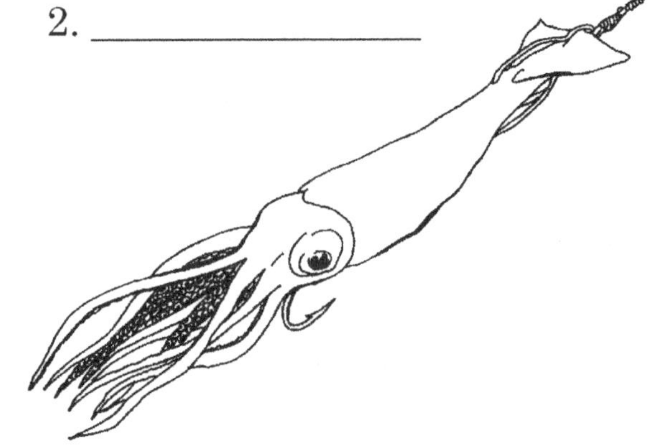

3. ____________________

4. ____________________

5. ____________________

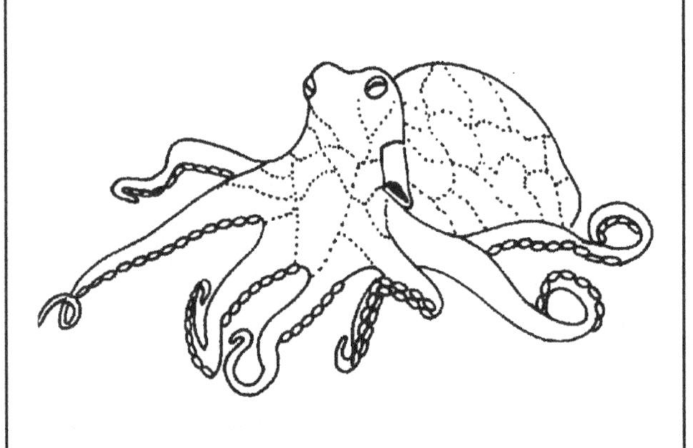

6. ____________________

Nektons are <u>strong</u> swimmers. The believers needed the added <u>strength</u> of the Holy Spirit to do the work before them. So do we today!

(Day 1)

"The Spirit of Truth"

**"And suddenly there came a sound from heaven as
of a rushing mighty wind,
and it filled all the house where they were sitting."
"And there appeared unto them cloven tongues like as of fire,
and it sat upon each of them."**
Acts 2:2-3

Read the verses and color the picture.

(Day 2)

Nekton—Fish

The flashlight or Lantern-eye fish is a strange black foot-long dweller of the waters of the Indo-Pacific. Its name comes from an unusual organ beneath its eye that glows with a brilliant cream-colored light, flashing at 5-10 second intervals as it rotates up and down. The light is actually produced by a colony of luminous bacteria that live in the fluid within the organ; since the fish cannot turn them off and on, it must rotate the organ to produce the flashing light.

The purpose of the "flashlight" is still mysterious; the fish may use it to navigate, to attract prey, to scare off predators or to communicate with its own kind. (Day 2)

Deep-Sea Anglers

Living at depths of 3,000-12,000 feet, these brown or black 2 1/2–4 inch anglers are truly deep-sea fishermen. In each species, it has parts on the front of the head and has muscles and appendages, enabling the fish to use it like a rod and lure to attract prey. In most species the rod glows with a blue-green light produced by bacteria in its cells to attract its food.

Color this picture.

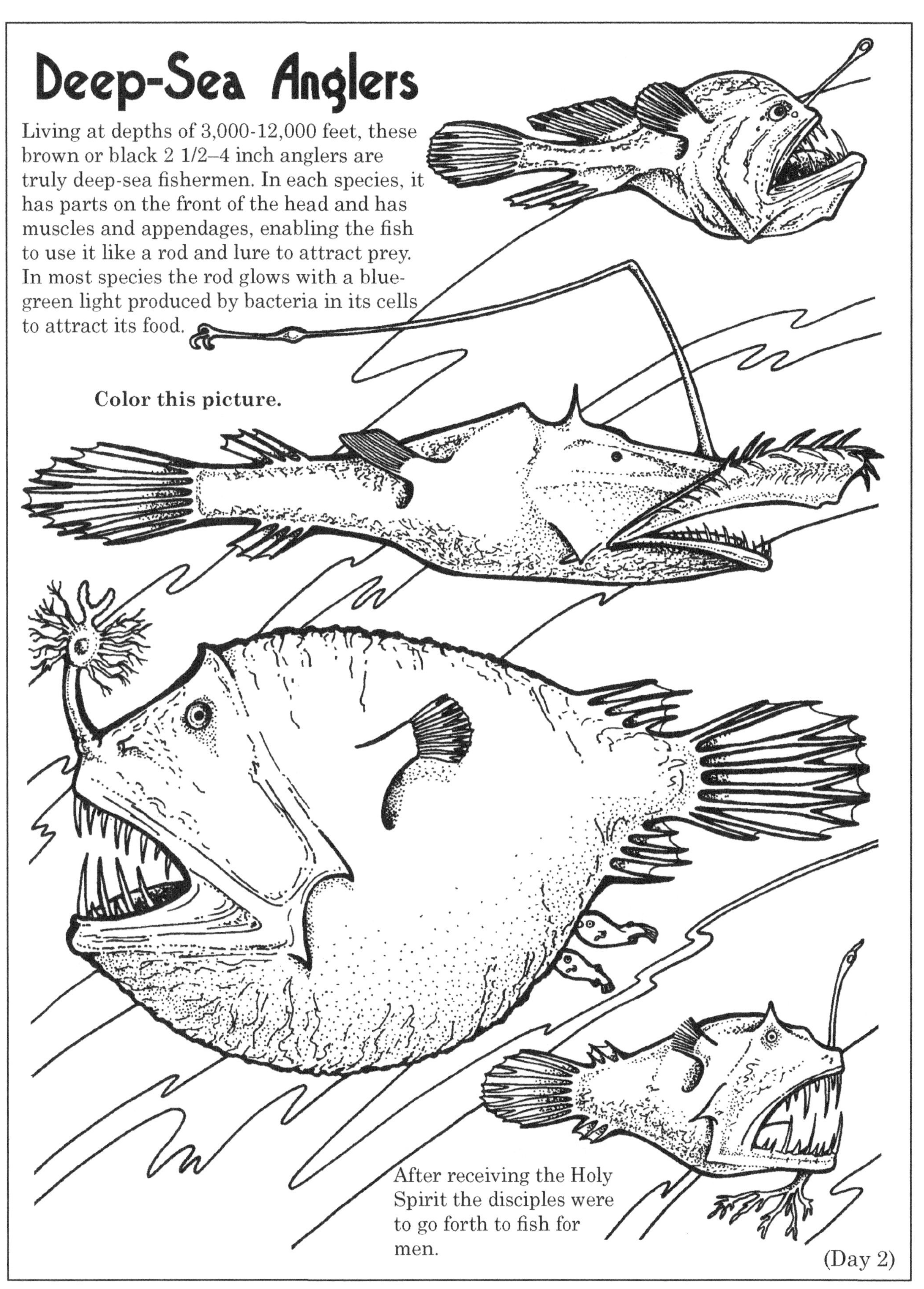

After receiving the Holy Spirit the disciples were to go forth to fish for men.

(Day 2)

Help and Influence of the Blessed Holy Spirit

It is the work of God, I own,
To melt this stubborn heart of stone;
My soul to change, my life to mend,
Or seek to Christ, that generous Friend.
'Tis God's own Spirit from above,
Fixes our faith, inflames our love,
And makes a life divine begin,
In wretched souls long dead in sin.
That most important gift of heaven,
To those that ask and seek is given;
Then be it my immediate care,
With penitent, believing prayer,
To seek it in a Saviour's name,
Who will not turn my hope to shame.
God from on high His grace shall pour,
My soul shall flourish more and more;
Press on with speed from grace to grace,
Till glory end and crown the race.
Since then, the Father, and the Son,
And Holy Spirit, Three yet One,
Glorious beyond all speech and thought,
Have jointly my salvation wrought;
I'll join them in my songs of praise,
Now, and through heaven's eternal days.

—*Unknown*

(Day 2)

Pure Religion

"I suppose Maria will say I'm a fool," reflected Nancy Dean, taking off her spectacles and laying them across the open Bible in her lap. "And perhaps I am; but somehow it's born in me to do this thing. Who knows but it's a leading of the Spirit? Again she placed the glasses on her nose, and following the words on the printed page with her finger, slowly read aloud:

"Verily I say unto you, inasmuch as ye have done it unto one of the least of these my brethren ye have done it unto me."

"Now, Nancy," She said, "If these words mean anything, they mean for you to just go ahead in this matter and not stand parleying here with Satan. Never mind what Maria says. If the Lord has put this thing into your heart, He will stand by you."

Having reached this righteous decision, Miss Nancy left the inner room, to which she had retired for meditation, and went into the little shop, where she did quite a thriving business in fancy goods and small wares. These two rooms, with a diminutive kitchen in the rear, were the lonely woman's home. It was somewhat out of the city, and very convenient for the people who lived near by to run in there for a spool of cotton or a bit of braid which they had forgotten to purchase in Boston. Besides she had a few regular customers, who patronized her cheerful establishment because her brave efforts to secure a livelihood, when smarter shops threatened to swallow up her trade, commanded their respect. But the summer was apt to be a slow time, and of late years, in common with her neighbors, Miss Nancy took a vacation, going to the old home in Maine where "Maria" lived. She, too, was struggling to support herself by carrying on the farm, which was the sole income of the two sisters after their parents died. They were far from being poor; but, with true New England thrift, they were careful to lay by something for their old age and for a decent burial, so that rigid economy had become their rule of daily living.

It was a hot day in August, and Miss Dean had been reading about the suffering among the poor children in Boston. Early in the season she had sent a small donation to the Fresh Air Fund for giving horse-car rides to the sick and poor, but

(Day 2)

even this did not satisfy her conscience; and today, when pondering the parable of the last judgment and thinking of her own meager ministry to the King, she resolved to take a child home with her when she went to Maine.

"It isn't much, to be sure," she thought, "but it will make one less to be scorched by this heat. Let me see," she mused, tying her bonnet strings, "I'll run around to the orphanage. They always have needy children there, and they will be thankful to get rid of one for a couple of weeks."

On reaching the orphanage and making known her errand to the matron, that weary woman's face lighted up as she said earnestly: "God bless you, Miss Dean. This is truly an act for one of Christ's little ones."

On the way to the nursery the visitor said, with a touch of uneasiness in her voice: "I am in no ways used to children, and maybe I can't get one to go with me."

"We'll see," said the matron, willing to trust the children's instinct in the matter.

The room was neat and clean, but oh! so stifling, and the air that came through the windows seemed like the breath from a furnace. Something seemed to trouble Miss Dean's eyesight. It may have been the change from the glare of the street to a partially darkened room, or perhaps the heat affected her; at any rate, she could scarcely distinguish the little form that stood by her side and clutched at her dress, until she heard the matron say:

"Poor Willie! I believe it will give him a new lease of life; and he's such an affectionate child, Miss Dean, I know you'll become attached to him."

"Is it a boy? Why, really! I don't think...the truth is...well, I hadn't thought of taking a girl. What will Maria say?"

This fear scattered the mist from her eyes, enabling her to look with a clear vision at the boy. One gaze into the depths of the truthful brown eyes, and then she gathered the child into her arms; and while his fingers crept over her thin face, or toyed with the old-fashioned broach at her throat, the bargain was made.

The next few days Nancy Dean seemed to be living in a dream. The mother-love, latent in every true woman's heart, had swept like a great tidal wave into her being. Fervent indeed were the prayers that were whispered night and morning into the Heavenly Father's ear for a blessing upon "His little one," as she secretly called Willie.

At length the preparations were completed, and among the hundreds of passengers that crowded the "down East" boat one August evening were no happier souls than Miss Dean and her little protege'. They had a queer look, as if mismatched somehow; but people were too absorbed in their own affairs to pay much attention to them. When the stewardess came along for the fares, it was funny to see the important air with which Miss Dean said: "For myself and a child."

"What age, ma'am?" said the stewardess.

"Five, next September," replied Miss Dean proudly.

"No charge for children under five," said the stewardess, and passed on.

The next morning a difficulty arose. It was a comparatively easy matter to get the boy out of his clothes, but dressing him was quite a different process. Miss Dean examined the stocking-supporters in despair. The whistle had sounded for Rockland, and in half an hour the boat would be at the pier, where a stage-coach connected for Maria's inland home. She fussed and fumbled, and at length took out her spectacles for a closer examination of the complicated article.

"Maria and I never wore such things. Mother hooked up our stockings with a pin, till we were old enough to knit good sensible garters for ourselves," she muttered. Opening the stateroom door, she spied a little girl playing about the walkway, and called out, "Sissy, come here a minute!" The child obeyed, and Miss Dean unburdened her heart to the small maiden, whose nimble fingers not only adjusted the socks but helped otherwise. After receiving Miss Nancy's profuse thanks, the child ran back to her mother and related the adventure, saying:

"O mamma, I do believe she isn't even the little boy's aunt, nor his grandma, for she didn't know anything about his clothes."

This report naturally led Mrs. Lecomte to look at her fellow-passengers as they emerged from the state-room. A question about the place of landing opened the way for a conversation, and Miss Nancy confided the story of her own and Willie's vacation to the elegant stranger. It was only a chance seed dropped by the wayside, but destined to bring forth fruit an hundredfold.

Miss Dean grew somewhat fidgety as she drew near the old home. "What will Maria say?" was the refrain to her every thought, and the sister soon spoke for herself.

"Who on earth is that child?" she asked, as the two alighted from the stage. Nancy meekly explained.

"Well, if it isn't a load off my mind," said Maria, leading the way to the house. "The fact is, I read about them poor children in Boston more than a month ago, and I said to myself, "I suppose Nancy will call me a fool, but I'm going to send for one of these little tots this summer." They will be a lot of company for each other."

These New England women were people of few words, so Nancy's only comment on this surprising announcement was: "I know the Lord will stand by us."

And He did in a most unexpected way; for Mrs. Lecomte visited the old homestead and made arrangements with the Dean sisters to convert it into a Summer Home for Children, providing liberally for its support from her own abundant means. Nancy Dean's vacation was indefinitely extended, and the small shop in the suburbs of Boston was given up for the larger service of caring for the cities orphans.

—Frances J. Dyer

"<u>Pure</u> religion and undefiled before God and the Father is this, to visit the fatherless...in their affliction...."
James 1:26

Tongues

What words or pictures belong on the Day of Pentecost?

Circle the numbers. Color the words and pictures.
Read Mark 16:17.

1. 	2. Purity
3. Sin	4. 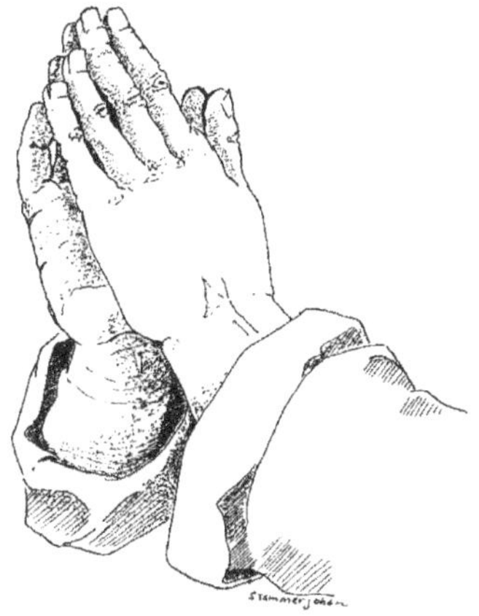
5. 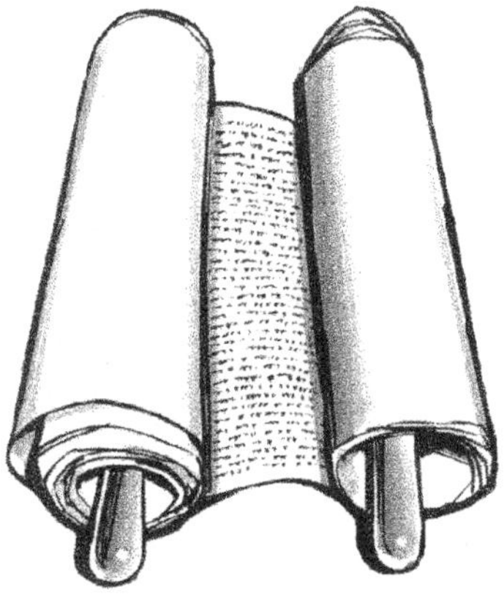	6. Guilt

(Day 3)

The Rain

Read this Bible verse and Zechariah 10:1 then color the words.

"...He will cause
to come down
for you the rain,
the former rain,
and the latter rain
in the first month."

Joel 2:23

(Day 3)

Other Nektons—Squid

Finish drawing the squid below. Review today's Nature Lesson.

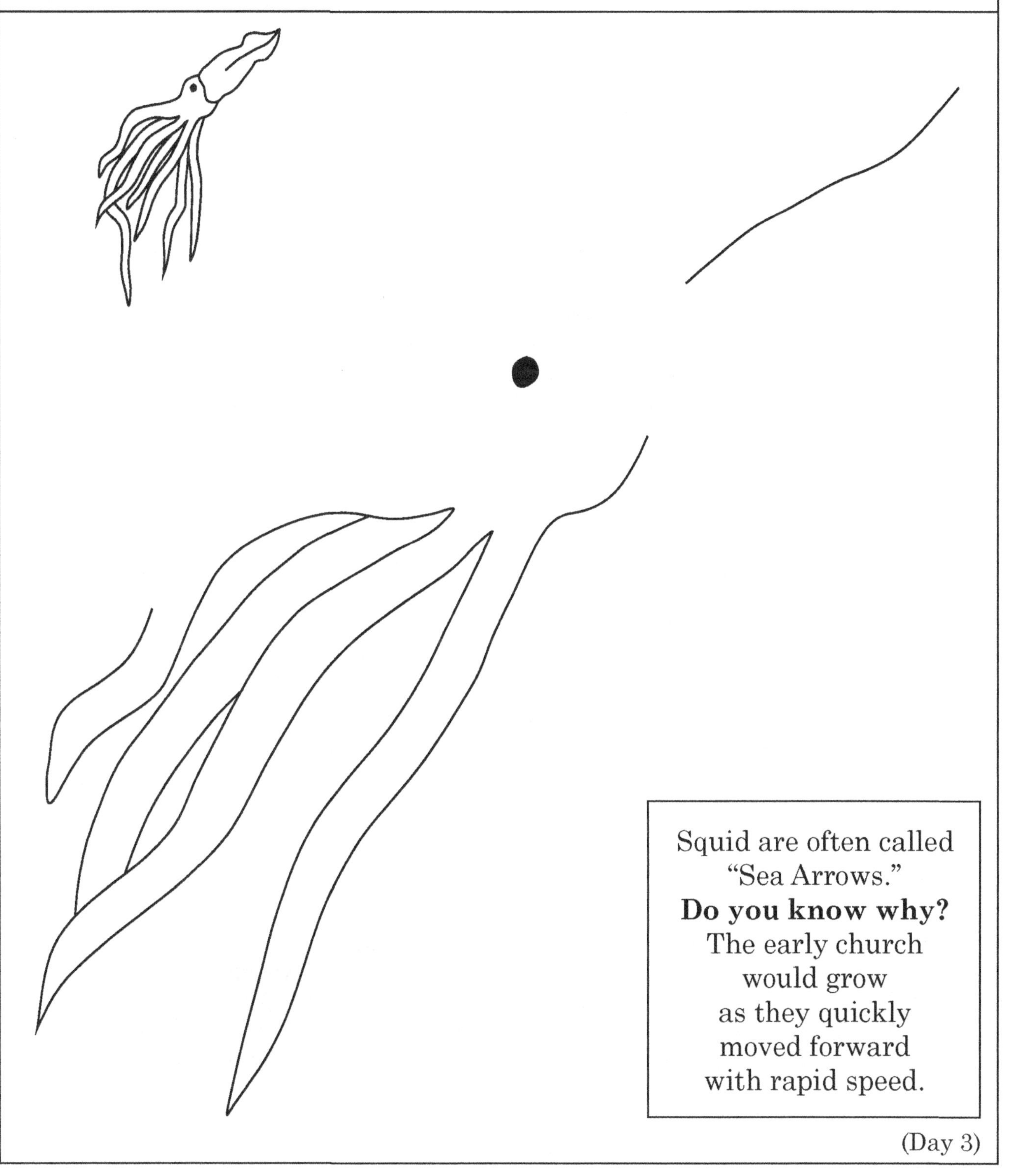

Giant Squid
The brick-red giant squid has been known to grow to 57-60 feet and may weigh over 4 tons. Its eye is the size of a beach ball. It normally lives in the deep ocean and is rarely seen on the surface; when provoked, however, it has the strength to pull a good-sized dinghy beneath the waves. It has eight regular tentacles; two longer tentacles with special suction cups and retractable claws are used for capturing prey. Scars from these claws have often been found on sperm whales, consequences of deep-sea battles.
Read and color.
Explain about the "Ink Sac." Reread Psalm 143:9.
(Day 3)

Peter Speaks for Christ

Review today's Bible Lesson and color this picture.

(Day 4)

More Nektons—Manatees

1. What are Manatees sometimes called? What do they eat? About how much do they eat in a day?

2. How many kinds of Manatees are there? What are they?

3. Describe what a Manatee looks like by looking at this picture.

(Day 4)

"No Not Even Once"

"Go with us, tomorrow, Hal?" said Fred Bean to Henry Lane, as they passed up the street amid a group of schoolboys.

"Can't afford it, Fred," replied Harry, a fine looking lad.

"Poor boy! out of cash!" sneered another boy.

"No," answered Harry good humoredly, "I have got ten dollars, all my own earnings."

"Stingy, then!"

"No, sir," answered Fred, "you don't know Harry Lane. There isn't a stingy bone in his skin. Come, Hal, why not go?"

"I told you, Fred, I could not afford it, and I cannot," said Harry with an air that said plainly, "I've told you all I want to about it; now leave me alone." But they were not satisfied, and Fred continued:

"Come, Hal, there won't be any fun without you. Go, just for once. The whole thing, dinner, wine, and all, wont cost more than two dollars. I'd rather pay myself, than not have you go."

"I can't, Fred, it would cost me a guilty conscience," said Hal in a low voice.

"Why, he's pious!" said the sneering voice again, in a most aggravating tone, "Let the saint alone, boys."

"Hold your tongue!" said Fred sharply, "pity you hadn't piety enough in your disposition to give you a few manners!" Then turning coaxingly to Harry, he said again, "Come, Harry, just for once!"

"No," said Harry firmly, "Not once. I don't go to any place where liquor is sold, if I can help it, and not even once."

The victory was won. Harry's firmness had won it; and though some boys called him "a saint," he was never urged to go to any of their foolish and wicked frolics. Boys, when "*sinners entice you,*" set your feet down firmly against the very first temptation. Say with brave Harry Lane, "No, not even once."

(Day 4)

The Things That are Pure

Lilies white that gem the vale;
Crystal dew-drops nights exhale;

Penciled moonbeams' silvery sheen;
Night's deep blue, when stars are seen;

Snow-wreaths twined o'er loved ones' graves;
Pearls that sleep beneath the waves.

Angel-guarded infant sleep;
Pledge of love which true hearts keep;

Silvered locks of righteous age;
Beams of truth from sacred page;

Hearts in Jesus' blood made white;
Death-damp brows' encircling light.

Pearly gates and walls of light;
Streets of gold and robes of white;

River of life flowing free;
Great white throne and crystal sea;

Harps of gold and blood-washed throng;
Jesus, theme of every song.

—Unknown

(Day 4)

Look to Jesus Christ

"blessed are the pure in heart for they shall see God."
Matthew 5:8

Build the early church by adding letters in each row of words until you have built the main words describing the believers.

Examples:

P

put
purity

P

pace
place

(Acts 2:1)

O

(Acts 2:1)

F

(Acts 2:4)

T

(Acts 2:8)

H

(Acts 2:37)

R

(Acts 2:38)

B

(Acts 2:38)

(Day 5)

another nekton—octopus

Octopus comes from two Greek words meaning "eight feet."

Color this picture.

Giant Pacific Octopus

There are suction cups on the underside of each of the eight arms. These can fasten tightly to any object. Peter made his points and the Holy Spirit fastened them firmly in the minds of the people.

(Day 5)

a harvest of souls 1

Use the word list on the next page and reconstruct Acts 2:43-47.
Which word is not in these verses but describes the early believers? ______________

43 ____

____

____

44 ____

____

____

45 ____

____

____

46 ____

____

____

47 ____

____

____

____

(Day 6)

a harvest of souls 2

2	3	4	5	6
by	and (13)	fear	every (2)	things
to (3)	the (5)	came	signs	common
as (2)	all (4)	upon	their (2)	parted
in	had	soul	goods	accord
of	men	many	daily (2)	temple
be	man	were (2)	bread	**purity**
	had	done	house (2)	having
	one	that	heart	favour
	did	sold	added	people
	eat	them	saved	church
	God	need		should
		they		
		with (2)		
		from		
		meat		
		with		
		Lord		
		such		

7	8	10	11
wonders	apostles	continuing	possessions
	believed	singleness	
	together		
	breaking		
	gladness		
	praising		

What are some things that the believers did under the guidance of the Holy Spirit?

(Day 6)

GROWING

"Praising God, and having favour with all the people. And the Lord added to the church daily such as should be saved."

Acts 2:47

Trace the words in the above verse with colored pencils.
Color this picture.

(Day 6)

More About the Octopus

The octopus has the ability to change its colors quickly for purposes of camouflage, and may be red-brown, grayish blue, or any color that matches its surroundings. Many people were changed by the Holy Spirit and became followers of Christ.
Color the octopus and color its surroundings that it might blend into it.

Purity—Are You Eating From a Garbage Can?

The terrible flood which swept through the great Ohio Valley some years ago left wreckage and ruin and death behind it. But an even greater tragedy is overtaking youthful America today in the raging flood of printer's ink and the computer world.

The rivers that were out of bounds serve a useful purpose when flowing within their own banks; also, they beautify the landscape and contribute in various ways to the pleasure of those who live in the cities, towns, and country settings along their course. But when excessive rains swelled them to flood stage then came disaster!

Just so with the printed page and visual materials of the internet. We cannot doubt that it is a great gift. The human brain is incapable of estimating even a small fraction of the good that has came to the world as a result of Johannes Gutenberg's invention of movable type and in more modern times the use of computers and other such devices. It has been a wonderful blessing to humanity. But the devil was quick to see its value in furthering his own interests. His agents have been busy all through the centuries, and now, as never before, wreckage and ruin are being spread abroad, not in one particular locality, but—everywhere! For there is scarcely a corner of the globe to which the printed page or internet has not found its way, and in which it does not in some measure wield its influence for good or ill.

What are you reading? What are you watching? Now—today? Are you spending your leisure hours poring over cheap reading or online watching impure things or other such garbage?

Garbage can material is being made very attractive these days—so attractive, in fact, that the large majority are eating at its table.

There are current materials that offer informative, interesting articles to the reading public or the viewing public. These afford us opportunity to use the good common sense God gave us and choose the **pure** kernel of the wheat, ignoring the chaff and the husks. But when you have such in hand, do you use discrimination? Or do you read or watch first, and then ask *"...Whatsoever things are true, whatsoever things are honest, whatsoever things are just, whatsoever things are **pure**, whatsoever things are lovely, whatsoever things are of good report; if there be any virtue, and if there be any praise, think on these things"* (Philippians 4:8). Have you ever feasted on them sort of "under cover" of Father's and Mother's notice?

(Day 6)

A lecturer looked over the fine group of young people who made up his audience, and wondered what they were reading and watching? "I'll find out," he thought; and during his talk he mentioned the titles of several books and movies that were <u>impure</u>. When he asked for a frank show of hands, all but two of those young people admitted they were partaking regularly of one or more of these garbage can materials.

Why fill the mind with trash when there is an abundance of good, wholesome, **pure**, brain food available? Why weaken the mind by such deliberate abuse? Just as sure as you live, the mind that is fed on such a diet soon becomes weak and unable to retain worth-while things.

Why waste precious time in poring over slushy, sentimental materials that soil the person, not only mentally, but morally as well? For that is just exactly what this garbage-can stuff does to those that partake of it.

A mother came home one day and found her daughter reading a popular book. Questioned, the girl said that she wished to get the moral lesson out of the story. It had a good moral—so she had been told.

The wise mother said no more, but several hours later she asked her daughter to put on her best clothes and go with her for a walk. As they started, instead of turning toward the better section of town, she led the way toward the dump, and made their way around it to the edge of a dirty pool of water. There the mother, who had picked a beautiful white rose as they left the home yard, dropped the flower out into the middle of the pool as though by accident, and asked the girl to get it. "But, mother, why do you want it?"

"Oh, it's pretty, and I'd like it."

"But think how dirty I'll get! It will simply ruin my clothes!"

"Yes? Well, what about the garments of your mind, which you are dragging through—[and she mentioned the name of the materials she was reading] to get a 'good moral'?"

And the girl, being intelligent and really eager at heart to do right and choose the best, saw the point and revised her habits.

For not one of us, young or old, wants an <u>impure</u> mind, do we? What are you reading? What are you watching? What are you thinking? Are you preparing your mind for the "Baptism of the Holy Spirit" and the return of Jesus?

What is **purity**? It is living in the visible presence of God daily and this showing itself by the refinement of thought and manner!

(Day 6)

5 – A Crippled Man Healed

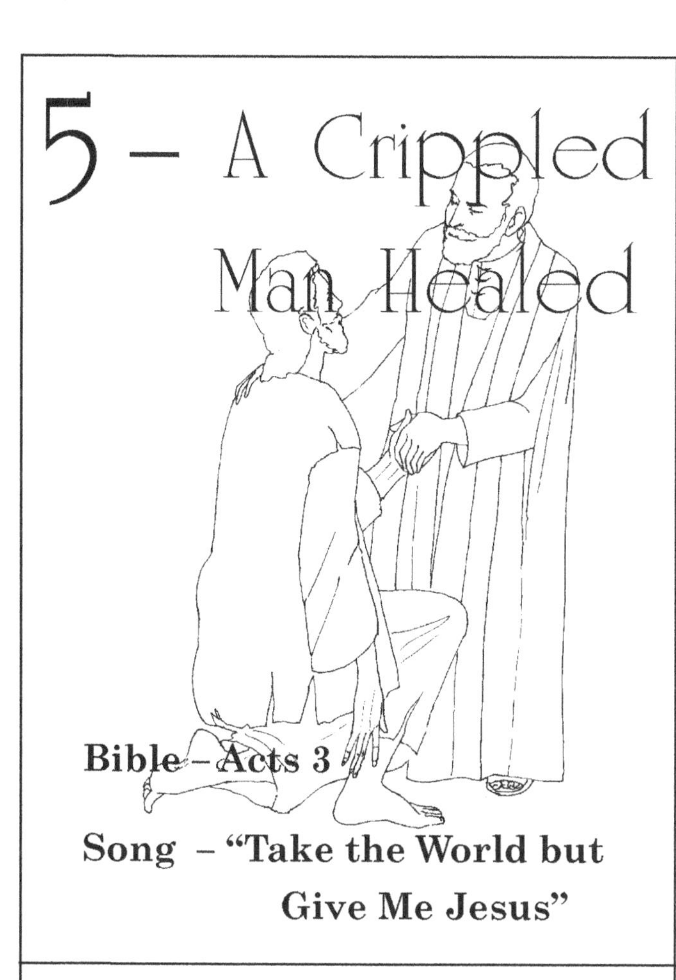

Bible – Acts 3

Song – "Take the World but Give Me Jesus"

Nature – Life in the Sea—Benthos

Character Quality

Giving vs Stinginess
Giving means to convey something and make it available to another to bless their life and glorify God's name.

Stone Crab

Memory Verse

Lobster

"And the prayer of faith shall save the sick, and the Lord shall raise him up; and if he have committed sins, they shall be forgiven him."
James 5:15

Benthos

Jesus was called the Star of Jacob.

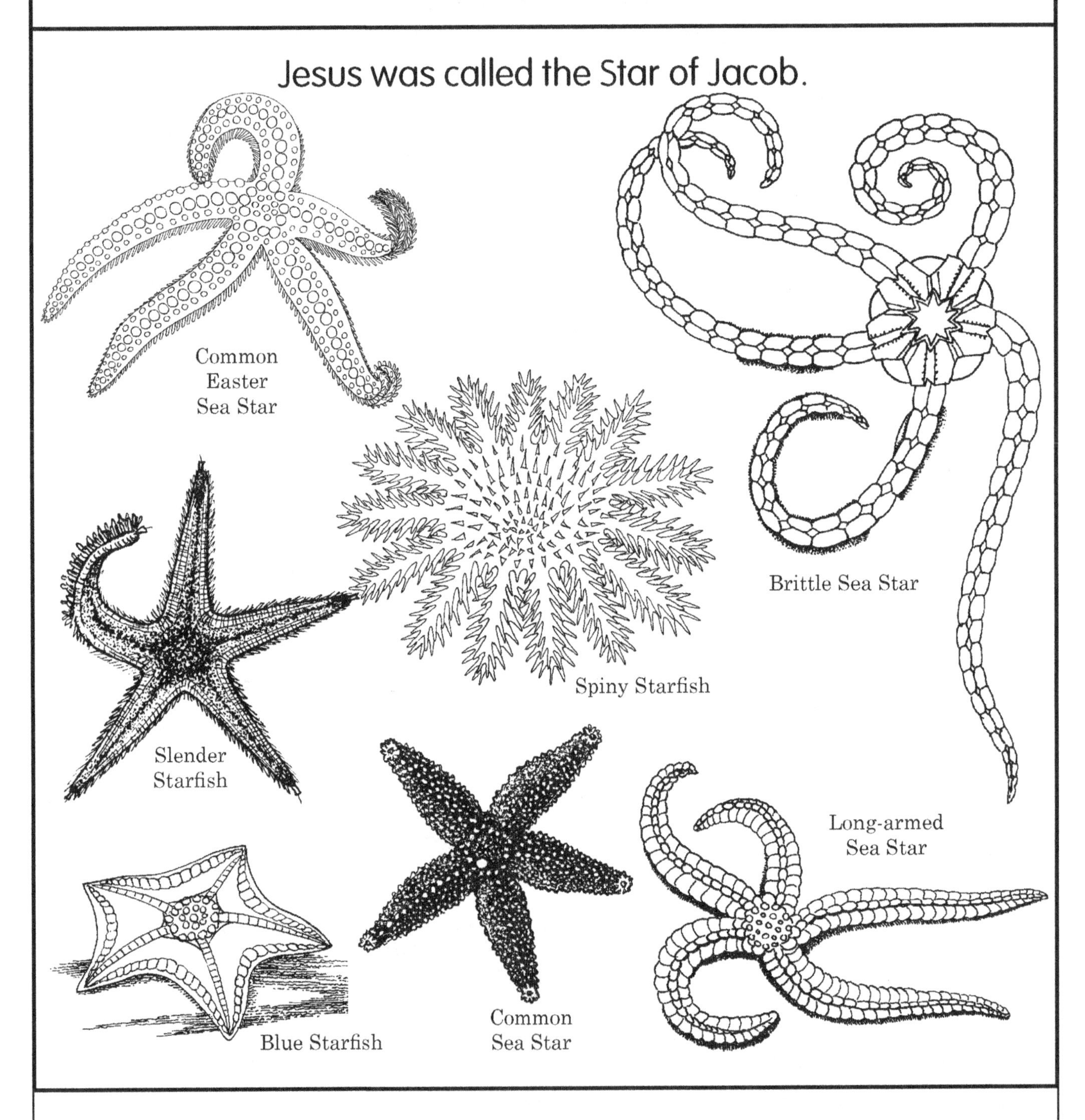

Color one Starfish in this picture
for each day this week
you study your lesson,
and say your memory verse.

"Earnest Prayer"

"Now Peter and John went up together into the temple at the hour of prayer, being the ninth hour."
Acts 3:1

Do the crossword below by using Acts 3:2. Follow these instructions:

1. Make a list of each word from the verse and how many letters in each.
2. Use every word only once. You will have some repeat words from the verse.
3. Mark out these words from using in the puzzle: a, man, his, was, whom, they, laid, and which.
4. Mother's is counted as 8 letters.
5. Start with the word beautiful. (3 Across)
6. Every word must go into the right squares or they will not work.
7. Use a pencil.

There will be 23 words used.

(Day 1)

BENTHOS

Mark the benthos below with a "b,"
plankton with a "p," and nekton with an "n.""

1. ____________________

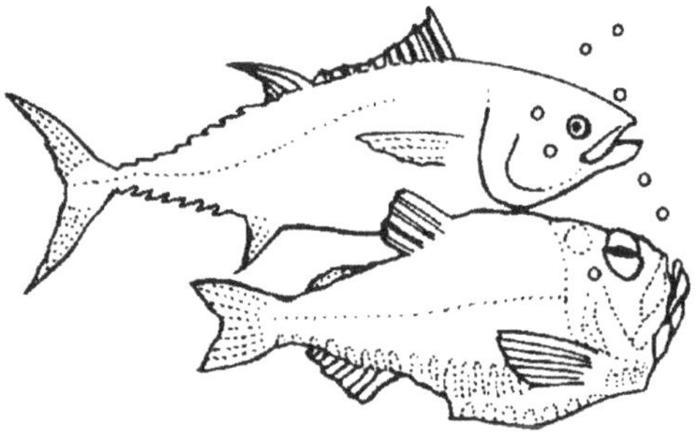

2. ____________________

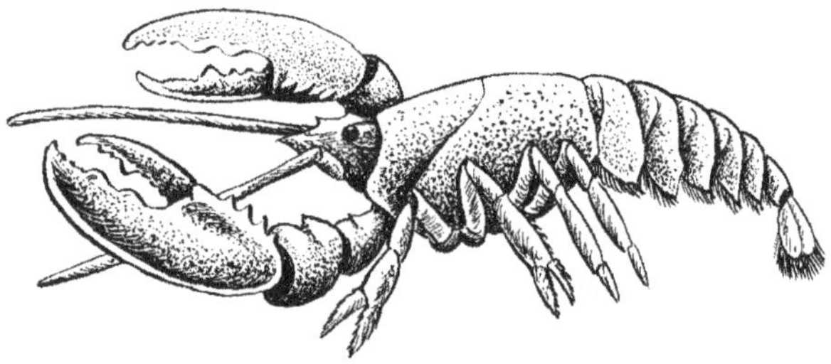

3. ____________________

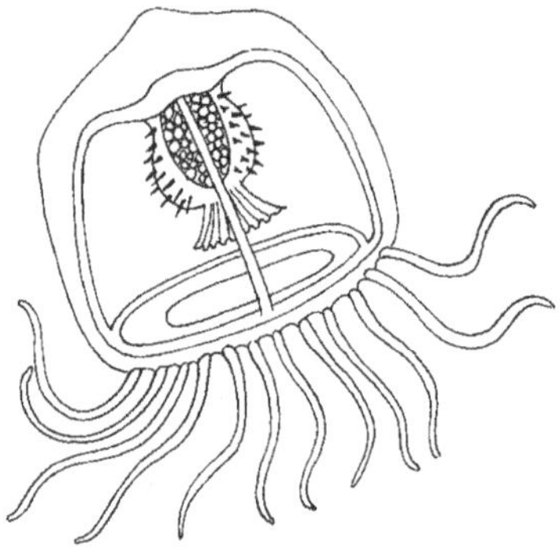

4. ____________________

5. ____________________

6. ____________________

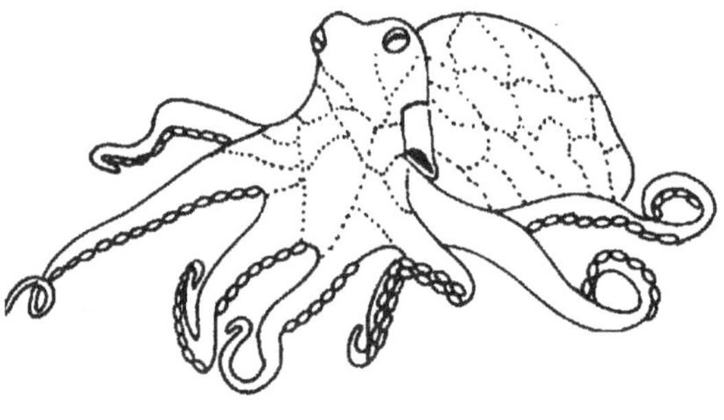

The sea is a busy, active place.
It was a very busy and active place at the Beautiful Gate.

(Day 1)

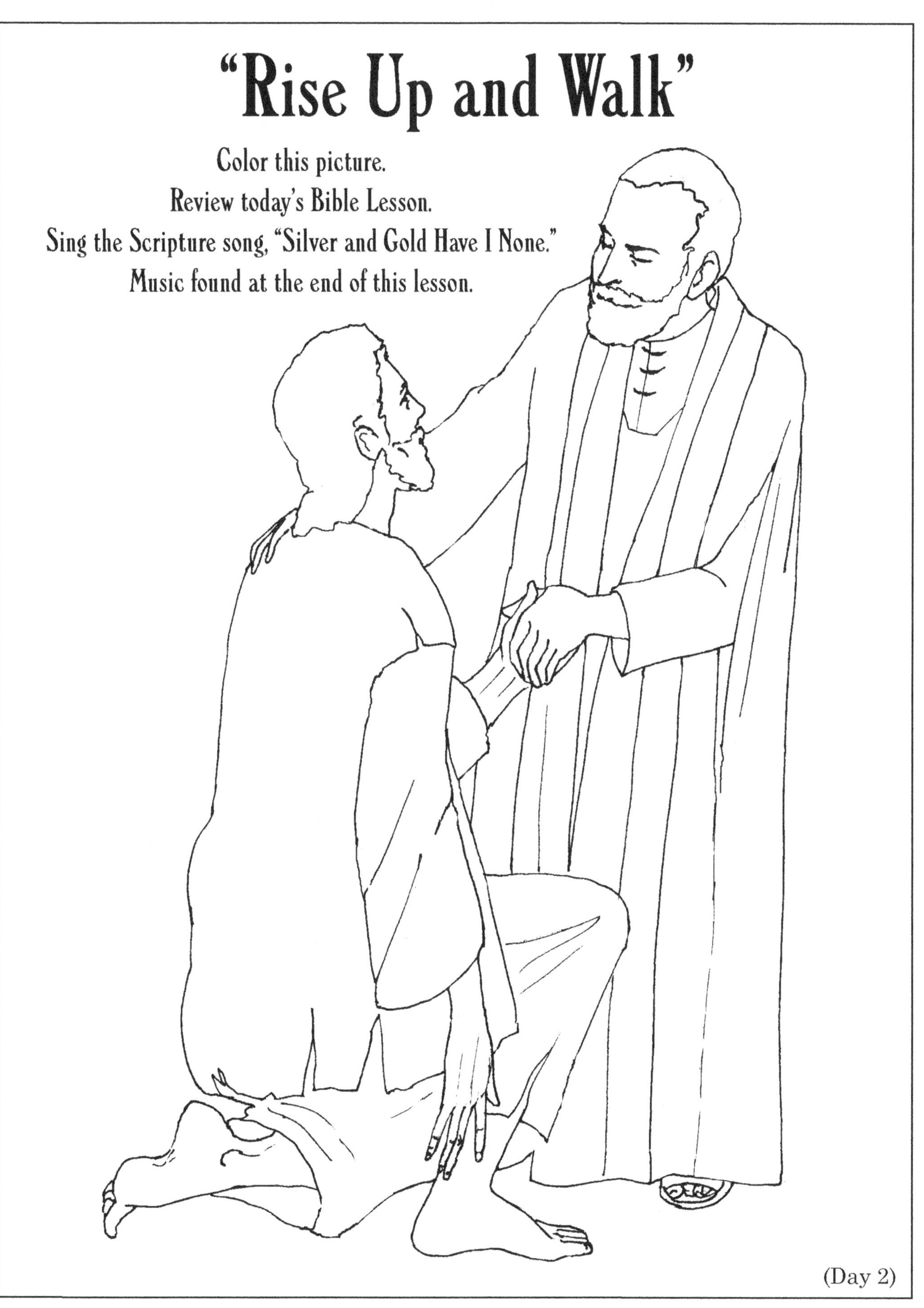
"Rise Up and Walk"
Color this picture.
Review today's Bible Lesson.
Sing the Scripture song, "Silver and Gold Have I None."
Music found at the end of this lesson.
(Day 2)

Silver and Gold

"Then Peter said, Silver and gold have I none; but such as I have give I thee: In the name of Jesus Christ of Nazareth rise up and walk."
Acts 3:6

The result of the man being healed is told in verse 8. Read the answer below by using a ruler and drawing a neat, straight line between each word, and add the punctuation.

"ANDHELEAPINGUPSTOOODANDWALKED
ANDENTEREDWITHTHEMINTOTHETEMPLE
WALKINGANDLEAPINGANDPRAISINGGOD."

How did the people respond? See verses 9-10.

"ANDALLTHEPEOPLESAWHIMWALKING
ANDPRAISINGGODANDTHEYKNEWTHAT
ITWASHEWHICHSATFORALMSATTHE
BEAUTIFULGATEOFTHETEMPLEANDTHEY
WEREFILLEDWITHWONDERANDAMAZEMENT
ATTHATWHICHHADHAPPENEDUNTOHIM."

Color the gold and silver.

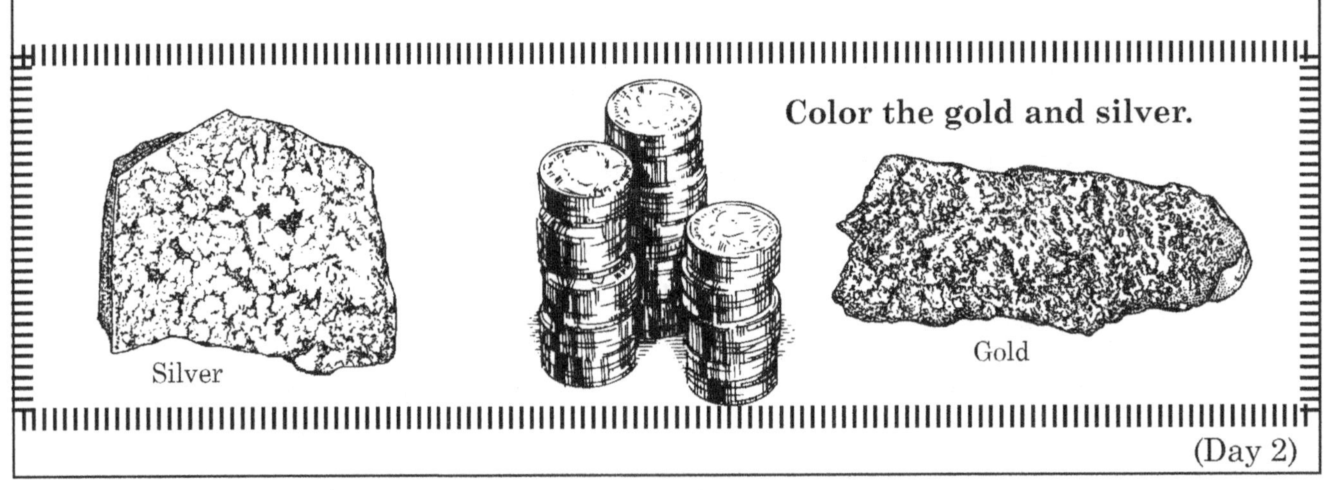

(Day 2)

Benthos—Kelp 1

Hollow-Stemmed Kelp

What is another name for kelp?

What is a kelp forest?

One spiritual lesson is......

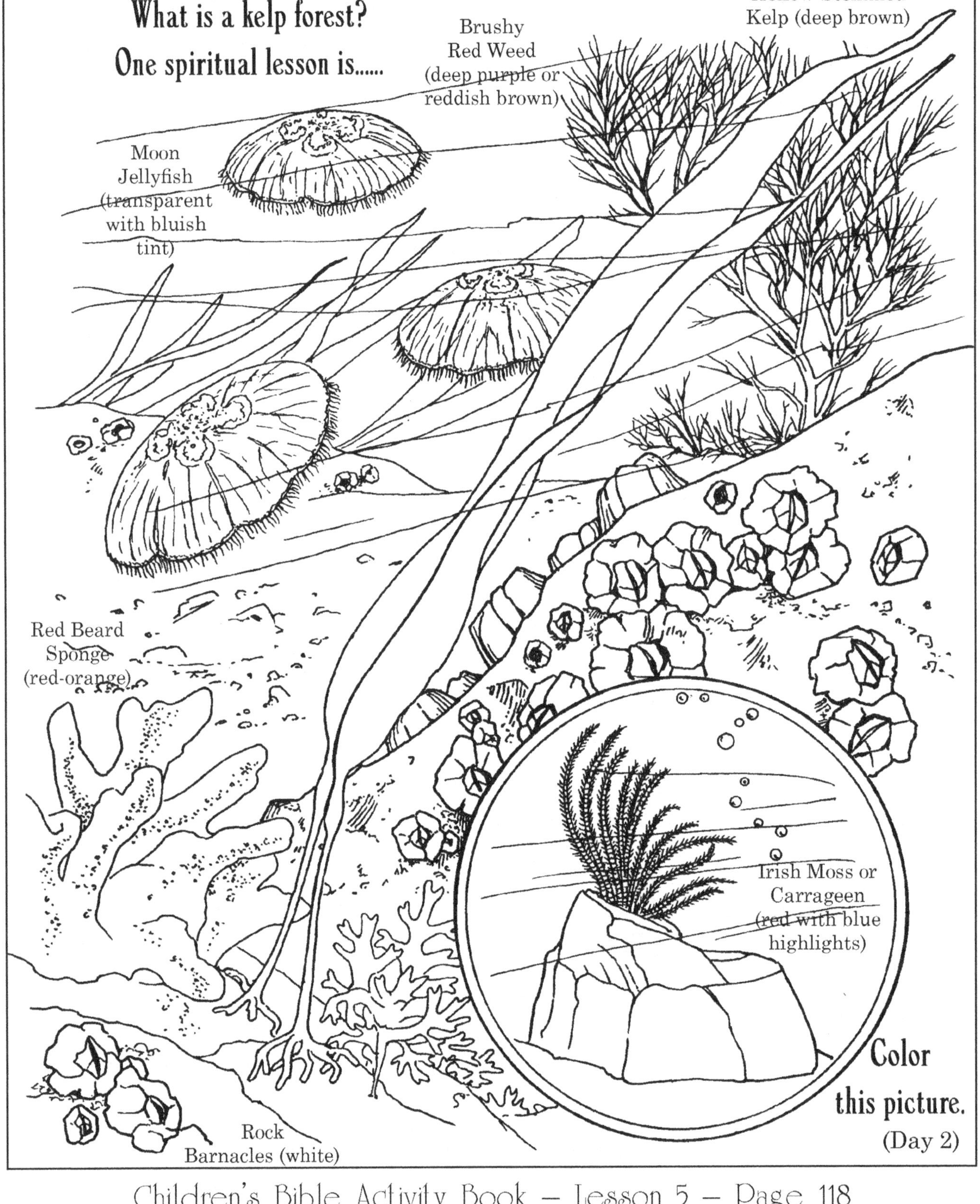

Hollow-Stemmed Kelp (deep brown)

Brushy Red Weed (deep purple or reddish brown)

Moon Jellyfish (transparent with bluish tint)

Red Beard Sponge (red-orange)

Irish Moss or Carrageen (red with blue highlights)

Rock Barnacles (white)

Color this picture.

(Day 2)

"ALL FOR THE BEST"

A traveler, during a dark and tempestuous night, had fallen into a ditch by the wayside. He was very anxious to reach home, from which he had been absent for a longtime. He had been abroad in a foreign country, and was returning with the fruits of his industry; and when he had almost reached home he was overtaken by a storm of wind and rain. Darkness increased; he could not see his way before him; the road was washed into gullies; he stumbled and fell. He had broken his leg, so that he could proceed no farther on the journey.

The poor man in the ditch, with his leg broke, bemoans his sad fate. His wife and children are expecting him this very night. They trim the midnight lamp, and anxiously await his arrival. He comes not; and as they hear the howling winds and driving tempest outside, they are filled with direful apprehension. The disabled traveler, as the storm beats upon him in the ditch, is ready to exclaim, "All these things are against me." He is, perhaps, tempted to murmur against Providence, when he was at the point of reaping the reward of a long season of toil and privation, to be thus thrust back when upon the threshold of the realization of his hopes, and to be thrown, groaning into a ditch.

But wait awhile, and it will be seen "tis all for the best."

When the morning light appears, the dismal traveler is filled with joy and gratitude at his wonderful deliverance. Had he proceeded a few rods, or even feet, farther on his journey, he would have fallen from the broken bridge, sunk, and perished, in the foaming flood beneath. When upon the brink of destruction a kind Providence turns his feet aside and prevents his moving from a place of safety. His family, also, are kindly cared for and preserved. That very night a plan was to be put in execution to rob, and perhaps murder, the inmates; but the midnight lamp showed that the master of the house had nor arrived with the expected treasure.

Thus we often perceive, as in the light of the noonday sun, the truth of the saying that "affliction has been a mercy." We doubtless are preserved from many dangers unseen by what are termed the mis-

(Day 2)

haps of life. Let us not deny the truth of the proverb, because we see so many good men live in suffering and die unrelieved, and so many bad men arrive at the summit of wealth and outward prosperity. By looking forward to another life, we discover its full meaning. "Our trials and troubles here will only make us richer there." Even here, we often find the trials of life are like the bracing wintry winds which invigorate our frame, or like the fire that tries and purifies the gold.

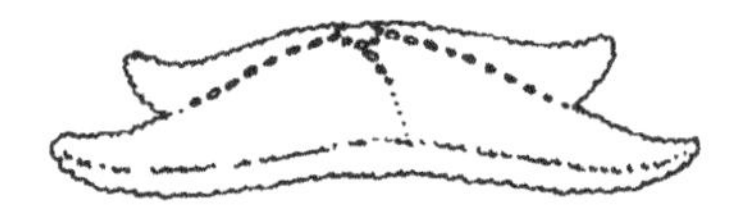

Let us, therefore, pursue our onward way, like Bunyan's pilgrim, through the mire of the Slough of Despond and up the Hill of Difficulty, or down the Valley of Humiliation, with courage, confidence and submission. Let us confide in the wisdom that is above us. Men are but shortsighted beings. "Behind a frowning Providence is seen a smiling face." Whatever may befall us, or whatever afflictions may attend us, they will, if rightly met, prove but blessings in disguise; and if not here, we shall hereafter see that they were "all for the best."

Sabbath Day

"Now Peter and John went up together into the temple at the hour of prayer...."

Acts 3:1

I'll awake at dawn on the Sabbath day,
For it's wrong to doze holy time away;
With my lessons learned, it shall be my rule
Never to be late at the Sabbath-school.
Birds awake betimes; every morn they sing,
None are tardy there, while the woods do ring;
So, when Sabbath comes, it shall be by rule
Never to be late at the Sabbath-school.
While the tuneful birds and the summer's sun
All it time are found with their works all done,
Shall not I, more blest, ever keep this rule,
Never to be late at the Sabbath-school?
When the summer's sun awakes the flowers again
They the call obey-none are tardy then;
Now shall I forget that it is my rule
Never to be late at the Sabbath-school?
While the days of youth swiftly glide away,
Let us seek the path to the realms of day;
We shall not regret that we kept this rule,
Never to be late at the Sabbath-school.

—*Unknown*

(Day 2)

Hymn to the Sea

Read each verse of this poem and then each Bible text.

O Sea, thy deep, unchanging blue,
As changeless as the blue on high,
Is emblem of the constancy
Of Him who rules both sea and sky
—Isaiah 49:15-16

Thy yawning depths, so dark and drear,
That never know the sun's clear light,
Are like the deeper, darker chasm,
Wherein our sins sink from His sight.
—Micah 7:19

Thy restless waves that ceaseless roll,
And cover o'er thy bosom bright,
Are emblems of His righteousness,
That robes His saints like garments white.
—Isaiah 48:18

Thy boundless stretch, so vast, so far
Beyond the reach of human ken,
Is like the love, so full and free,
He beareth to the sons of men.
—I John 3:1

O Father, Sovereign of the sea,
In all Thy works we own Thy sway!
O manifest Thy power in us,
For our salvation, day by day!
—Colossians 1:13-14, 16
—*Unknown*

(Day 2)

The "Beautiful Gate"

1. The people were ______________________ "that the disciples could perform miracles similar to those performed by Jesus.

2. How long had the man been helplessly crippled?

3. Explain how he was responding to this miracle.

4. What is the *"Beautiful gate"* today?

5. How will the great work of the gospel close in the end?

6. Will you be like Peter and John today?

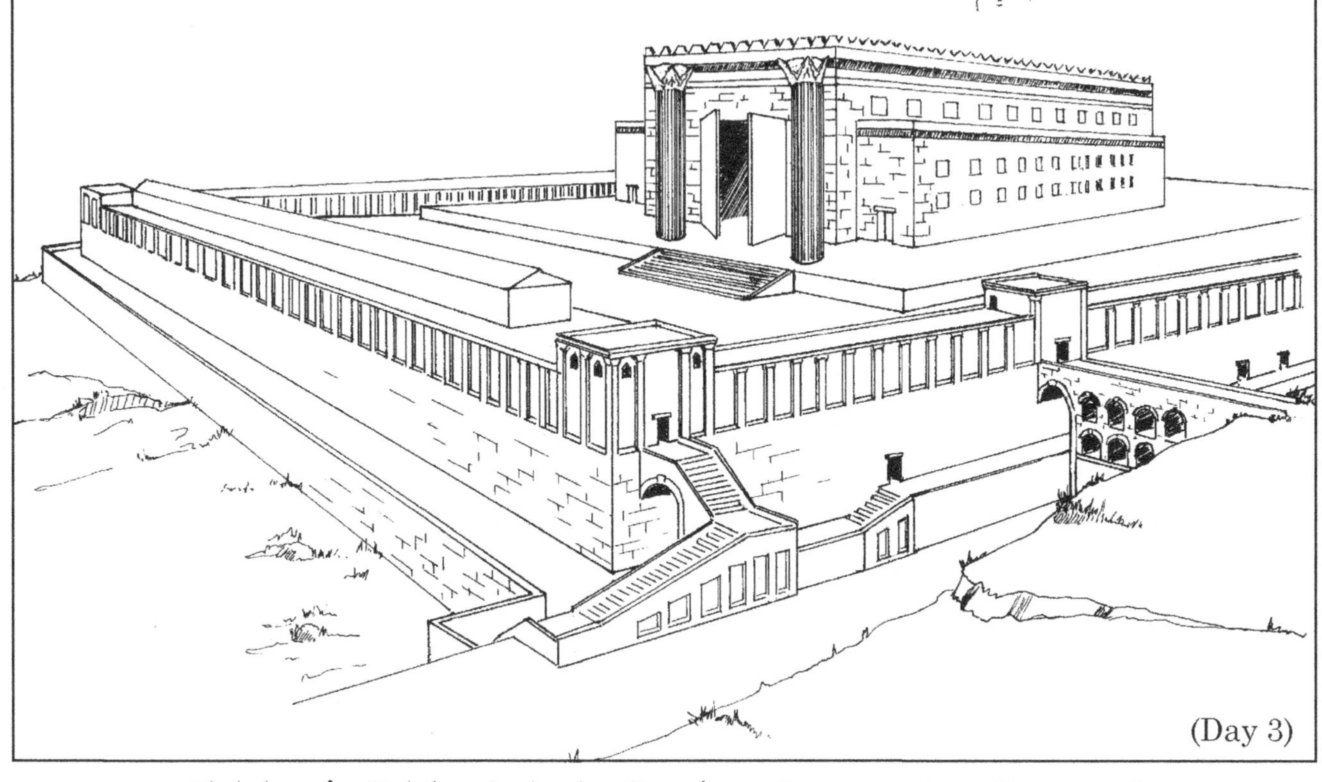

(Day 3)

Benthos—Kelp 2

Remember, the temple was to be a place of spiritual shelter
like the kelp beds.

Draw or place seals of sea creatures among the kelp.

Sugar kelp has crinkly fronds and wavy edges.
A sweet tasting white powder forms on the drying surface of the plant.
It is considered by some to be a special treat in the Far East.
It was a sweet experience for the crippled man
to not only be given health, but to also learn more about Jesus.

(Day 3)

"Repent and Be Converted"

Read then color the words and pictures.

"Repent ye therefore,
and be converted,
that your sins
may be blotted out,
when the times
of refreshing shall come
from the presence
of the Lord."

Acts 3:19

(Day 4)

Benthos—Starfish 1

Find the Starfish in this letter.

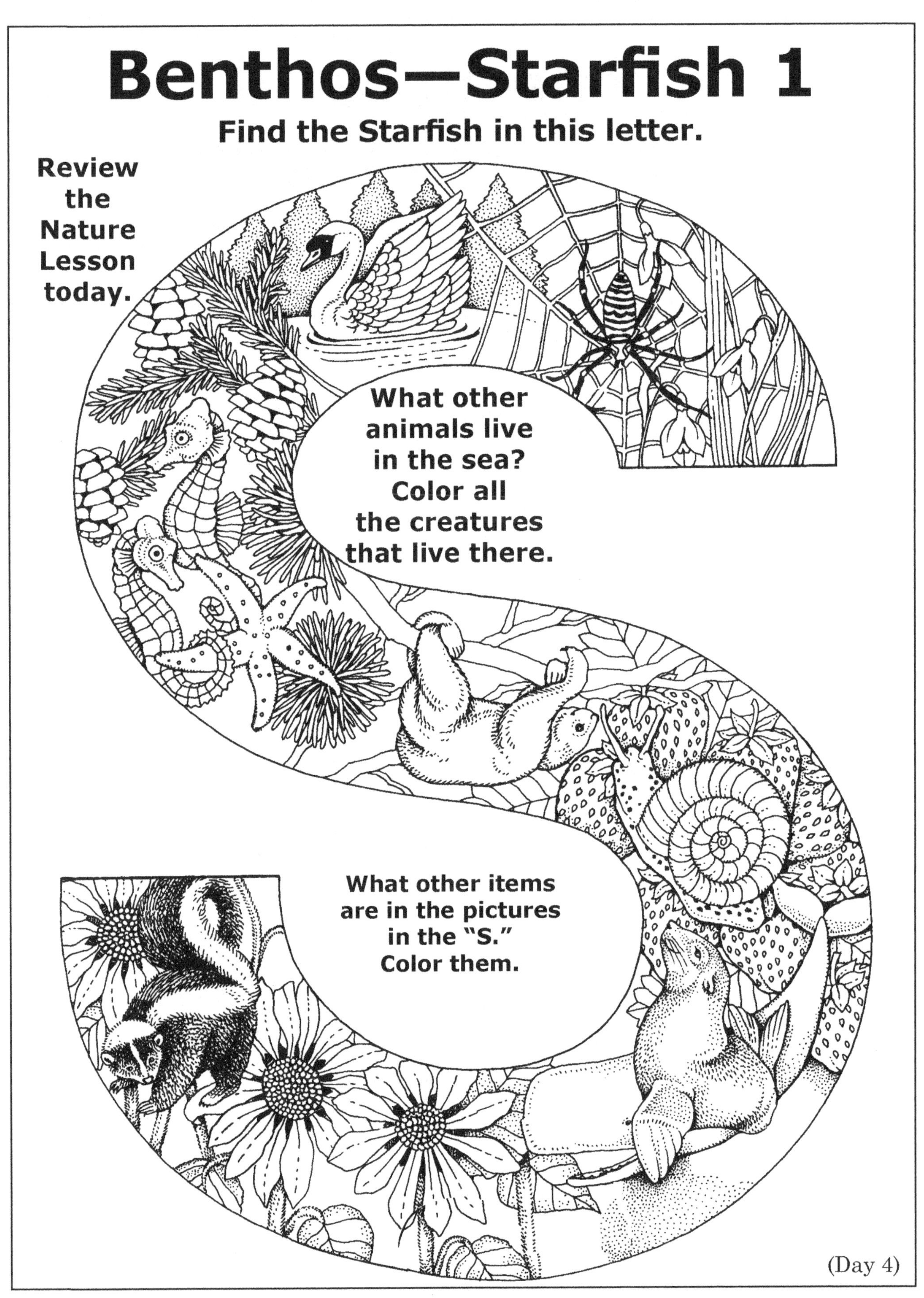

(Day 4)

"True Giving"

God has **given** us all that we have, and if we remember this, gratitude for these gifts should make us willing to give to Him whenever we have the opportunity.

One day a gentleman **gave** a little boy a gold dollar. "Now you must keep that," said the gentleman.

"Oh, no, " said the boy; "I shall half it first. Maybe I shall keep my half."

"Your half?" said the gentleman, "why, it's all yours."

"No," answered the child, with an earnest shake of the head; "No, it's not all mine. I always go halves with God. Half I shall keep, and half I shall give to Him."

"God owns the world; He does not need it," said the gentleman; *"the gold and the silver, and the cattle on a thousand hills belong to Him."*

The little boy looked puzzled for a moment. He had never thought of this. Presently he said: "Any how, God goes halves with us, and don't you think we ought to **give** Him back His part?"

That was the right feeling. This little boy felt grateful to God for all the good things He had given him, and it was the gratitude he felt that made him desire to "go halves with God."

But then Jesus **gave** Himself to die for us, and gratitude for this should made it easy for us to learn the lesson of **giving**.

"For God so loved the world, that he gave his only begotten Son, that whosoever believeth in him should not perish, but have everlasting life."
John 3:16

(Day 4)

Reward

The earth gives us treasure four-fold all that
We give to its bosom;
The care we bestow on the plant comes back
In the bud and the blossom.

The sun draws the sea to the sky,
O, stillest and strangest of powers,
And returns to the hills and the meadows
The gladness of bountiful showers.

The mother regains her lost youth in the beauty
And youth of her daughters;
We are fed after many long days by the bread
That we cast on the waters.

Never a joy do we cause but we for
That joy are the gladder,
Never a heart do we grieve,
But we for the grieving are sadder.

—Carlotta Perry

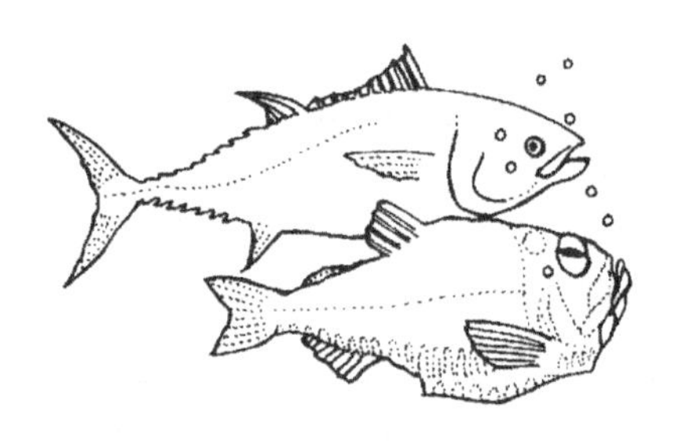

(Day 4)

Right Words

Find these quotes in *Steps to Christ*, pages 23 and 33.
Fill in the missing words.

"Repentance includes ______________ for sin

and a __________ away from it.

We shall not ____________ sin unless

we see its ____________;

until we turn away from it in____________,

there will be no real ___________ in the life."

"Every act of ________________, every neglect or rejection

of the ____________ of Christ,

is reacting upon yourself; it is _____________the heart,

_____________ the will, ____________ the understanding,

and not only making you less inclined to yield,

but less capable of yielding,

to the _____________

_____________of God's Holy Spirit."

Parents and older children can read pages 13-36 in *Steps to Christ*.

(Day 5)

Preaching

In **giving** to others the precious words about Christ we become stronger ourselves and grow in Him.

A message is below for you to discover. Use the key.

"__________ __________ __________ __________

__________ __________ __________ __________

__________ __________ __________ __________."

The Acts of the Apostles 60

Key Words

and	seed	the
bore	sown	up
fruit	sprang	Saviour
had	that	The

(Day 5)

Benthos—Starfish 2

Finish drawing the starfish by following the numbers. Start with 1.
Color the starfish.
What colors should it be?
Describe a starfish.
What spiritual lesson
can it teach us?

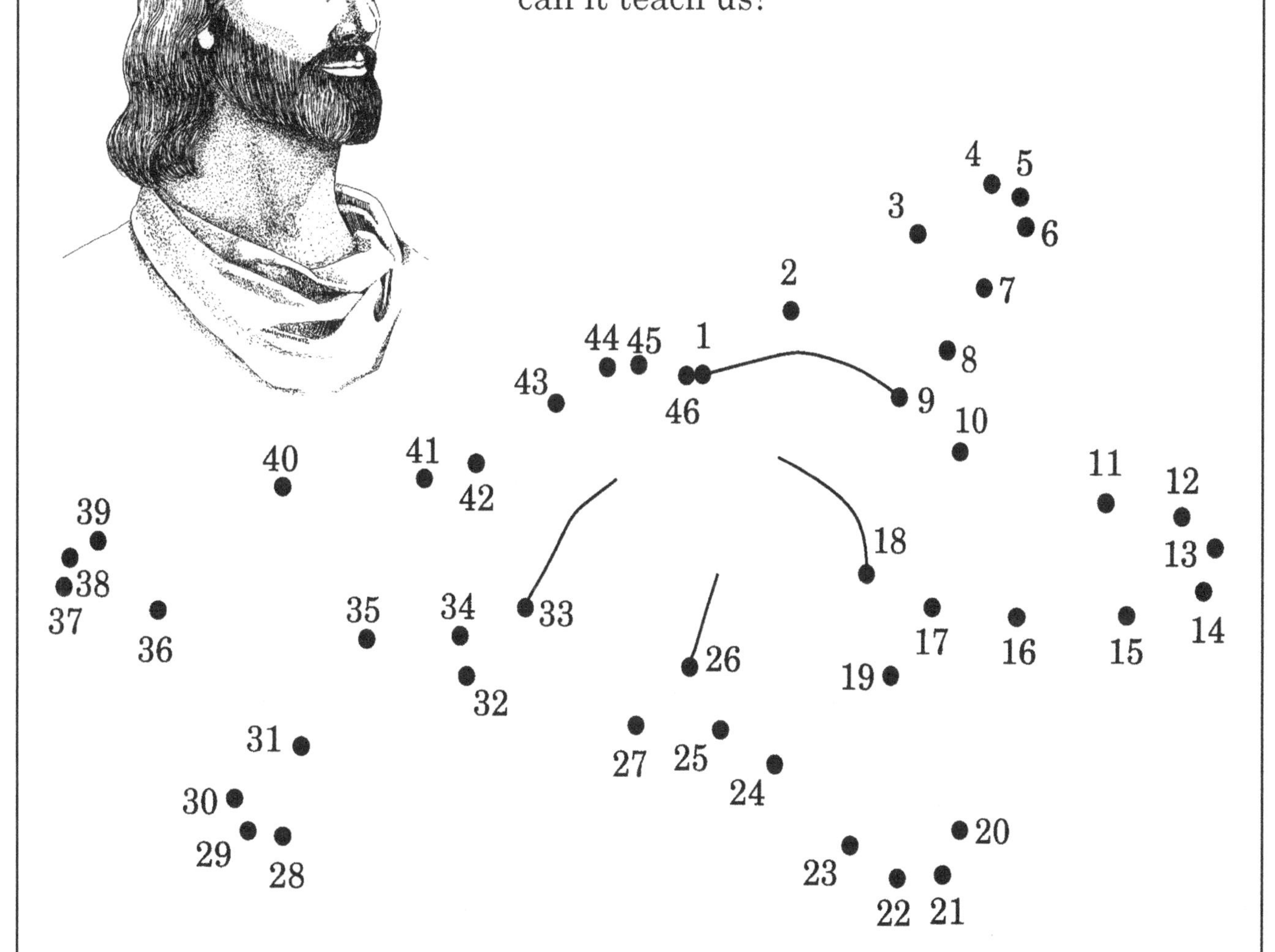

As the starfish is called sea star, so Jesus was called the Star of Jacob.
It was through the **giving** of His power
that the crippled man was healed. (Day 5)

"They Believed"

1. What was the disciples' main message?

2. Who was waiting for this testimony?

3. How did they respond?

4. Why?

5. What happens when we give to others the precious words about Christ?

(Day 6)

Benthos—Starfish 3

Trace this starfish.
Cut it out.
Fold it on the dotted lines on the bottom side starting from the tip of each leg all the way across the body. Then refold only the section of each line running between each leg to the center of the starfish in the opposite direction.

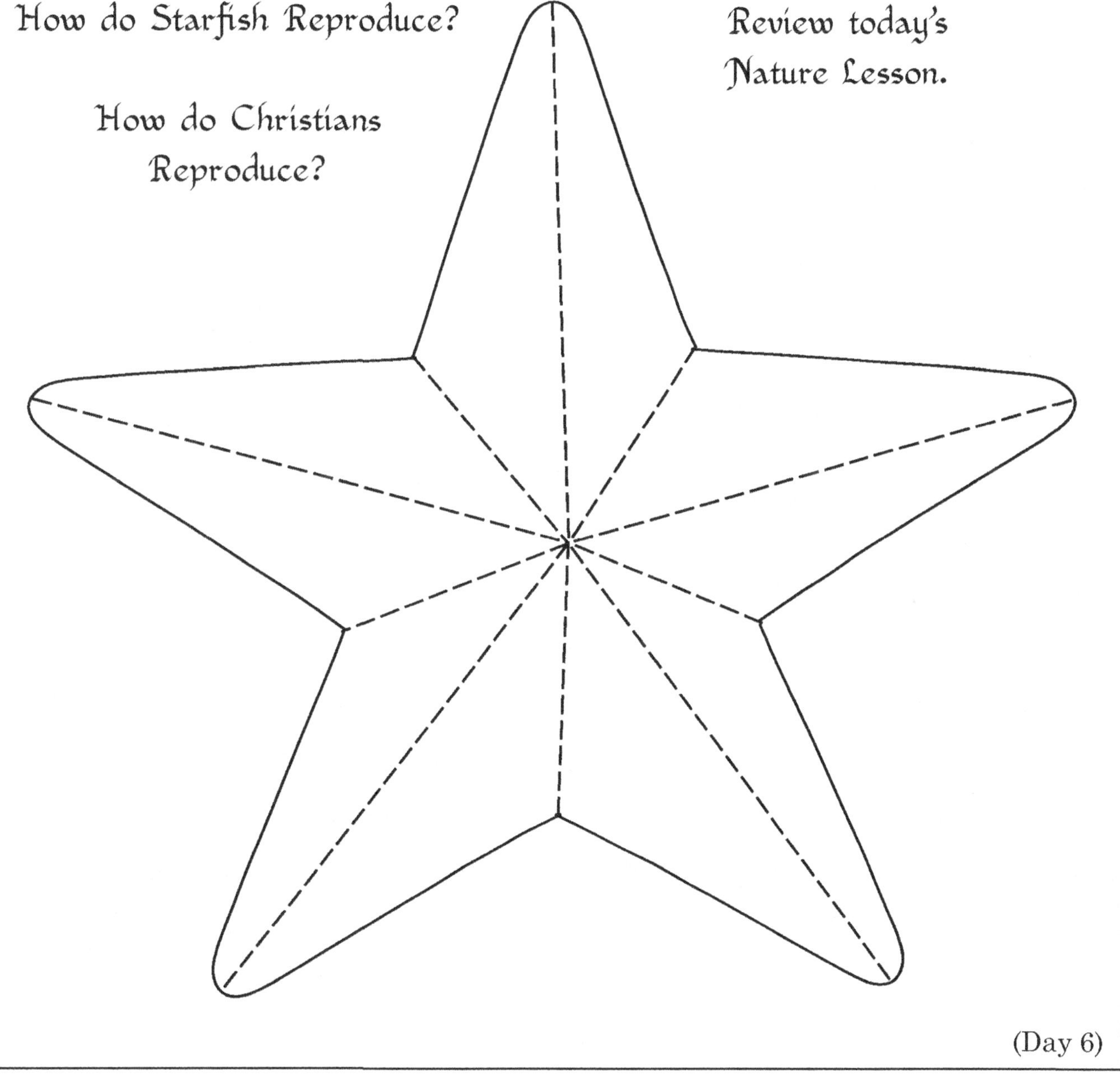

(Day 6)

Tide Pools

Study this picture for 60 seconds. Take the picture away,
then tell your teacher what was in the picture.
Next, bring it back and find the items, name and color them.

(Day 6)

Sarge

How beautiful and costly is the life of Jesus who gave it for you!

Back in the 1930s when on the farm, a neighbor of mine constructed a homemade electric fence by using 220-volt direct current, which packed quite a wallop.

One day my five-year-old brother and an uncle were walking in an orgon rain with our pet bulldog, Sarge. My brother, being an inquisitive child, decided to see if the wire of the electric fence would really shock a person in the rain. Again, being a typical boy, he had walked through every mud puddle, thoroughly soaking his feet, thus providing electricity with excellent grounding.

Needless to say, my brother got severely shocked—to the point where he could not let go.

When my uncle saw what had occurred and tried to release him, he found that the two of them were "frozen" together by the charge of the high-voltage electricity. They would both surely have died within minutes.

Somehow, Sarge perceived the trouble in which my little brother and my uncle had placed themselves. With those powerful bulldog jaws, he bit the wire in half.

It was as if Sarge knew that he had only a split second to do the deed or he too, would be frozen by the electrical charge and become as helpless as they were.

Although he accomplished the heroic deed, he could not escape the effects of the powerful electric charge. Sarge fell dead the instant his jaws snapped the wire. My brother and uncle survived only because of Sarge's unselfish act of sacrifice.

Later, the doctor who examined my brother said that his heart could not have handled very much more of the electrical current.

I have always wondered just how it was that old Sarge could have understood that my brother and uncle were being killed by the wire. And even perceiving that, how did he know that the wire must be cut in order to save their lives?

—Benjamin Smith

(Day 6)

Bulldogs

The bulldog has a height of 14-16 inches.
It weights about 40-50 pounds.
Color this picture.
Find a color picture of a bulldog to look at.
Bulldogs are found in these colors:
brindle, white, red, fawn, fallow, or piebald.

"My brother and uncle survived only because
of Sarge's unselfish act of sacrifice."
You are living today because of the unselfish act
of Jesus' sacrifice. GIVE your life to HIM now!

Silver and Gold Have I None

Jesus, Saviour, Pilot Me

Jesus, Saviour, pilot me
Over life's tempestuous sea;
Unknown waves before me roll,
Hiding rock and treacherous shoal;
Chart and compass come from Thee;
Jesus Saviour, pilot me.

As a mother stills her child,
Thou canst hush the ocean wild;
Boisterous waves obey Thy will
When Thou sayest to them, "Be still."
Wondrous Sovereign of the sea,
Jesus, Saviour, pilot me.

When at last I near the shore,
And the fearful breakers roar
'Twixt me and the peaceful rest,
Then, while leaning on Thy breast,
May I hear Thee say to me,
"Fear not, I will pilot thee."

—Edward Hopper, 1871

6 – Peter and John

Bible – Acts 4:1-33

Song – "Stand Up for Jesus"

Nature – Coral

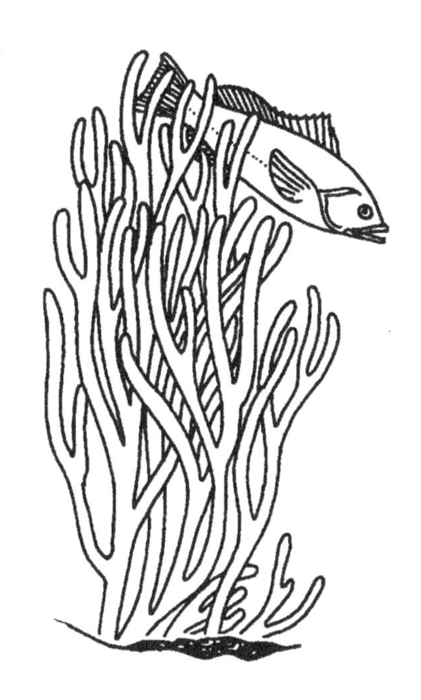

Character Quality

Boldness vs Fearfulness
Boldness is the courage that comes from doing what is right, because it will honor God.

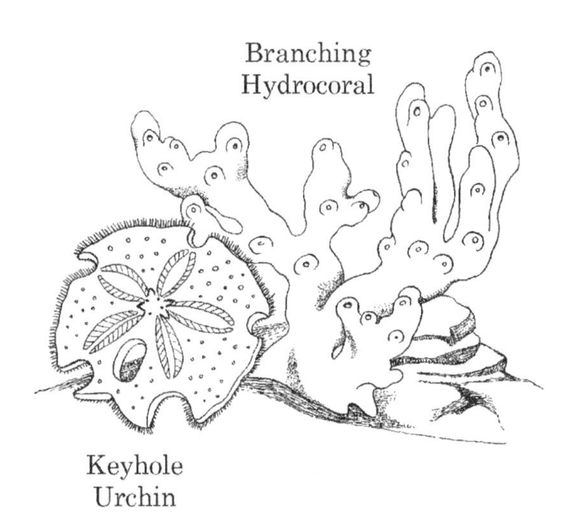

Memory Verse

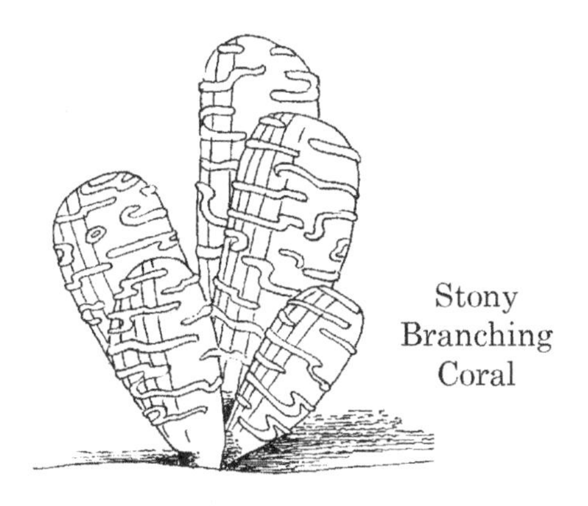

"Neither is there salvation in any other: for there is none other name under heaven given among men, whereby we must be saved."
Acts 4:12

Coral

Barrier reefs of coral stand up **boldly** to the sea
as the disciples did to the sea of people.

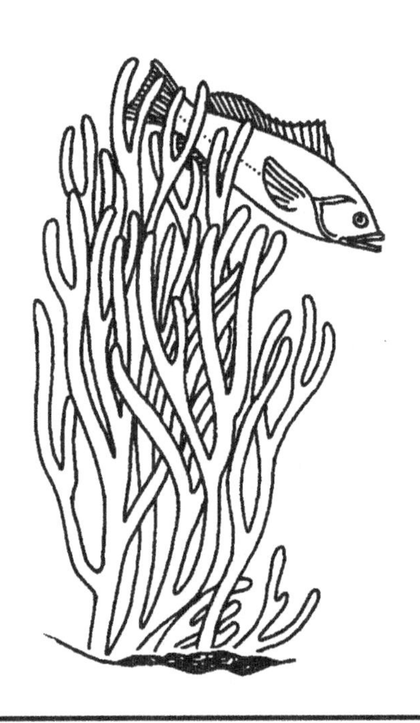

Draw a part of a coral reef
for each day this week
you study your lesson,
and say your memory verse.

Arrested

"And as they spake unto the people, the priests, and the captain of the temple, and the Sadducees, came upon them, And they laid hands on them, and put them in hold unto the next day: for it was now eventide."

Acts 4:1,3

What were the Jewish leaders afraid of?
To answer this question do the following.

1. Cross out all the lower case letters.
2. From the remaining letters, cross out every third letter.
3. Use the remaining letters to write your answer.

____

i	I	e	N	a
A	o	F	L	B
U	E	D	N	u
g	C	I	y	m
t	o	E	s	g

(Day 1)

Benthos—Coral

Answer the questions below by using the key.

1. What is coral?

2. What lives among the coral?

3. Where are some islands formed of coral?

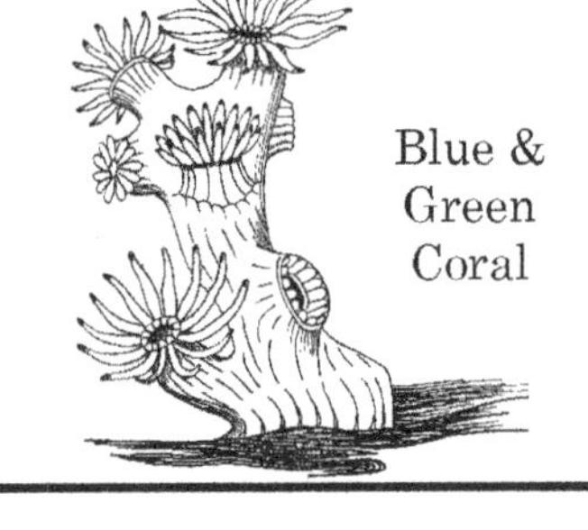
Blue & Green Coral

Key

A	B	C	D	E	F	G	H	I	J	K	L	M
1	2	3	4	5	6	7	8	9	10	11	12	13
N	**O**	**P**	**Q**	**R**	**S**	**T**	**U**	**V**	**W**	**X**	**Y**	**Z**
14	15	16	17	18	19	20	21	22	23	24	25	26

1. _ _ _ _ _ _ _ _ _ _ _ _
20 9 14 25 1 14 9 13 1 12 19

2. _ _ _ _ _ _ _ _ _
19 20 1 18 6 9 19 8

_ _ _ _
6 9 19 8

_ _ _ _ _ _ _ _ _ _ _ _
19 5 1 1 14 5 13 15 14 5 19

3. _ _ _ _ _ _ _ _ _ _ _ _ _
19 15 21 20 8 16 1 3 9 6 9 3

As sea creatures find homes in the coral reefs,
so God's people can find a refuge in the Truth.

(Day 1)

Trial

1. "On the day following the healing of the cripple," who all met together for the trial of the disciples?

2. What did Peter remember when he was brought before them?

3. What did those present think they could do to Peter?

4. Who was Peter's Helper?

5. How did Peter respond to the question put to him?

6. What did Peter's weak point become?

Answer the above questions. Color this picture.

(Day 2)

Coral Reefs

Answer these questions:

1. What is a Coral Reef?

2. What can we spiritually learn from a developing Coral Reef?

3. What is a Fringing Reefs; Barrier Reef; and Astoll?

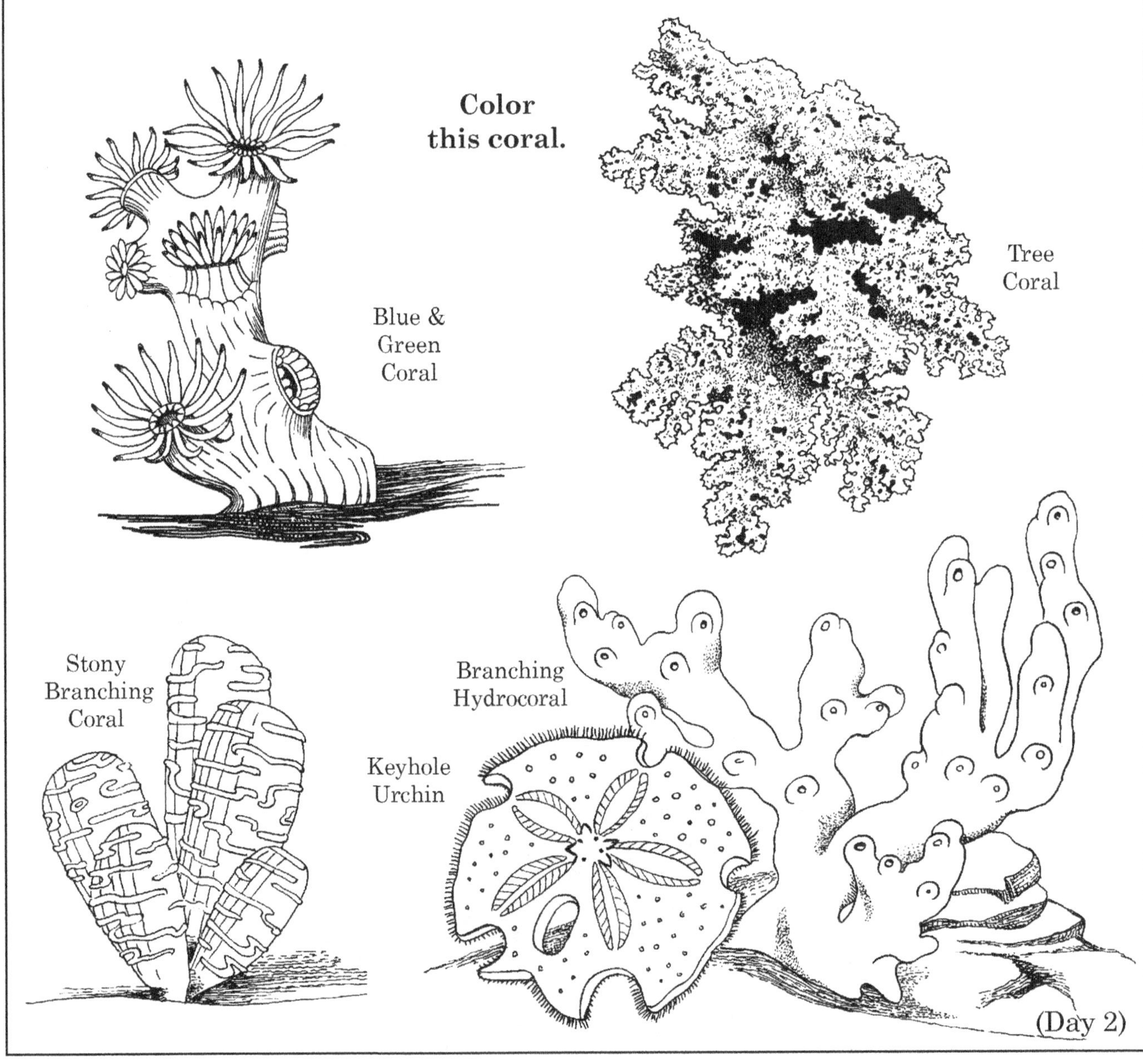

Children Can Preach

To the young, the following incident, given by an aged minister, will be very encouraging.

A little girl in one city, who had been early trained in the way of salvation, **boldly** entered the store of a merchant near by, and addressed him thus:

"I have come to tell you that Jesus died for sinners."

"What is that?" said the merchant, as though he did not understand her.

She **boldly** repeated with double emphasis, "I have come to tell you that Jesus died for sinners."

Having delivered her message, she retired to her own room; but the short and thrilling declaration left its impression. He thought of her object. He thought upon the address, and the angel-like simplicity in which it was delivered, and then reflected that it was to him. In vain did he try to rid himself of the conviction that was made upon his heart by the thrilling sermon of this little girl. Wherever he went, in whatever business he was engaged, whether measuring his cloth, or weighing his produce, the tidings still sounded in his ears, "Jesus died for sinners."

The little leaven continued to increase. The momentous truth to which he had listened, became to him an active reality. His condition as a sinner was clearly represented in the light of the Holy Spirit. He sought and in a short time realized that Jesus died for him, and he began to rejoice in a happy Christian experience.

How true it is that "*words fitly spoken are like apples of gold in pictures of silver*"! I would rather be that little girl, leading that merchant to Christ and to Heaven, than a Xerxes, leading a million of soldiers into Greece; and how much rather share in her reward! What must have been the gratitude of that converted merchant toward the little girl! and what exceedingly sweet notes of joy, at the moment of his conversion, fell upon "angelic ears"! "*Let us not be weary in well-doing, for in due season we shall reap, if we faint not.*"

—*The Young Pilgrim*

(Day 2)

When I look up to yonder sky,
So pure, so bright, so wondrous high,
I think of One I cannot see,
But One Who sees and cares for me.

His name is God! He gave me birth;
And every living thing on earth,
And every tree and plant that grows,
To the same hand its being owes.

'Tis He my daily food provides,
And all that I require besides;
And when I close my slumbering eye,
I sleep in peace, for He is nigh.

Then surely I should ever love
This gracious God Who reigns above;
For very kind indeed is He,
To love a little child like me.

——*Unknown*

(Day 2)

Council

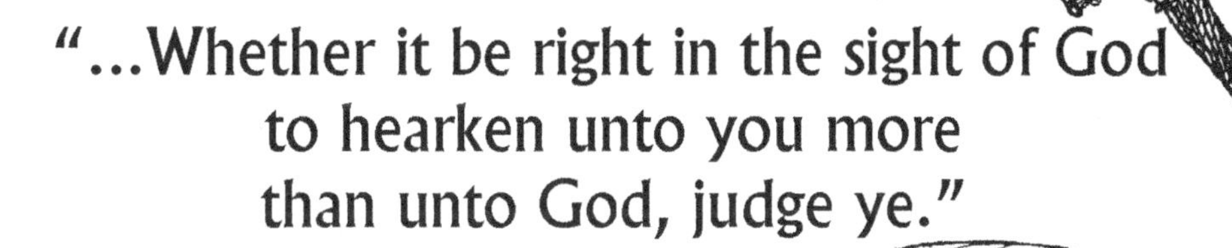

"...Whether it be right in the sight of God
to hearken unto you more
than unto God, judge ye."

Acts 4:19

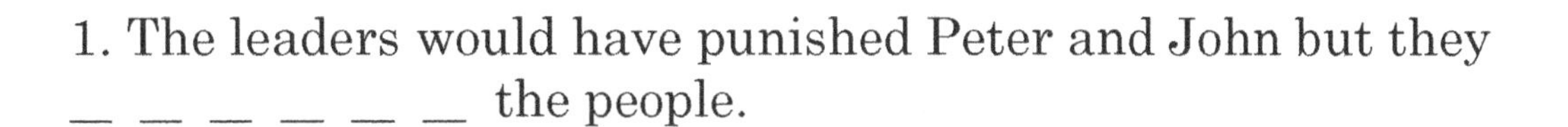

1. The leaders would have punished Peter and John but they _ _ _ _ _ _ the people.

T F H E R A E

R A E T D S

2. "So, with repeated _ _ _ _ _ _ _ _ and injunctions, the apostles were set at liberty."

Instructions

1. Start with letter two and color every other letter yellow for the first answer.

2. You will find the second answer in the first two lines of letters in the uncolored one.

(Day 3)

How Coral Is Formed 1

Read Acts 4:11-12 from the Bible.

______________ ________
are platforms of living coral under the sea that extend out from the shore.

1

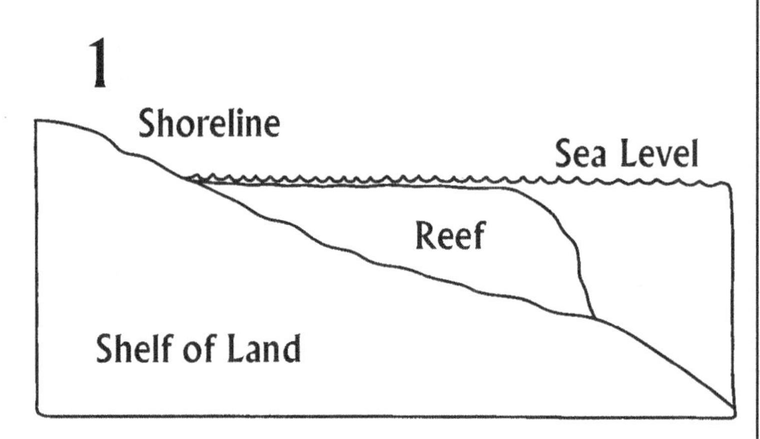

______________ ________
follow along the shoreline, but are separated from it by water.

2

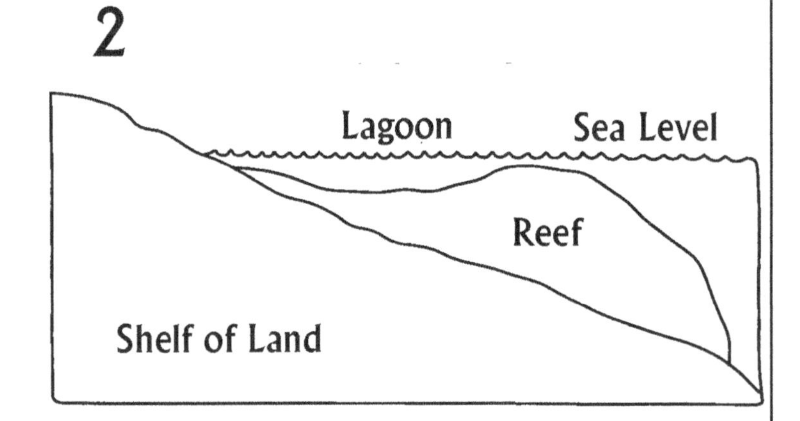

An ______________
is a ring-shaped coral island in the open sea.

3

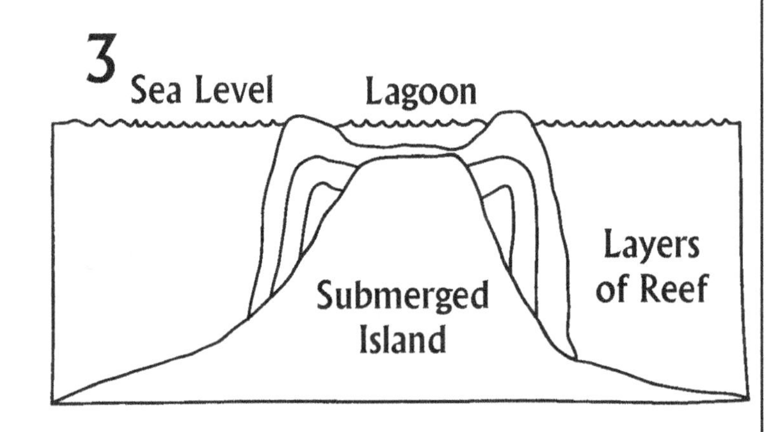

Directions: Draw a line from the information to the cross section picture then fill in the correct reef: Fringing Reef, Barrier Reef, and Atoll.

(Day 3)

Praying

"And now, Lord, behold their threatenings: and grant unto thy servants, that with all boldness they may speak thy words."

Acts 4:29

Review today's lesson and color this picture.

(Day 4)

Deliverance

Memorize this verse then color these letters gold.

"...He preserveth
the souls
of his saints;
he delivereth
them
out of the hand
of the wicked."

Psalm 97:10

(Day 4)

How Coral Is Formed 2

Coral Polyps

Fill in the blanks and answer the questions.

1. Coral polyps reproduce from ________ or by __________________.
2. Christians reproduce by ______________________.
3. Describe the budding of polyps.
4. What does budding do for the main colony?
5. __________________ under Christ is like the budding of coral polyps for it increases the ______________ of the believer and gives him _____________ to speak _____________.

Coral Polyps Develop

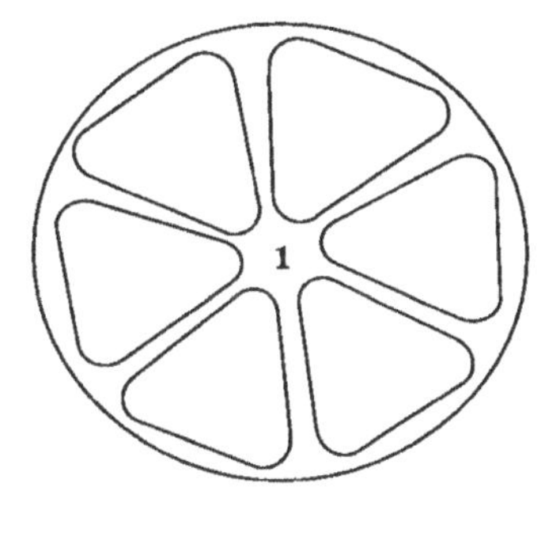

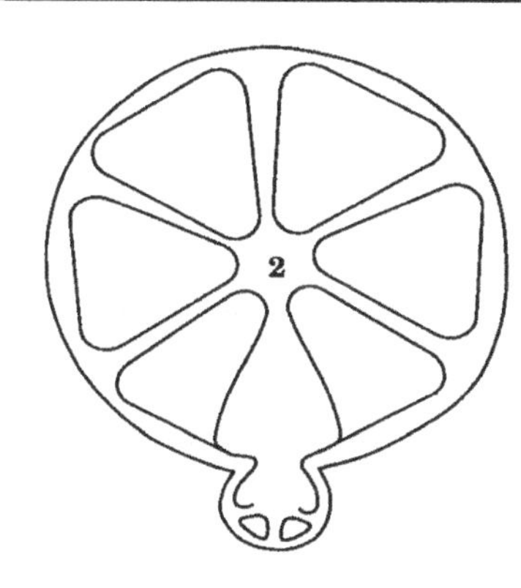

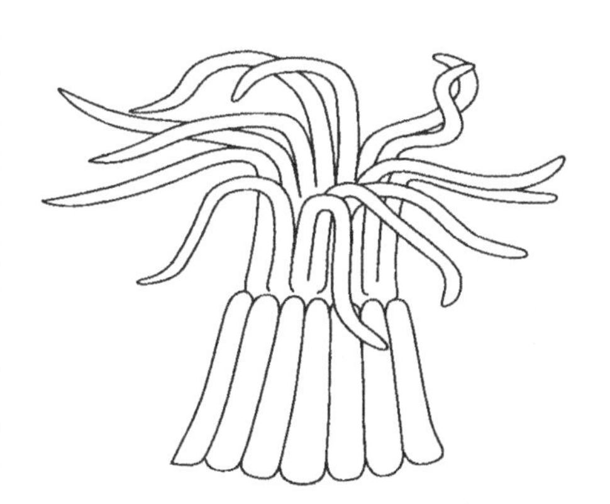

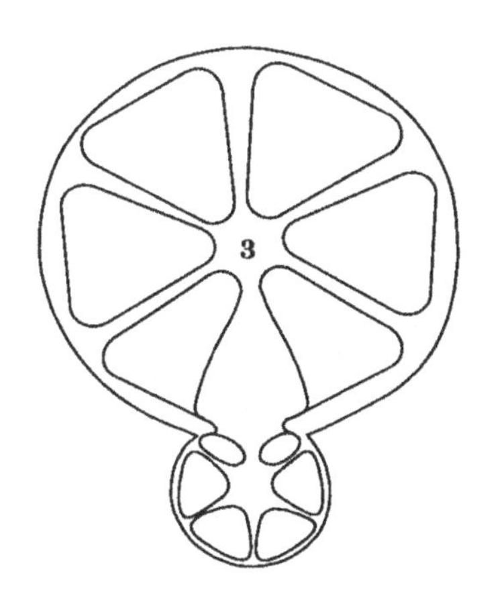

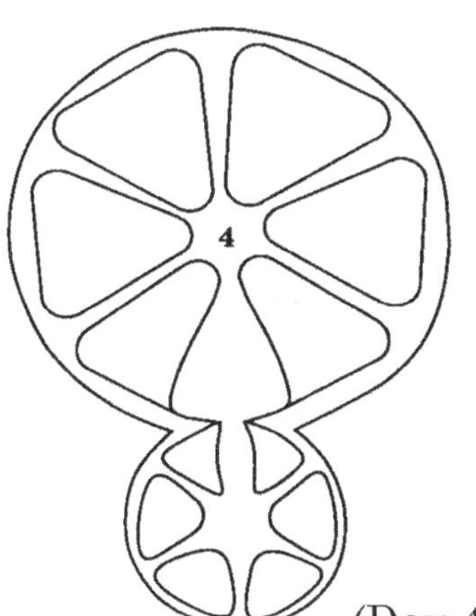

Color the polyps golden yellow.

(Day 4)

Coral with Polyps

Find in a sea identification book these plants and animals.
Color this picture using the illustration found in the Answer Key.

(Day 4)

What A Child May Do

Read this story then hand out tracts or magazines about the Sabbath!

A little boy in London, who attended a Sabbath School, having occasion every Lord's day to go through a certain court, observed a shop open for the sale of goods. Shocked at such a profanation, he considered whether it was possible for him to do any thing to prevent it. He determined to leave a tract about the "Lord's day," as he passed the shop in the course of the week. He did so; and on the following Sabbath he observed that the shop was closed. Surprised at this, he stopped and considered whether it could be the effect of the tract he had left. He ventured to knock gently at the door, when a woman within, thinking it was a customer, answered aloud: "You cannot have anything; we don't sell on the Sabbath."

Encouraged by what he had heard, the little boy still begged for admittance. Then the woman, recollecting his voice, said,

"Come in, my dear little fellow: it was you that left the tract here against Sabbath-breaking; and it alarmed me so that I did not dare to keep my shop open any longer; and I am determined never to do so again while I live.

—*Sabbath School Visitor*

Amazing Facts, Inc. has a new magazine
called "The Rest of Your Life!"
This is an excellent hand out to others
concerning the Sabbath.
Contact them at PO Box 1058
Roseville, CA 95678-8058
Phone: 916-434-3880; Fax: 916-434-3889

(Day 4)

The Bold Conqueror

This life is a battle with Satan and sin,
And we are the soldiers, the victory to win.
And Christ is the captain of our little band,
Whatever opposes, for Him we will stand.

To God for our armor, we'll fail not to go.
He'll clothe us with truth and with righteousness too,
The *"gospel of peace"* shall our footsteps attend,
The *"good shield of faith"* from all harm shall defend.

Though little temptations, the worst of them all,
Will often beset us to make us to fall,
We'll stand up for Jesus, and when life is o'er,
For us He'll be standing on Jordan's bright shore.

—Unknown

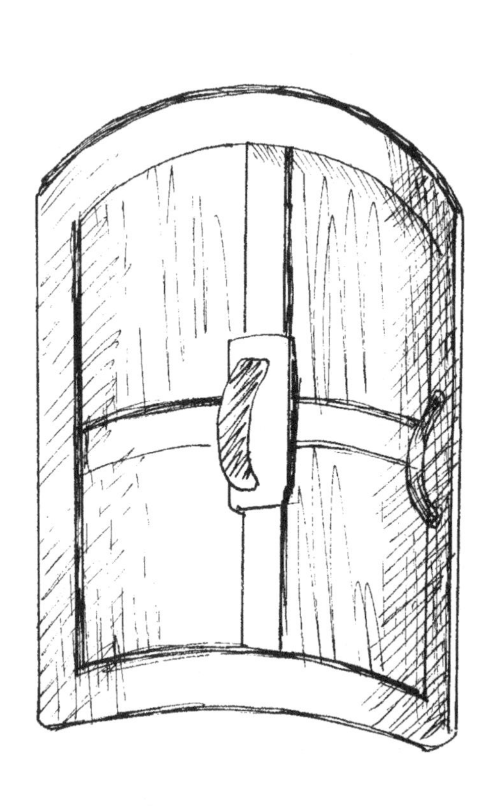

(Day 4)

Power of God

"And when they had prayed, the place was shaken where they were assembled together; and they were all filled with the Holy Ghost, and they spake the word of God with boldness."
Acts 4:31

"Only to those who wait humbly upon God, who watch for His guidance and grace is the Spirit given."
The Desire of Ages 672

Color the picture.

(Day 5)

How A Coral Reef is Formed

1. How is a coral reef formed?

2. What spiritual lesson can the above lesson teach us?

3. Who eats the living coral that are forming?

4. What creature can destroy stony coral colonies on many reefs of the southwest Pacific Oceans?

5. How can this statement remind us of a spiritual lesson: Scientists do not know why the starfish have become so numerous!

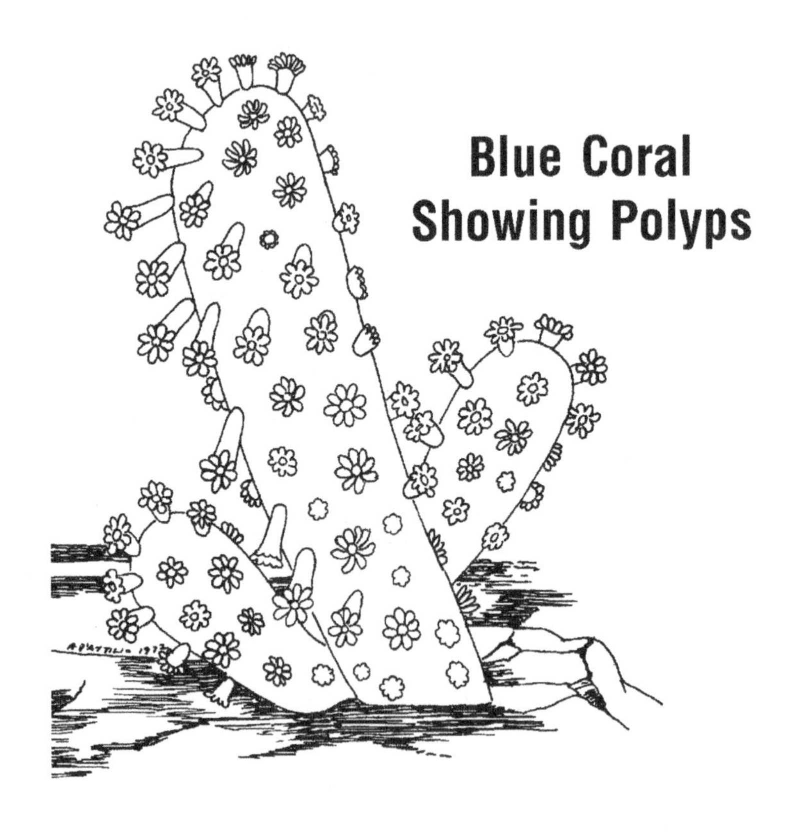

Blue Coral Showing Polyps

(Day 5)

"The crown of Christ is to be lifted above the diadems of earthly potentates [rulers]."

The Acts of the Apostles 69

Answer these questions with yes or no.

1. Are we to be **bold** for the Lord? _________

2. Are we to be disrespectful of those in authority? _________

3. Are human governments appointed by God? _________

4. Are we to obey human government as long as it does not require us to disobey God? _________

5. Do we believe in law and order? __________

6. Are we to continue to work for God if government says we cannot? _________

7. Would you keep the Sabbath if government said you had to worship on Sunday? _________

"In matters of conscience the majority has no power...."
"This principle we in our day are firmly to maintain. The banner of truth and religious liberty held aloft by the founders of the gospel church and by God's witnesses during the centuries that have passed since then, has, in this last conflict, been committed to our hands."

The Acts of the Apostles 68-69

(Day 6)

Precious Corals

Color each coral the color indicated.

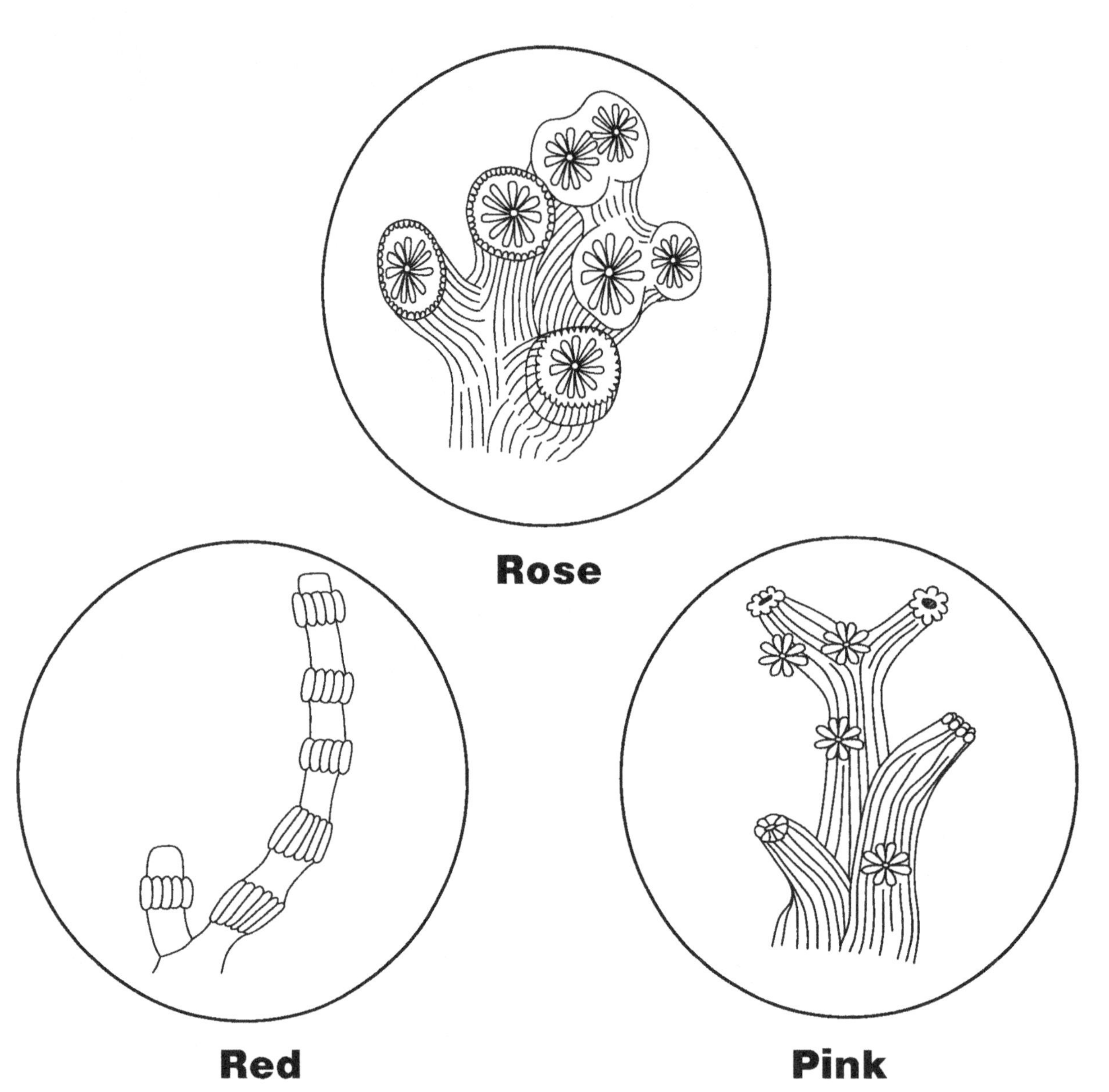

Precious coral is the kind that is valued for jewelry.
Jesus has other precious souls the disciples were
to search out with holy **boldness**.

Find the Mediterranean Sea and the Sea of Japan on a map.
Remember, this is where precious coral is found.

(Day 6)

Coral Coral Coral Coral

1. ______________________________

2. ______________________________

3. ______________________________

Find the Brain Coral, Burrowing Shrimp, and the Spotted Snail in the picture below and print on the lines above.

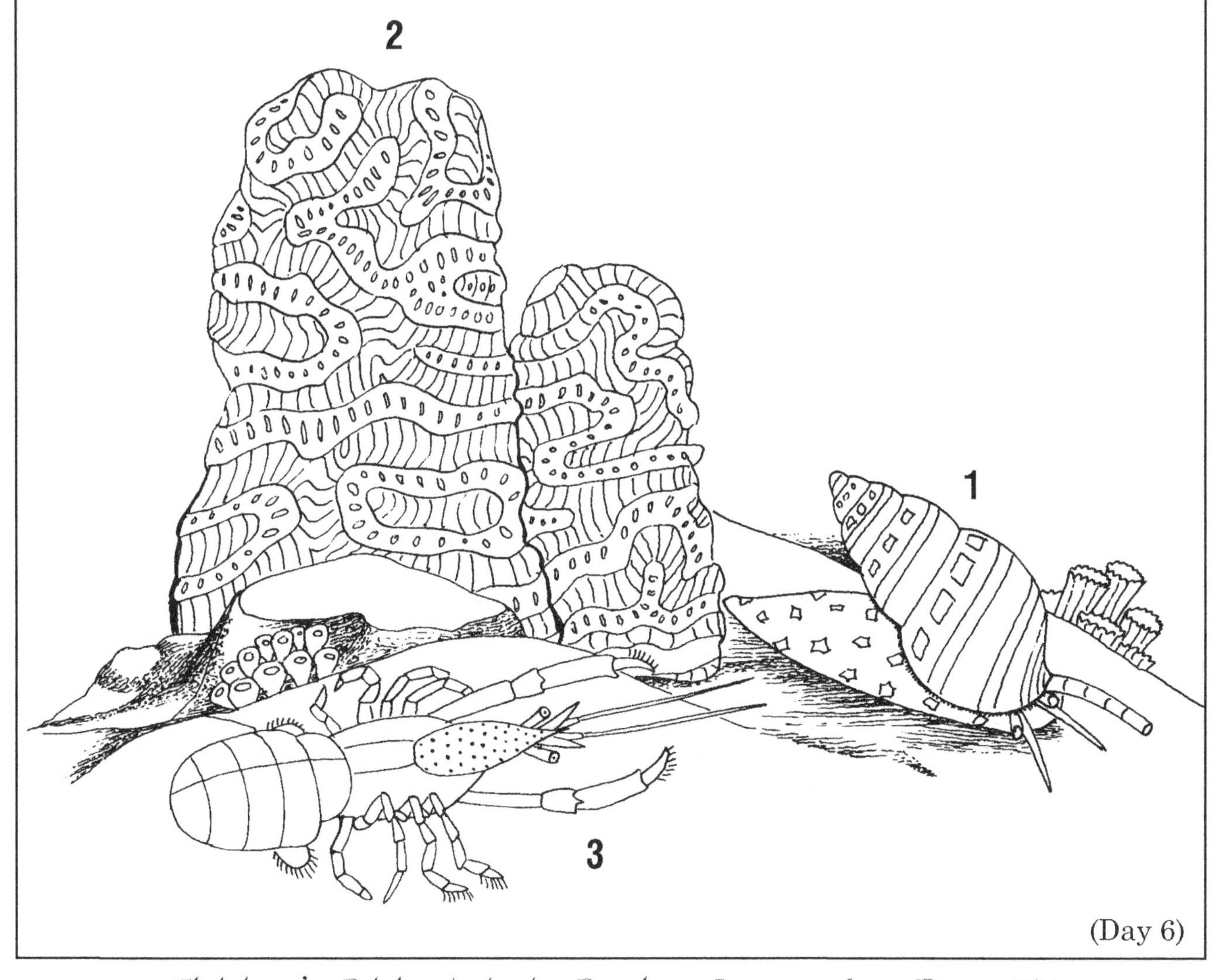

(Day 6)

Coral Coral Coral Coral

Color this picture.

1. **Which coral is named for an animal?**
2. **Which coral is named for a fungus?**
3. **Do more study about Astrangia Coral.**

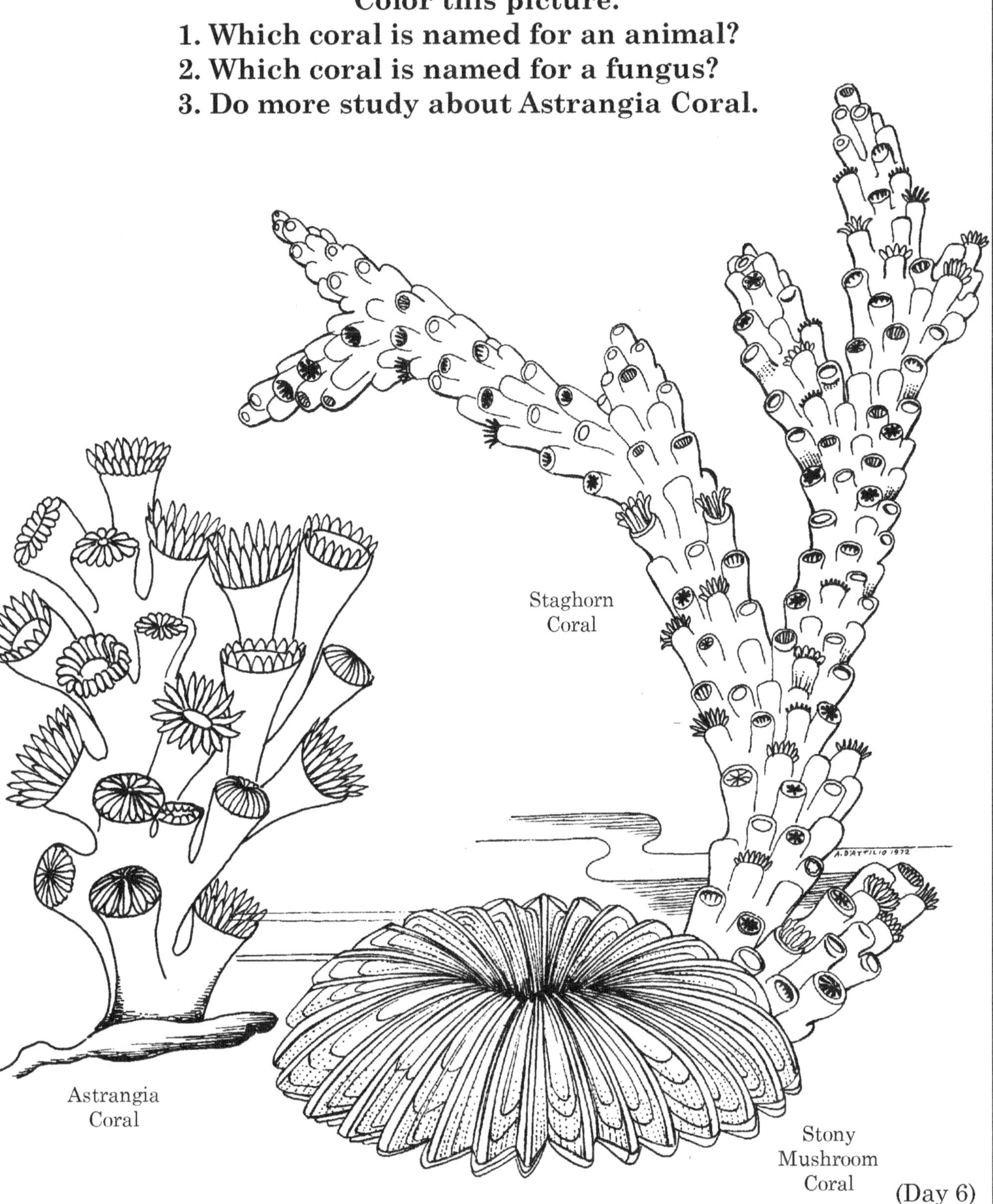

(Day 6)

Fear

"...I will send a faintness
into their hearts in the lands of their enemies;
and the sound of a shaken leaf shall chase them;
and they shall flee, as fleeing from a sword;
and they shall fall when none pursueth."
Leviticus 26:36

Can you imagine a person so fearful that he runs in terror at the sound of a falling leaf? Guilt-filled, he flees from imaginary foes, finally falling even though no one is pursuing him. Constantly, thousands fall into mental, physical, and emotional collapse because of fear. And most of the things they fear never happen.

Fear causes us to do strange things. Mr. Jones spent much time in the woods, for he loved everything in nature. He not only learned the name of every bird and tree but found out about the life of each.

On one of his walks he came to a small, quiet stream spanned by a little bridge. Something hanging on the underside resembled a bird's nest. This was new to him. He must find out what bird occupied it, yet there seemed to be no way to get to it without getting wet. Noticing many rocks in the stream, he decided to step from rock to rock to get close enough to investigate. All went well. Only one more rock and he could peer inside.

Suddenly two birds flew at him. The mother bird flew at his nose, turned and quickly zoomed back toward his eyes. The father bird's wings knocked his glasses into the water. Surprised at this attack, Mr Jones jumped back quickly, missed the rocks and splash! He was sitting in the stream. The parent birds were very small, yet fear caused him to do a funny thing. Although he had studied birds all his life, he scrambled out of the water in double-quick time and ran for home as it two bears were after him.

His was only momentary fear sparked by two small birds whose sharp bills could peck him. The fear expressed in our verse has a deeper cause. Those who run when nothing pursues are filled with fear because they do not listen to God or keep His commandments. Are you filled with imaginary fears possibly caused by following self instead of God? Fear can be sin. Jesus can give you peace when you submit your life to Him. You are living in the land of the enemy, but Jesus will take away your faintness of heart. Ask Him to do it right now.* (Day 6)

**Stop, Look, Listen*

Meditate

Fear or Fearless

"As the priests listened to the apostles' fearless words,
'they took knowledge of them, that they had been with Jesus.'"
The Acts of the Apostles 64

"Gladly would the priests have punished these men
for their unswerving fidelity to their sacred calling,
but they feared the people;
'for all men glorified God for that which was done.'
So, with repeated threats and injunctions,
the apostles were set at liberty."
The Acts of the Apostles 67

"The principle for which the disciples stood so fearlessly when,
in answer to the command not to speak any more in the name of Jesus,
they declared, *'Whether it be right in the sight of God to hearken
unto you more than unto God, judge ye,'*
is the same that the adherents of the gospel struggled
to maintain in the days of the Reformation."
The Acts of the Apostles 68

"When the mouse laughs at the cat, there is a hole nearby!"
—*Nigerian Proverb*
(Explain this saying.)

(Day 6)

7 – Ananias and Sapphira

Bible – Acts 4:34-37; 5:1-11

Song – "We Give Thee But Thine Own"

Nature – Sea Anemones and Sea Cucumbers

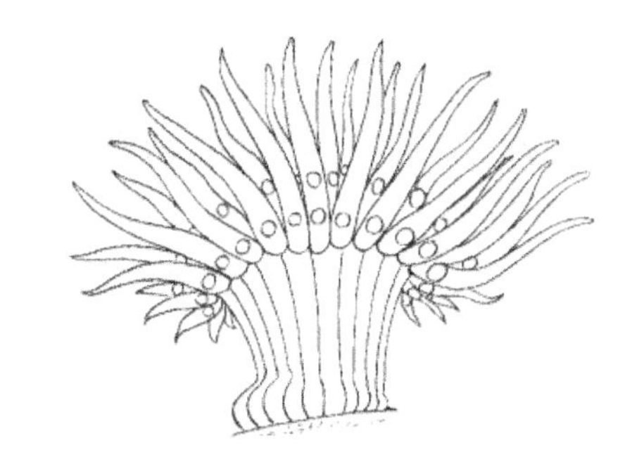

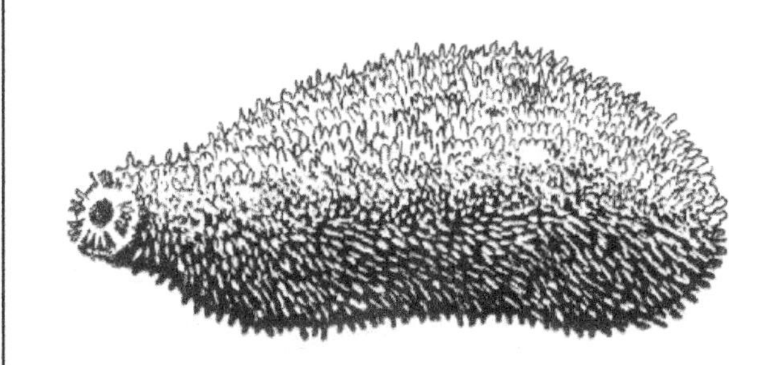

Character Quality

Carefulness vs Neglectfulness
Carefulness is heedful in guarding against evil and providing for safety.

Memory Verse

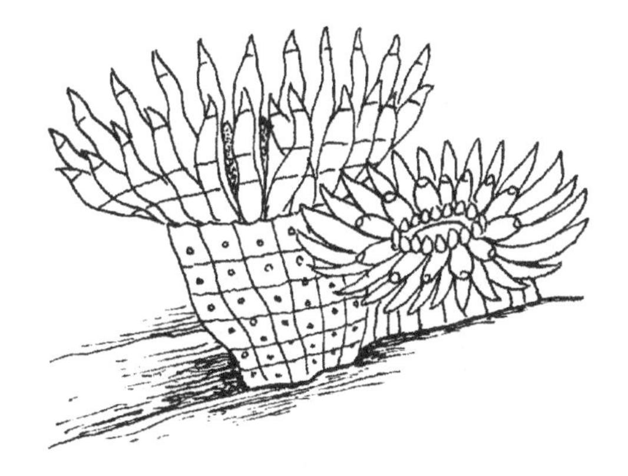

"Wherefore putting away lying, speak every man **truth** *with his neighbour: for we are members one of another."*
Ephesians 4:25

And also sing Proverbs 13:5.

Sea Anemones and Sea Cucumbers

The wartlet anemone has wart-like knobs on its body and that is how it got its name. These apparent defects remind us of the defect of selfishness and lying, which were defects of character in Ananias and Sapphira.

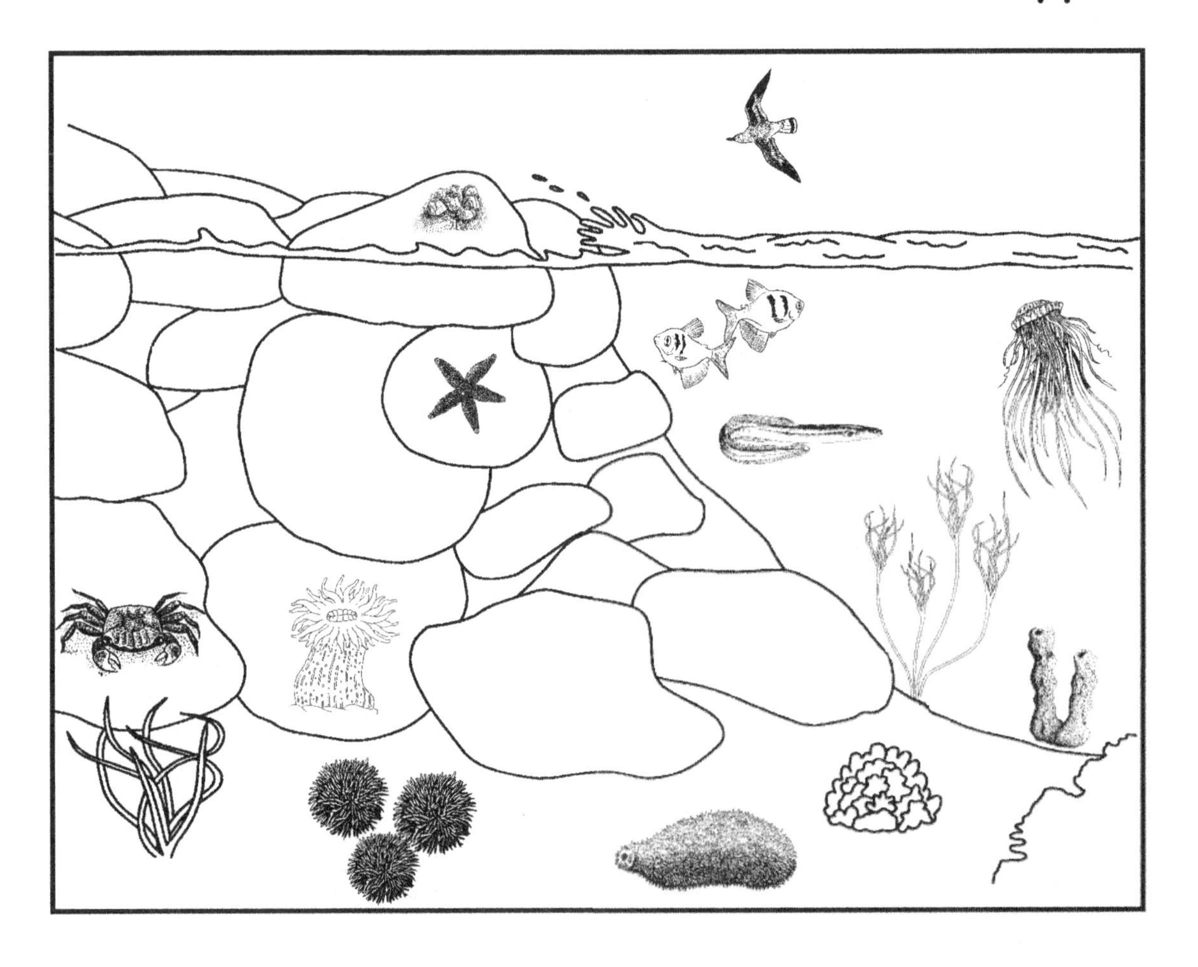

Color one or more sea creatures for each day this week you study your lesson, and say your memory verse.

Sharing

Find the words in the word-find below that describe the early church. Use the word list.

Word List

APOSTLES
BROUGHT
DISTRIBUTION
DOWN
FEET
HOUSES
LACKED
LAID
LANDS
NEED
POSSESSORS
PRICES
SOLD

S	A	D	E	K	C	A	L
R	P	I	E	O	S	A	A
O	T	S	L	E	I	E	N
S	B	T	S	D	N	S	D
S	H	R	O	U	G	E	S
E	S	I	O	T	D	S	O
S	E	B	I	U	S	U	L
S	C	U	T	R	G	O	D
O	I	T	I	N	B	H	U
P	R	I	W	F	E	E	T
A	P	O	S	T	L	E	S
T	D	N	I	O	N	L	A

(Day 1)

Sea Anemones 1

Sea anemones look like flowers. Our Bible story this week tells about two people who appeared like Christians, but were not.

Color the sea anemones bright colors like the flowers they resemble.

(Day 1)

Advancing the Gospel

Review today's Bible lesson while coloring this picture.

"He that hath pity upon the poor lendeth unto the LORD; and that which he hath given will he pay him again."
Proverbs 19:17

(Day 2)

Sea Anemones 2

Read the information then color the picture of the hermit crab. Review the rest of today's nature lesson.

A Hermit Crab has no hard carapace to cover the lower portion of its anatomy. These crabs must find and live in empty snail shells to protect their soft abdomens. As the crabs grow, they seek larger shells. These "homes" are carried with them everywhere. Formidable claws seal off the shell's entryway and threaten predators. However, sometimes the anemone's latch on to the crab's shell and protect it with its stinging tentacles. It is the crabs friend and they help each other. The early believers helped one another. Draw an anemone on the shell of the crab.

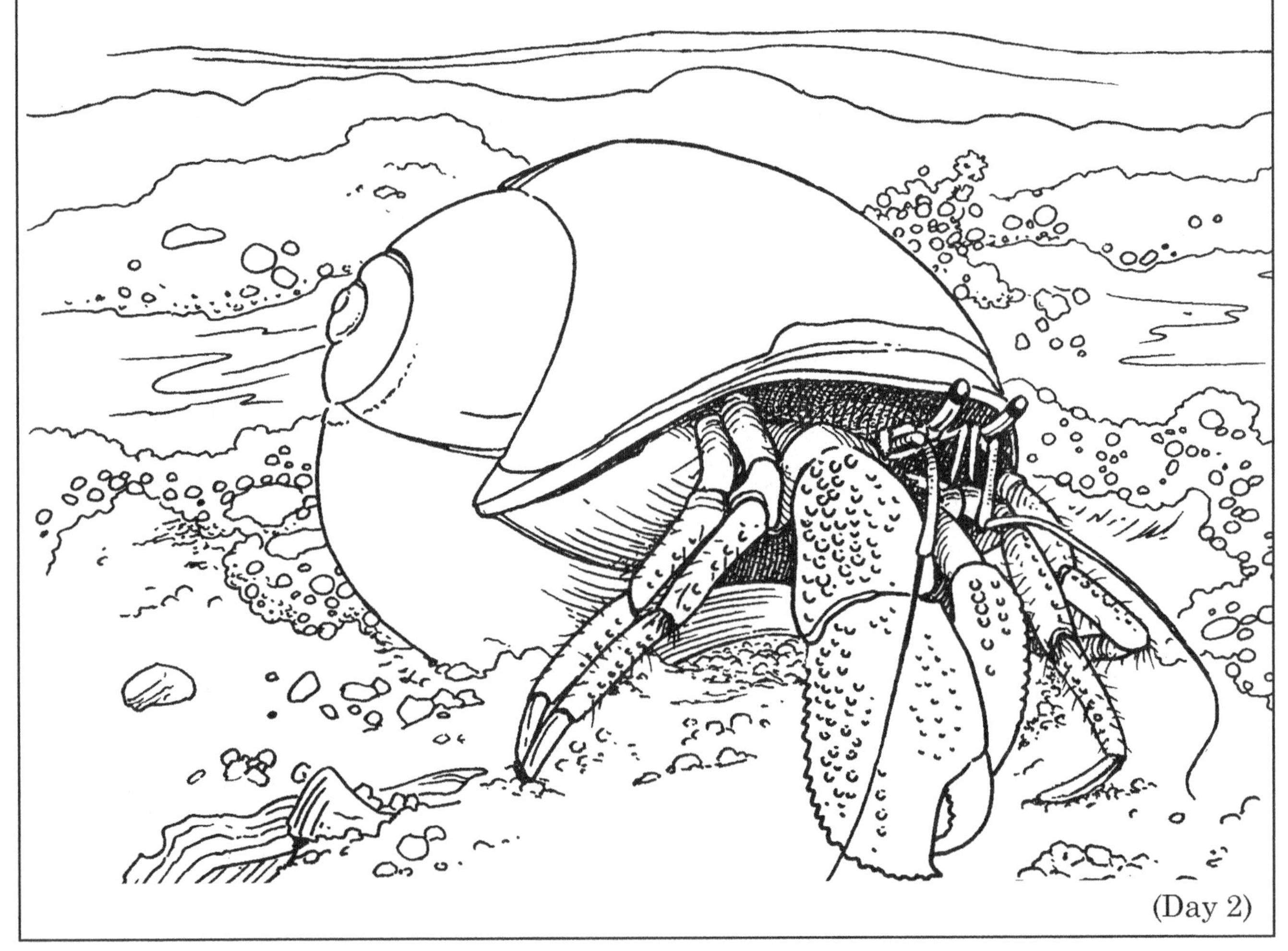

(Day 2)

"Thy Word Is A Lamp Unto My Feet"

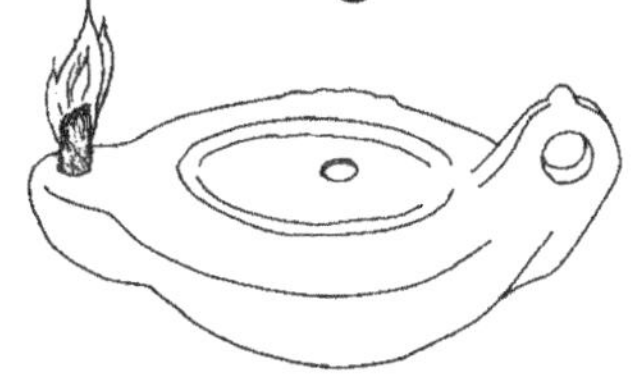

A ragged errand boy was carefully printing with chalk on a gate this Bible text.

So interested was he with his work that he did not notice a kind-looking old gentleman who, after walking slowly past twice, returned and stood beside him.

"M–y," said the boy, repeating the letters aloud as he formed them with care. F –double e–t, feet."

"Well done, my boy, well done!" said the old gentleman. "Where did you learn that?"

"At church sir," replied the boy, half frightened, and thinking the old gentleman was going to deliver him up to the police for writing on the gate.

"Don't run away; I'm not going to hurt you. What is your name?"

"Nicholas."

"So you learned that text at church. Do you know what it means?"

"No, sir," said Nicholas.

"What is a lamp?"

"A lamp why, a lamp is a thing that gives light!"

"And what is the word that the text speaks of?"

"The Bible, sir."

"That's right. Now, how can the Bible be a lamp and give light?"

"I don't know, unless you set it afire," said Nicholas.

"There is a better way than that, my lad. Suppose you were going down some lonely lane on a dark night with an unlighted lantern in your hand and a box of matches in your pocket, what would you do?"

(Day 2)

"Why, light the lantern, sir," replied Nicholas, evidently surprised that any one should ask such a foolish question.

"What would you light it for?"

"To show me the road, sir."

"Very well. Now, suppose you were walking behind me some day, and saw me drop a shilling, what would you do?"

"Pick it up, and give it to you again, sir."

"Wouldn't you want to keep it for yourself?"

Nicholas hesitated; but he saw a smile on the old gentleman's face, and with an answering one on his own, he said, "I should want to, sir, but I shouldn't do it."

"Why not?"

"Because it would be stealing."

"How did you know?"

"It would be taking what wasn't my own, and the Bible says we are not to steal."

"Ah!" said the old gentleman, "so it's the Bible that makes you honest, is it?"

"Yes, sir."

"If you had not heard of the Bible you would steal, I suppose?"

"Lots of the boys do," said Nicholas, hanging his head.

"And the Bible shows you the right and safe path, the path of honesty?"

"Like the lamp!" said Nicholas, seeing now what all these questions meant. "Is that what the text means?"

"Yes; there is always light in the Bible to show us where to go. Now, my boy, do you think it worth while to take this good old lamp and let it light you right through life?"

"Yes, sir."

"Do you think you will be safer with it?"

"Yes, sir."

"Why?"

"Because if I'm honest I shall stand no chance of going to prison."

"And what else?"

Nicholas thought for a few minutes. "If I mind the Bible I shall go to heaven," he said at last.

"Yes, that's the best reason for taking the lamp. It will light you right into Heaven. Good-bye, my lad, here's a shilling for you, and mind you don't keep the Bible light covered up by not reading it."

"Yes, sir," said Nicholas, grasping the shilling, and touching his ragged cap; "I'll mind."

When Robert Raikes started religious-schools a hundred years ago in a place where the boys and girls, before that, used to spend the day in swearing and fighting, the Bible was like a lantern to many poor boys like Nicholas, to show them the right way to speak and act and walk, and to keep them from going wrong, and to show them how to go to Heaven. Since then these schools have multiplied, until fourteen millions of people, mostly children, now go to religious-school, and get the Bible as a lantern to show them how to go in this world and how to get to heaven at last.

If we have God's words in our memories, and can repeat them to help others, our hearts also will be like lanterns, to show people the right way. That is what Jesus means when he says, *"Ye are the light of the world"; "Let your light shine."*

In England they call matches "lights," and so the match-sellers cry, "Have a light, sir?" When a little boy said that to an old minister, he replied, smiling, "Don't you know that I am one of the lights of the world?" The mischievous little fellow, not understanding the Bible words, answered, "Well, then, I wish you was hung up in our alley, for it's an awfully dark one." There are alleys and streets "awfully dark" with drunkenness and swearing and sin and sorrow; and we can help to lighten them up with temperance and religion and joy, by kind words of our own and Bible words from our memories, and by acts of kindness and love.

Like a Little Candle

—F. E. Belden

Sing this song with music found in Christ in Song number 501.

Jesus bids us shine with a clear, pure light,
Like a little candle shining in the night.
In the world is darkness, we must shine,
You in your small corner, I in mine.

Jesus bids us shine thro' the gloom around,
Many kinds of darkness in this world are found;
Sin, and want, and sorrow: so we shine,
You in your corner, I in mine.

When we shine for others we shine for Him,
Well He sees and knows it if our light is dim;
He looks down from heaven, sees us shine,
You in your corner, I in mine.

Jesus is a bright light of love divine,
When on Him we're looking, then it is we shine,
Like the silver moon, with borrowed light,
Each in his corner, doing right.

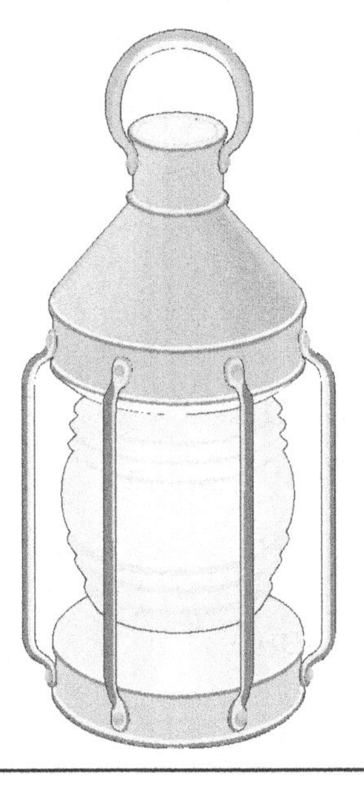

(Day 2)

A Pledge

Use the letters in the top word at least once to help complete the other words below. Other letters may be needed—Count each row of boxes. See Acts 5:1-2 for clues of the letters in the right places!

Color the picture of Peter Confronting Ananias.

(Day 3)

Sea Anemones 3

Grayish Beadlet Anemone

Color the stubby body with pastel rainbow colors. Color the tentacles gray.

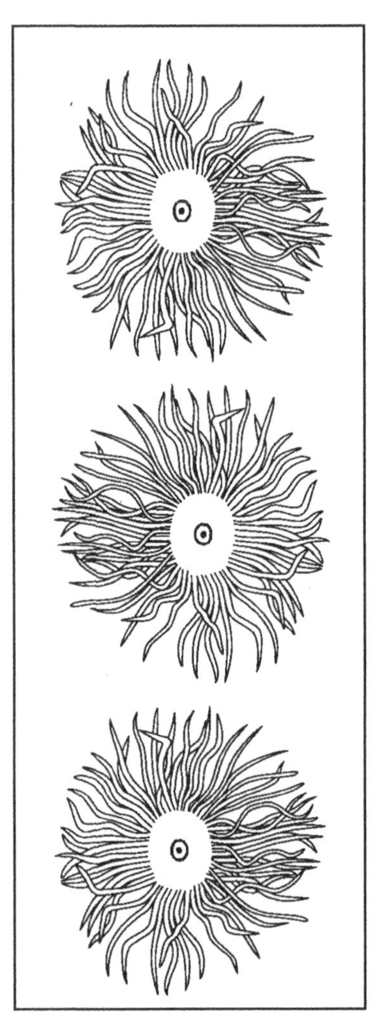

Traffic Light Anemone

Color these anemones green, gold, and red.

What spiritual lessons can these anemones teach us?

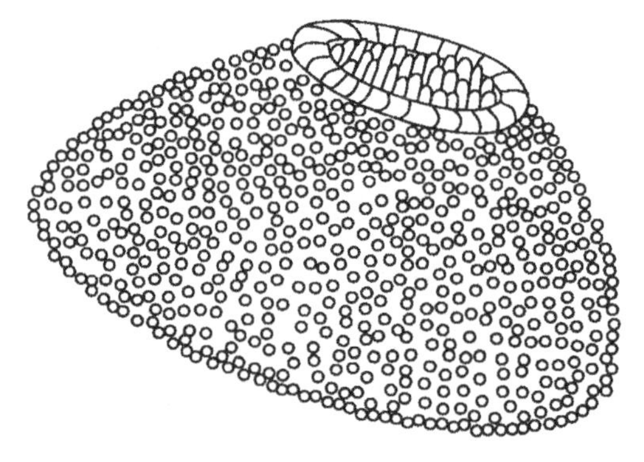

Wartlet Anemone

Color this anemone cream.

Giant Green Anemone

Color this anemone blue-green.

Make a spiritual lesson to parallel with the giant green anemone.

(Day 3)

Ananias

Review today's Bible lesson while coloring this picture.
Memorize Proverbs 12:22.

(Day 4)

Sea Cucumbers 1

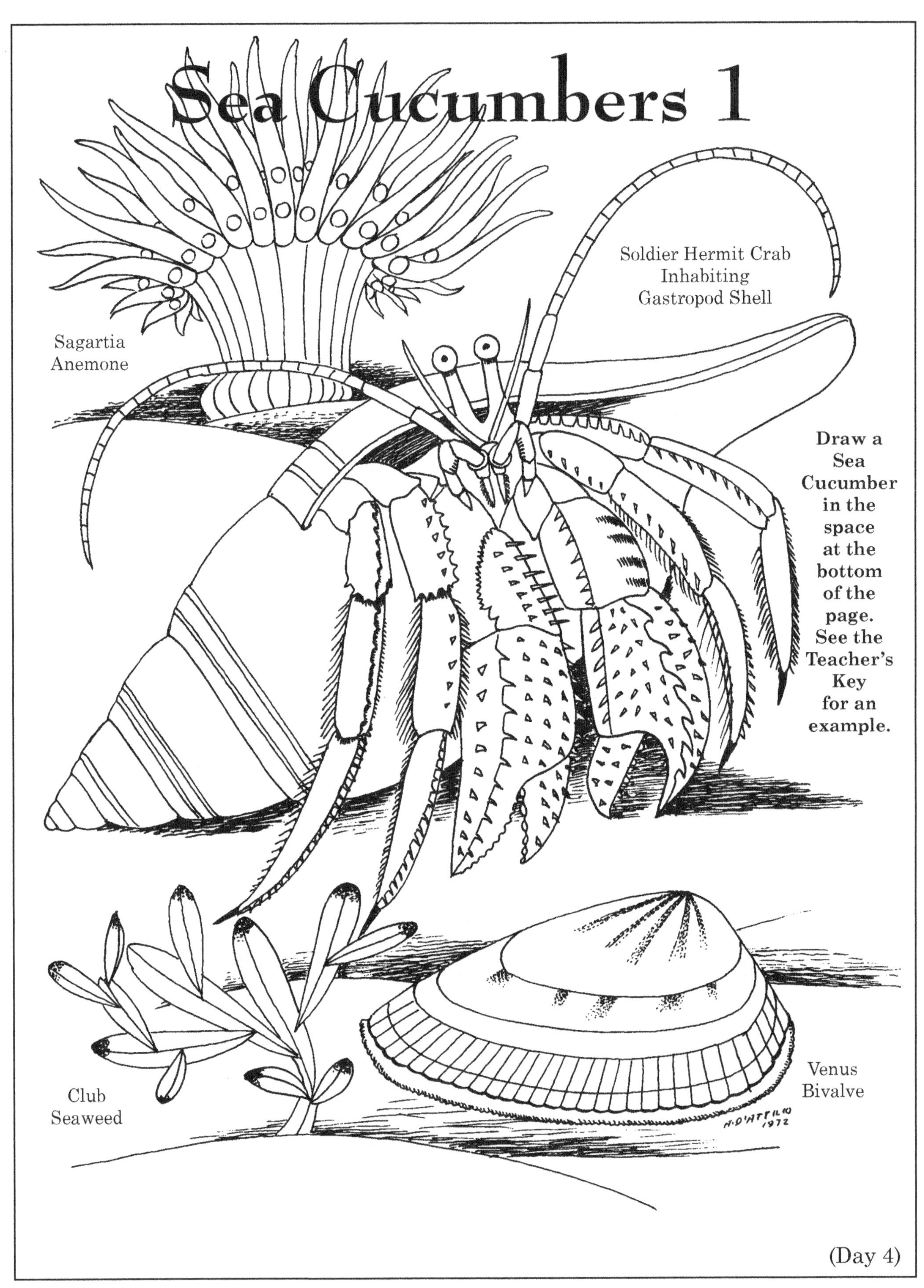

Draw a Sea Cucumber in the space at the bottom of the page. See the Teacher's Key for an example.

(Day 4)

Keep Your Promise

A boy borrowed a tool from a neighbor, promising to return it at night. Before evening he was sent away on an errand, and did not return until late. Before he went, he was told that his brothers would see the article returned.

After he had come home to go to bed, he inquired and found the tool had not been sent to its owner. He was much distressed to think his promise had not been kept, but was persuaded to go to sleep and rise early and carry it home the next morning.

By daylight he was up, and nowhere was the tool to be found. After a long and fruitless search, he set off for his neighbor's in great distress to acknowledge his fault. But great was his surprise to find the tool on his neighbor's doorstep! And then it appeared, from the prints of his little bare feet in the mud, that the lad had got up in his sleep and carried the tool home, and went to bed again, and knew it not.

Of course a boy who was **careful** and prompt in his sleep was **careful** and prompt when awake. He was respected, and had the confidence of his neighbors, and was placed in many offices of trust and profit.

If all the grown folks felt as this boy did, there would be a good many tracks of bare feet found some of these bright, sunny mornings, and what piles of tools, and utensils, and books, would be discovered lying at their owners' doors!

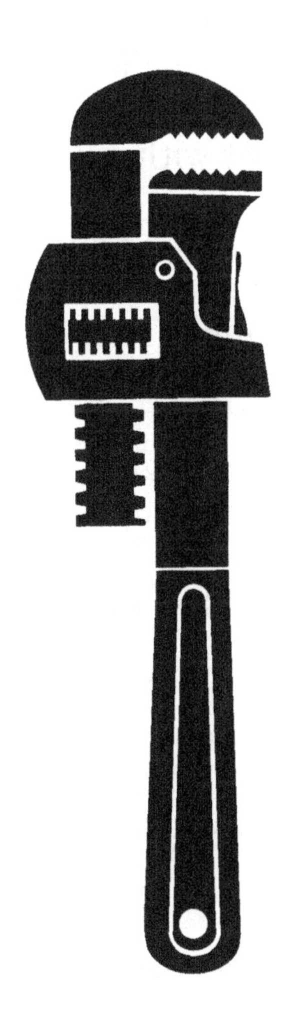

(Day 4)

Against Lying

O 'tis a lovely thing for youth
   To walk betimes in wisdom's way;
To fear a lie, to speak the truth,
   That we may trust to all they say!

But liars we can never trust,
   Though they should speak the thing that's true;
And he that does one fault at first,
   And lies to hide it, makes it two.

Have we not known, nor heard, nor read
   How God abhors deceit and wrong?
How Ananias was struck dead,
   Caught with a lie upon his tongue?

So did his wife Sapphira die,
   When she came in and grew so bold
As to confirm that wicked lie,
   Which just before her husband told.

The Lord delights in them that speak
   The words of truth; but every liar
Must have his portion in the lake
   That burns with brimstone and with fire.

Then let me always watch my lips,
   Lest I be struck to death and hell,
Since God a book of reckoning keeps
   For every lie that children tell.

—*Unknown*

(Day 4)

The Fruit of CARE

A poor girl in California picked up the cutting of a grapevine, thrown into the road. She carried it home and, though it was much worn and appeared good for nothing, she stuck it into the ground. "It has a little life left," she said, "I will try and save it." So she watered it, and watched it, and trimmed it, and took as much **care** of it as if it were the most promising shoot in the world.

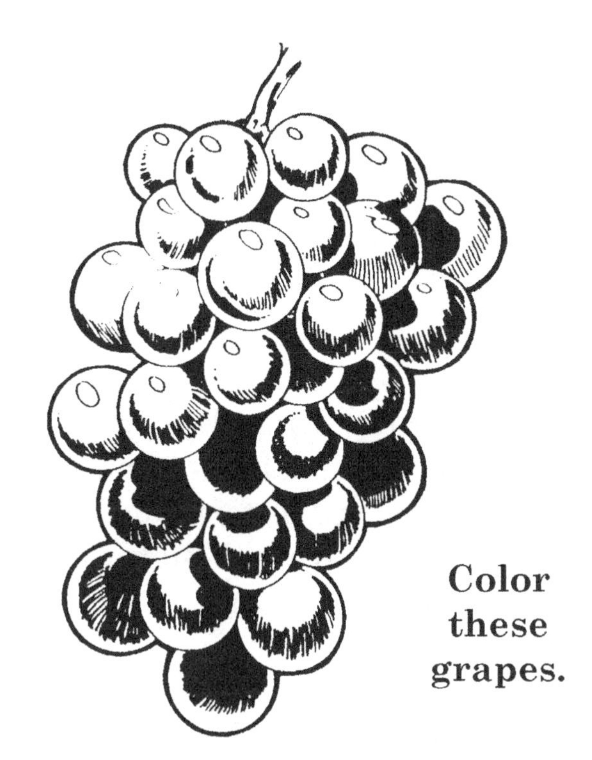

Color these grapes.

Well, how did it reward her? In the space of six years it bore five thousand bunches of grapes, and each bunch weighted one pound; these, on being sold, brought her a thousand pounds, which is nearly five thousand dollars.

(Day 4)

On Attending Public Worship

When to the house of God we go
  To hear His word, and sing His love,
We ought to worship Him below,
  Like all the saints in heaven above.

They stand before His presence now,
  And praise Him better far than we,
Who only at His footstool bow,
  And love Him, though we cannot see.

But God is present every where,
  And watches all our thoughts and ways;
He sees who humbly join in prayer,
  And who sincerely sing His praise.

And He the triflers too can see,
  Who only seem to take a part;
They move the lip, and bend the knee,
  But do not seek Him with the heart.

O may we never trifle so,
  Nor lose the days our God has given!
But learn, by Sabbaths here below,
  To spend eternity in heaven.

—*Unknown*

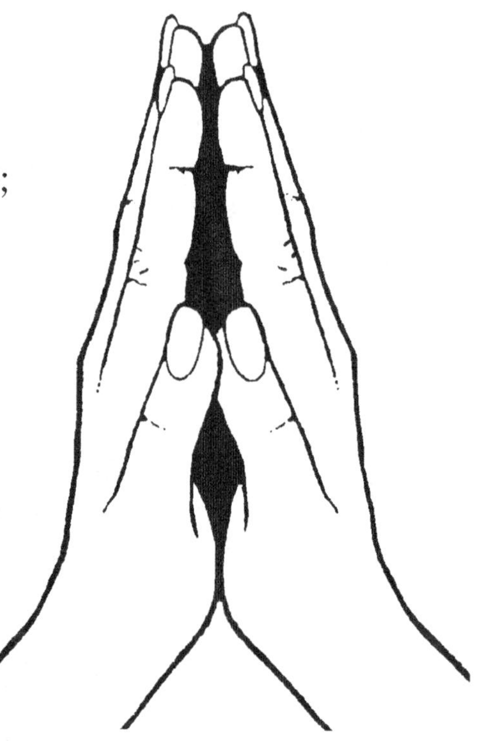

(Day 4)

Sapphira

There are three paths you will want to take in your life. Find them and color them green.

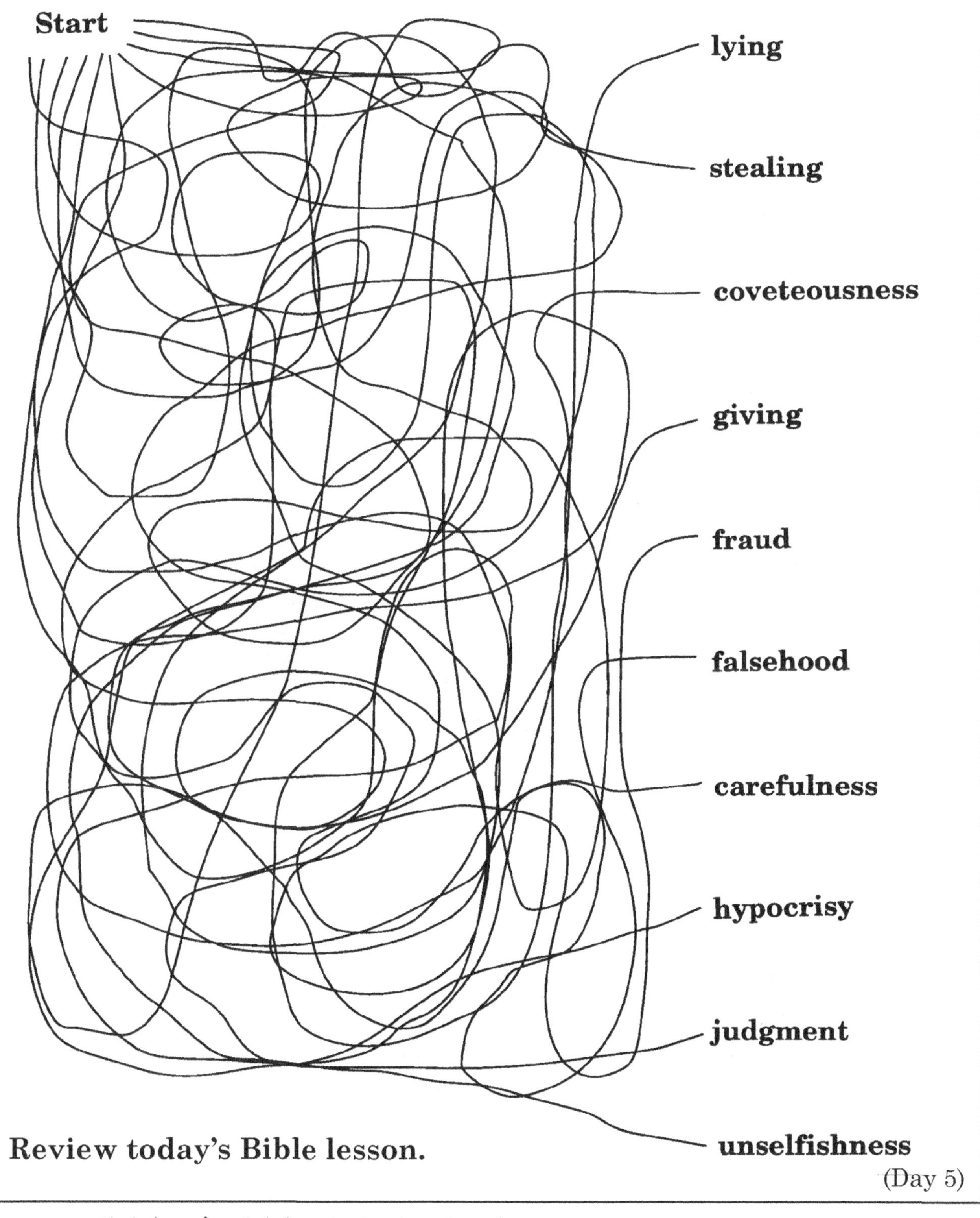

Review today's Bible lesson.

(Day 5)

Death of Sapphira

"And great fear came upon all the church, and upon as many as heard these things."
Acts 5:11

**Reread Acts 5:7-11
while coloring this picture.**

(Day 5)

Sea Cucumbers 2

Make a Sea Picture

Materials needed:
Blue construction paper
Other colors of construction paper
Shallow box lid
Glue
Thread
Plastic wrap
Real shells

Instructions:
Paste a sheet of blue paper in the back of a shoe box lid. Place real shells on the bottom. Trace and cut out patterns. Hang fish by thread. Glue some items to the back.

The sea cucumber protects itself by letting out streams of sticky tubes from the gut, covering the predator. It then inches away to safety leaving a fish or crab covered with sticky entrails. It regrows them in a few weeks. God protected the early church from falling into the sin of careless lying and covetousness by the speedy judgment upon Ananias and Sapphira.

(Day 5)

Other Unusual Creatures of the Sea

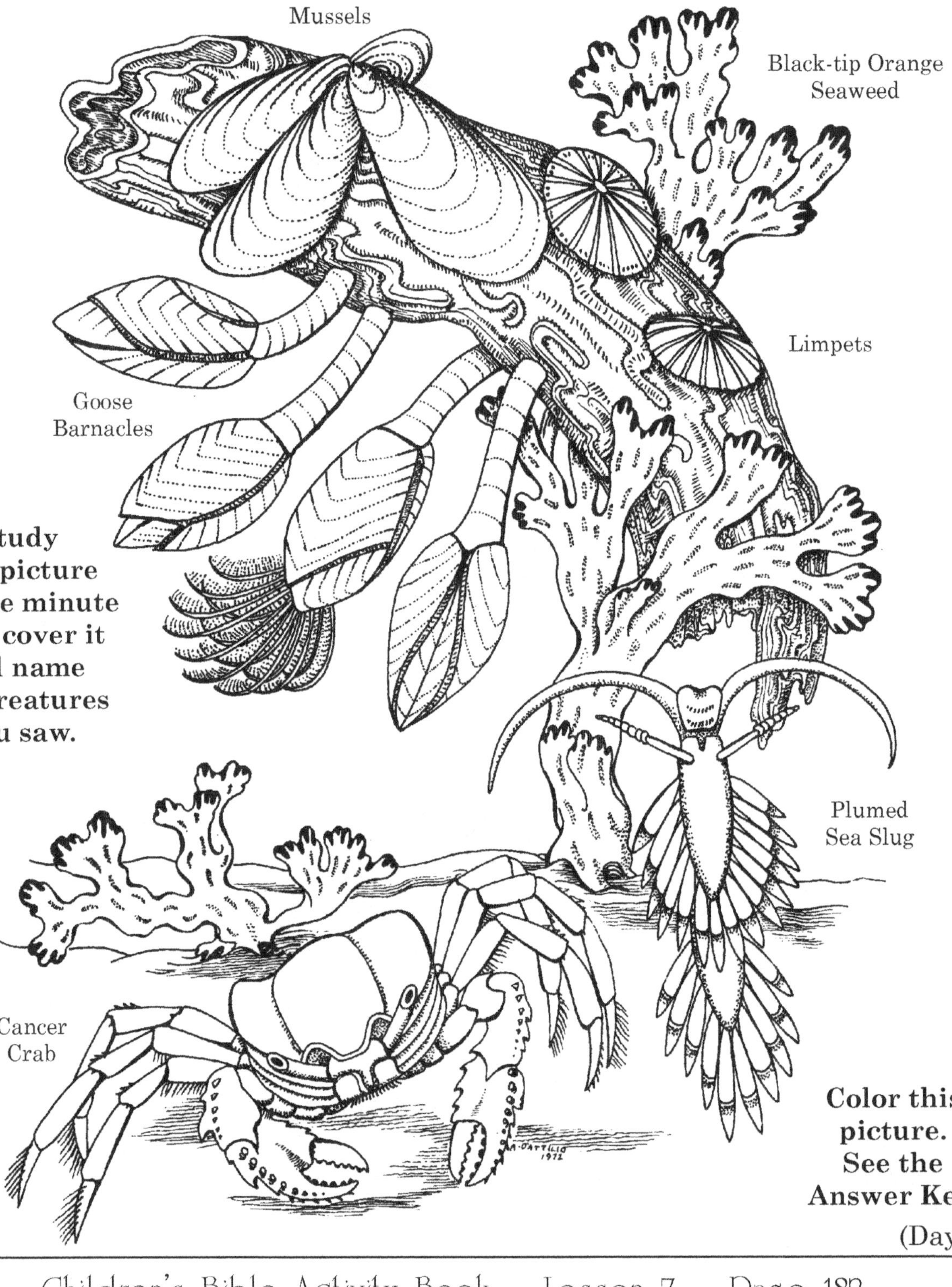

Mussels

Black-tip Orange Seaweed

Limpets

Goose Barnacles

Study this picture for one minute then cover it and name the creatures you saw.

Plumed Sea Slug

Cancer Crab

Color this picture. See the Answer Key.

(Day 5)

Guarding the Church

See how many small words you can make by using the letters of the following words below.

Carefulness

Covetousness

Truthfulness

Falsehood

(Day 6)

Sea Cucumbers 3

Finish drawing the picture below and then use the picture to tell the story and the lesson you learned today.

The Pearlfish
and
The Eyed Sea Cucumber

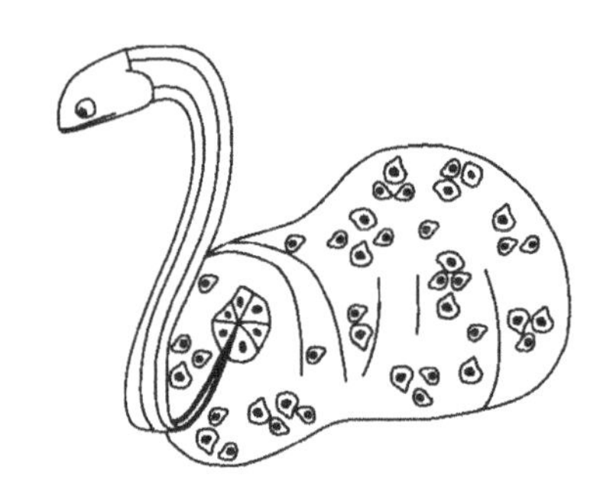

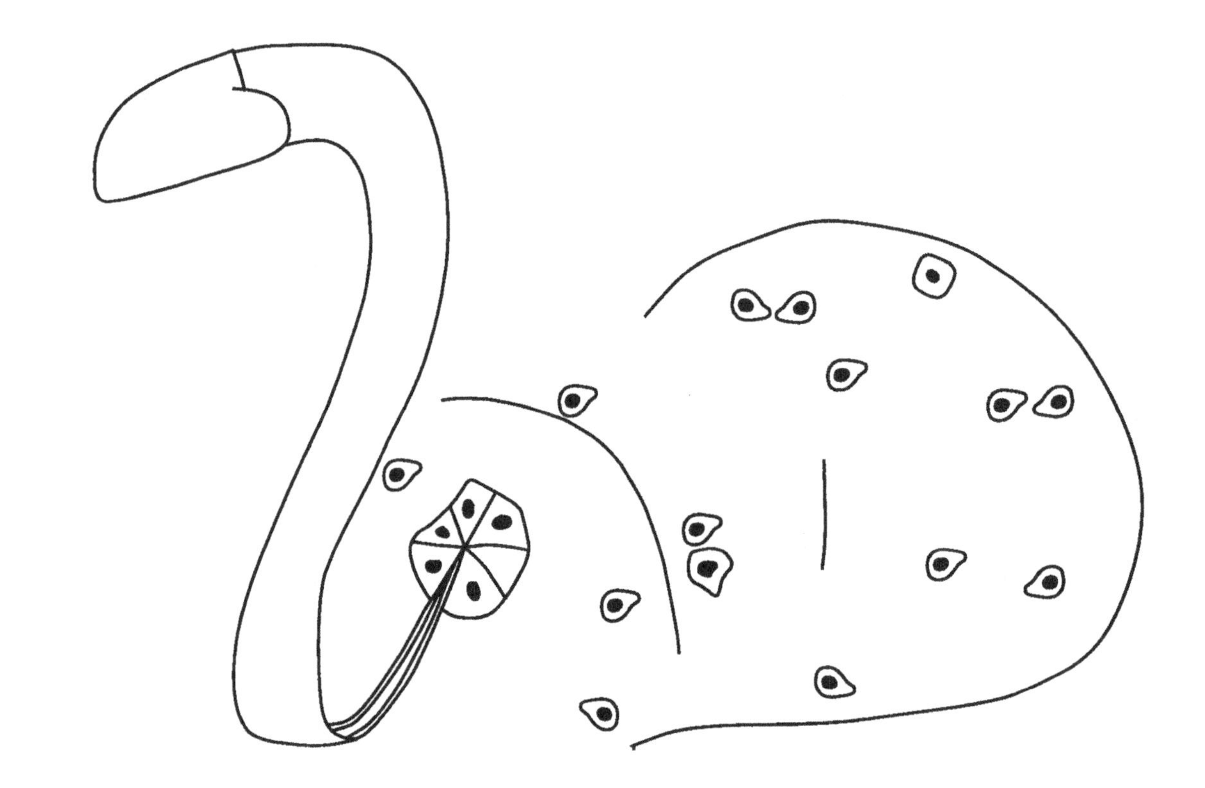

(Day 6)

Clothed in Beauty

"And the man of God sent unto the king of Israel, saying, <u>Beware that thou pass not such a place;</u> for thither the Syrians are come down."
II Kings 6:9

Sea anemones can teach us a completely different kind of lesson than what we have been studying this week. Why and How? Because the ocean has also come under the curse of sin and the animals that live there show both good and evil.

In the sea garden of tropical waters live the lovely sea anemones whose brilliant hues and fragile-looking tentacles add to the glories of the coral reefs. These beautiful flower-like animals dot the ocean floor with every color of the rainbow—pink, brown, orange, purple, yellow, and white. Their snake-like tentacles, so like the petals of a chrysanthemum, can be very slender or quite thick, but all are beautiful and graceful.

However, that beauty masks a murderous nature. Those lovely tentacles are armed with tiny nettle cells, which, at the slightest touch, shoot out poison darts or whiplike stingers on ends of threads. If a small fish brushes against these feelers, he is promptly paralyzed by the dart. Instantly those flower-like feelers disappear, forcing the fish into the anemone's mouth to be swallowed and digested. The gorgeous flower now appears as a dark, leathery bump of muscle on a rock.

As one fish after another disappears instantly into the mouths of these deceptive creatures, the observer finds himself disliking the sea anemone instead of admiring its beauty. The poor fish has no chance to warn others to stay away from this colorful attraction.

The world is filled with lots of sea-anemone attractions, but more fortunate than the hapless fish, you have been warned not to pass places where Satan masks his horrible traps with beautiful sights and sounds, smells and tastes. Hidden beneath the glamour of sin are the poison darts that paralyze good judgment. The victim, not able to pull away, is pulled into the pit. A death trap is still a death trap no matter how beautiful. A wicked movie is still wicked whether you see it at a theater, a school auditorium, or on the laptop. Caffeine is a habit-forming drug whether in coffee, tea, or coke. Bad music ruins lives no matter who sings it.

Sea anemones often live 60 years. If cut in pieces each grows into a new death trap. Satan, too, is constantly inventing prettier, more subtle attractions to lure men from God. But there is no need to be trapped if you will *"beware that thou pass not such a place."*

—Adapted from *Stop, Look, and Listen*

(Day 6)

A is for Anemone

Anemone
Clownfish
and Anemone

Color
this picture.

(Day 6)

8 – Delivered by an Angel

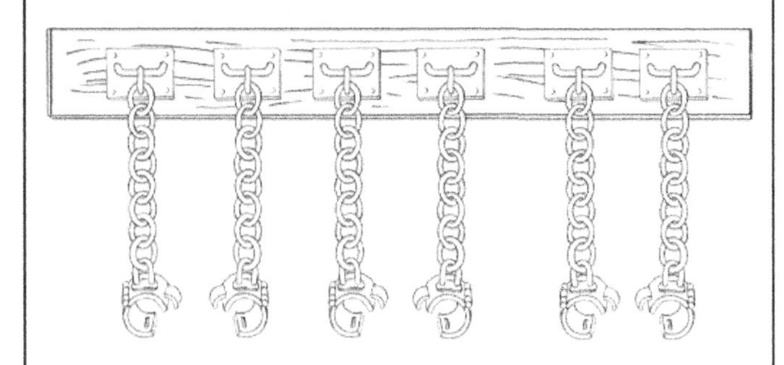

Bible – Acts 5:12-42

Song – "Gracious Father Guard Thy Children"

Nature – Benthos—Sponges

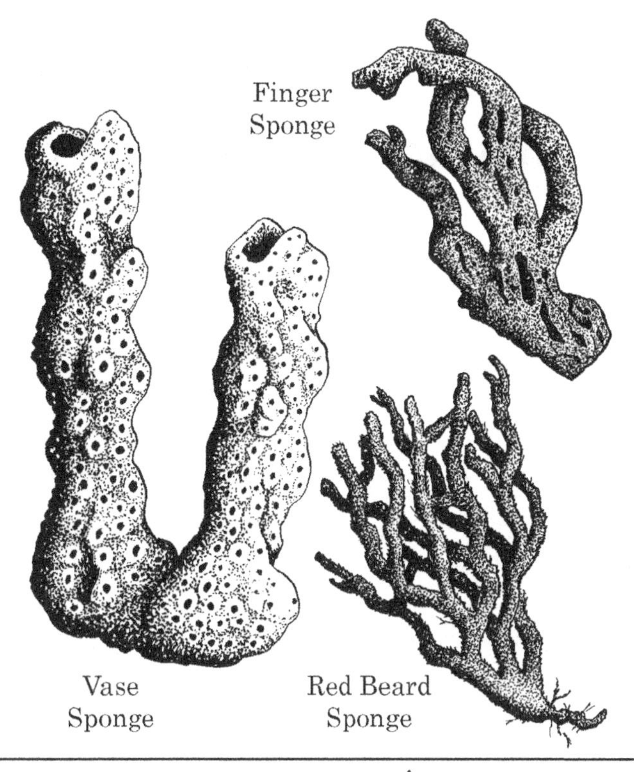

Character Quality

Obedience vs Willfulness

Obedience is compliance with God's commands done quickly and cheerfully.

Memory Verse

"Then Peter and the other apostles answered and said, We ought to obey God rather than men."
James 5:15

Benthos—Sponges

If a part of the sponge's body is lost or damaged.
it may be replaced or repaired.
The disciples would be beaten but God would heal them.

Bread Crumb Sponge

**Draw another "bread crumb" on the sponge
for each day this week
you study your lesson.
and say your memory verse.**

Signs and Wonders

"And by the hands of the apostles were many signs and wonders wrought among the people."
Acts 5:12

Use Acts 5:12-16 to answer the questions and fill in the crossword.

12. "...Many ____________ (11D) and _____________ (3A) wrought among the people...."

14. "And ______________ (14A) were the more ______________(16D) to the Lord, ____________________ (4A) both of ___________ (10A) and ______________ (9D)."

15. "...They ______________ (13D) _____________ (1D) the ____________ (7A) into the streets...that at the least the _______________ (8A) of Peter passing by might ________________ (12D) some of them."

16. There came also a multitude....bringing sick folks, and them which were vexed with _____________ (5D) ______________ (2D): and they were _______________ (15A) every one."

(Day 1)

Sponges

Many people think that sponges are plants,
having <u>confused</u> <u>ideas</u> about them.
In Jerusalem people had <u>confused</u> <u>ideas</u> about Christ,
so the disciples continued to speak with boldness
to explain the truth to the people.

**Color all the areas that have a dot
to find the animal called a sponge.**

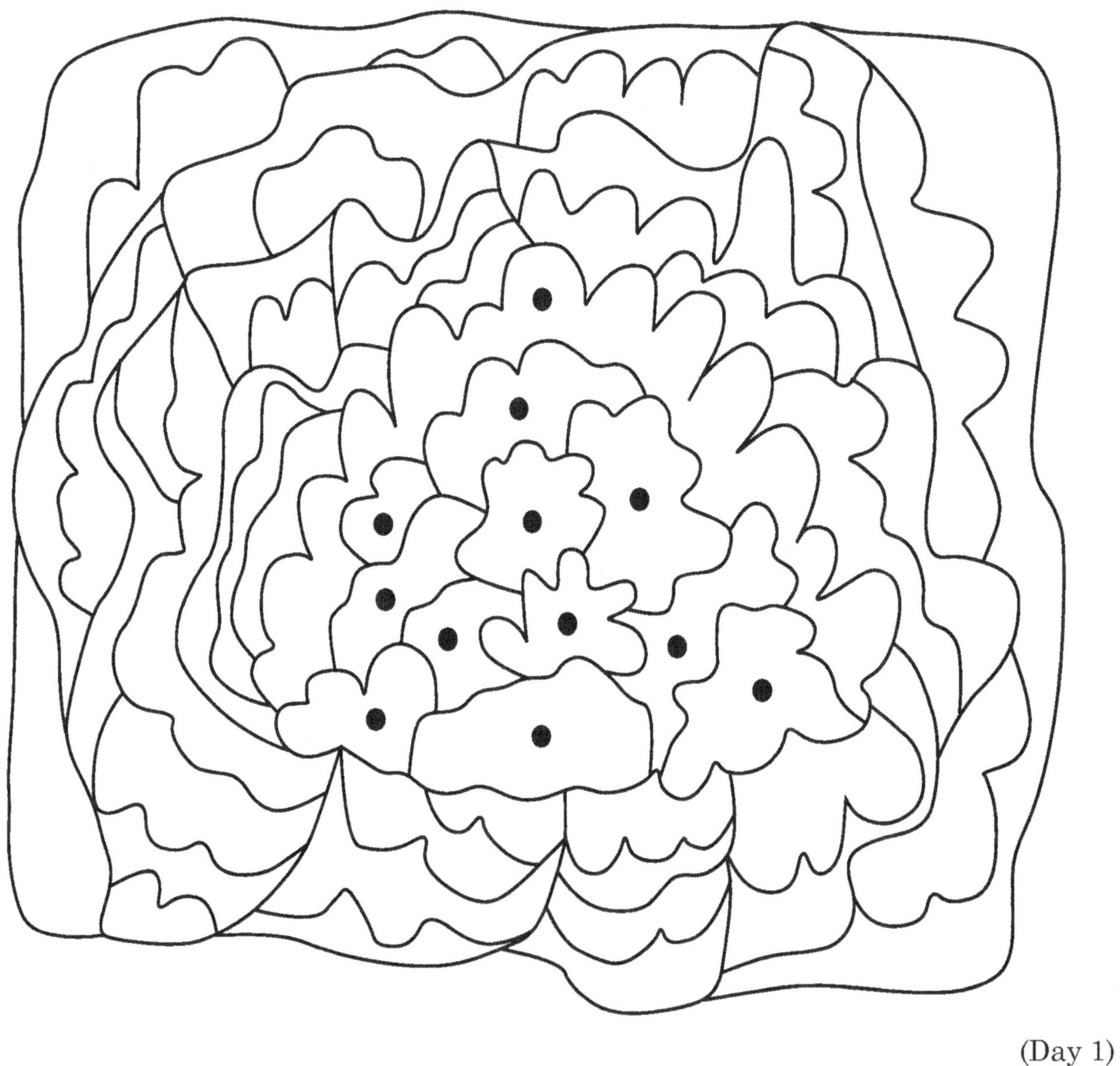

(Day 1)

Christ Only Christ

Answer the questions.

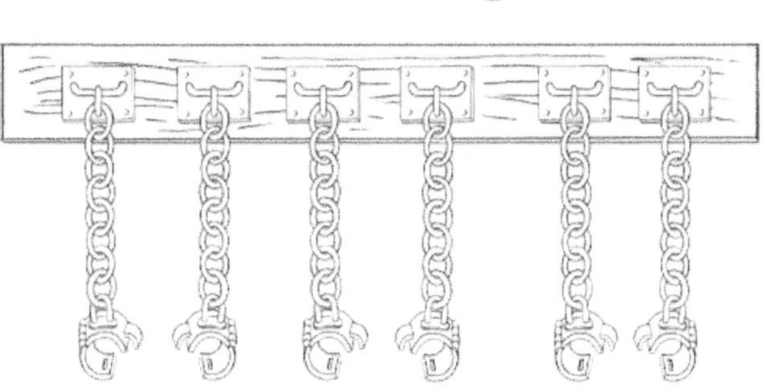

Color the pictures.

1. Why were the priests, rulers, Pharisees and Sadducees upset with the apostles preaching?

2. Who wanted this "new teaching" of the disciples stopped? Why? Thought Question: Was this a "new teaching?"

3. What did the Sadducees and Pharisees do to Peter and John?

4. What were the Jewish rulers content with in their lives?

5. What can happen to us sometimes?

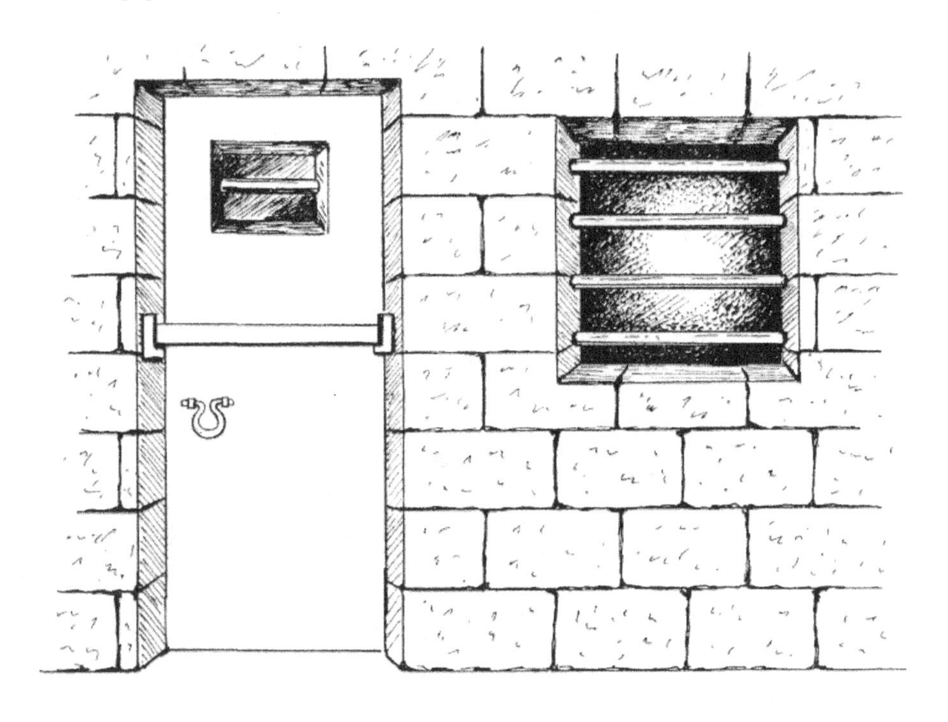

(Day 2)

The Bodies of Sponges 1

Review today's Nature Lesson. Color this picture. Find the sponge.

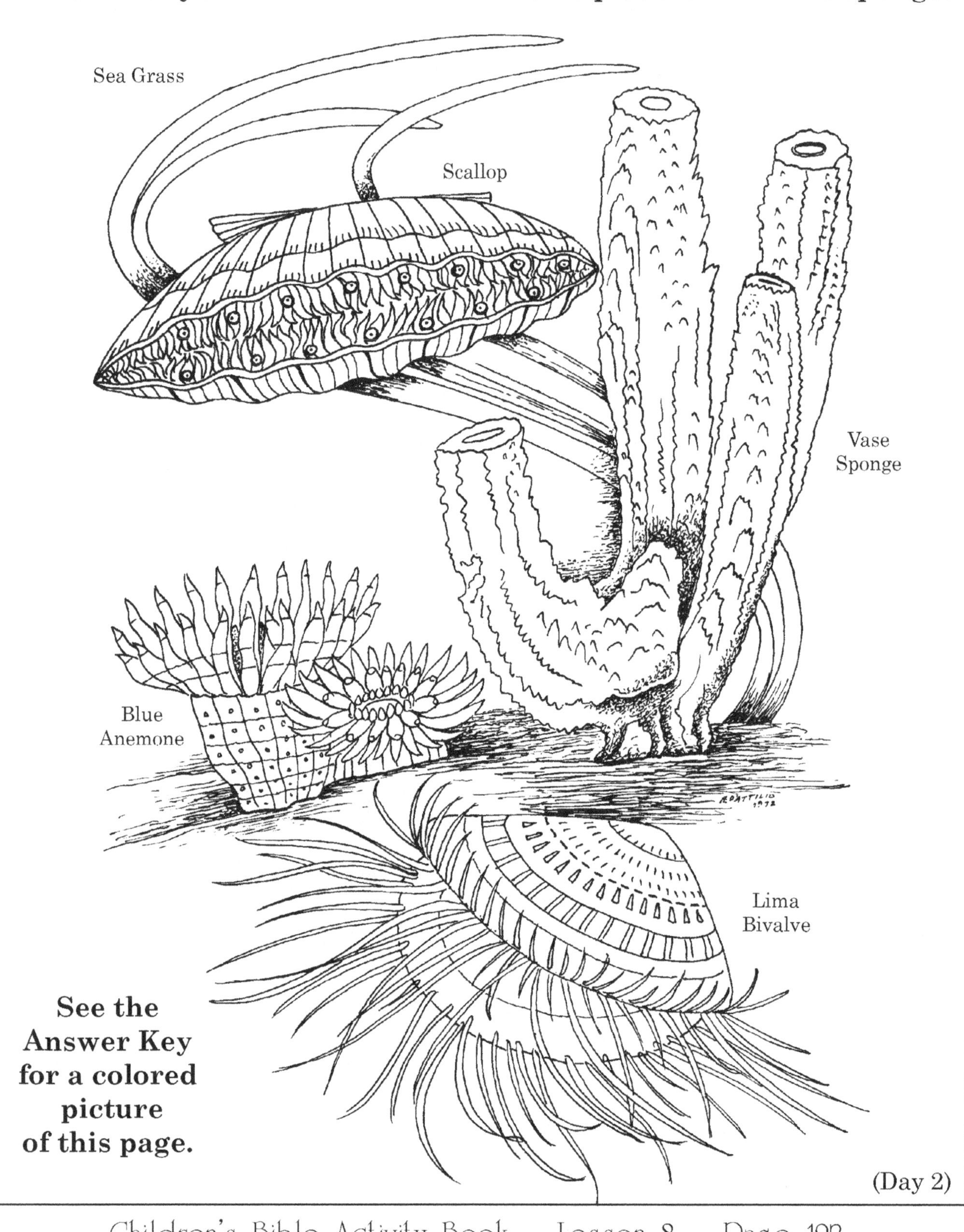

See the Answer Key for a colored picture of this page.

(Day 2)

A True Story For the Little Ones

A little girl, six years old, was one evening gently reproved by her pious mother for some of her faults during the day. She seemed very sorry; and shortly afterward, when she thought she was alone, some one passed by, and heard her talking; but in too low a tone for any one to understand what she said.

The next evening, after repeating her usual prayer at her mother's knee, the little girl asked earnestly: "have I behaved better today?" Her mother answered that she was much pleased with the day's improvement, and hoped that her little daughter would always behave as well. "Then," replied the child, "I must go and talk with God again. I told Him yesterday that I wanted to be good; and I asked Him to help me, and He has helped me all day long, so that I could not be naughty, even when I felt it in me."

Yes, dear children, the evil is in us all the time; and it is only by God's grace that we can subdue it. Go and talk to Him about it, and He will help you to avoid every evil way, and to **obey** the precepts of His holy Law, all the days of your life.

"Casting down imaginations, and every high thing that exalteth itself against the knowledge of God, and bringing into captivity every thought to the ***obedience*** *of Christ."*

II Corinthians 10:5

(Day 2)

Peter's Deliverance

'Tis midnight; and, the busy world
Has ceased from toil and care–
Why then is yonder weeping band,
Still bowed in fervent prayer?

Ah! one is from their number gone—
A brother, ever dear,
Who, when afflictions pressed around,
Wanted their hearts to cheer.

With them he sang their songs of praise,
With them he knelt to pray;
At length there came a ruthless band,
And bore him thence away.

Within the dreary prison walls,
He, bound in chains, doth lie;
The cruel monarch has decreed,
Tomorrow he must die.

But pray, What evil hath he done,
For which he has been tried?
'Tis only preaching pardon free,
Through Christ, the Crucified.

Ye mourners dry those falling tears;
For God has heard each prayer;
And He who watches o'er His saints,
Doth still for Peter care.

(Day 2)

Peter's Deliverance Continued

For lo! commissioned from on high,
In haste, as Angel flew—
Before him bolted doors gave way,
And light the prison grew.

"Peter arise," the angel cries,
"And put thy sandals on!"
And as the galling chains fall off,
They hasten to be gone.

They pass the door, although before
The guard in order stands,
And through the massive iron gate,
Which opens without hands.

And as the Angel guide withdrew,
And Peter left alone,
He hastens on his way to make,
His great deliv'rance known.

Once more he joins that faithful band,
And tells the joyful news,
How God hath saved him from the king,
And persecuting Jews.

With wonder, joy, and gratitude,
They all, with one accord,
Recount the wonders of that night,
The dealings of the Lord.

—*Susan Elmer*

(Day 2)

A Hymn of the Sea

The sea is mighty, but a mightier sways
His restless billows. Thou, whose hands have scooped
His boundless gulfs and built his shore, Thy breath,
That moved in the beginning o'er his face,
Moves o'er it evermore. The obedient waves
To its strong motion roll, and rise and fall.
Still from that realm of rain thy cloud goes up,
As at the first, to water the great earth,
And keep her valleys green. A hundred realms
Watch its broad shadow warping on the wind,
And in the dropping shower, with gladness hear
Thy promise of the harvest. I look forth
Over the boundless blue, where joyously
The bright crests of innumerable waves
Glance to the sun at once, as when the hands
Of a great multitude are upward flung
In acclamation. I behold the ships
Gliding from cape to cape, from isle to isle,
Or stemming towards far lands, or hastening home
From the Old World. It is thy friendly breeze
That bears them, with the riches of the land,
And treasure of dear lives, till, in the port,
The shouting seaman climbs and furls the sail.

—*Unknown*

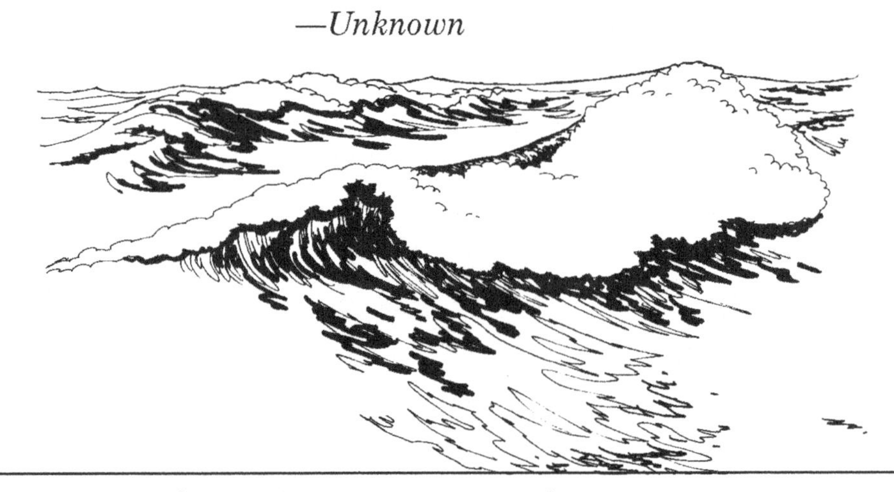

(Day 2)

Prison Doors Opened

When we obey the Holy Spirit's leading it sometimes can bring trials to our life but God has a way of escape.

Unscramble these words to see how God delivered the disciples. Then place the words in the correct order below.

1. GENAL
2. HOURGBT
3. ROSOD
4. TROHF
5. OG
6. FIEL
7. GINTH
8. NEDEPO
9. LEPOPE
10. SINROP
11. KEPAS
12. DANST
13. MEPTEL
14. DORWS

"But the ______ (1) of the Lord by ______ (7) ______ (8) the ______ (10) ______ (3), and ______ (2) them ______ (4), and said,"

"______ (5), ______ (12) and ______ (11) in the ______ (13) to the ______ (9) all the ______ (14) of this ______ (6)."

(Day 3)

Peter In Prison
Color this picture.
(Day 3)

The Bodies of Sponges 2

What is an ostia? ______________________________

____

What is an osculum? ______________________________

____

Decorate a small flowerpot to keep your sponges in after washing dishes.

Materials needed: Small flowerpot with hole in bottom
Plaster of Paris
Shells
Small rocks gathered by the water
Clear varnish
Paint brush

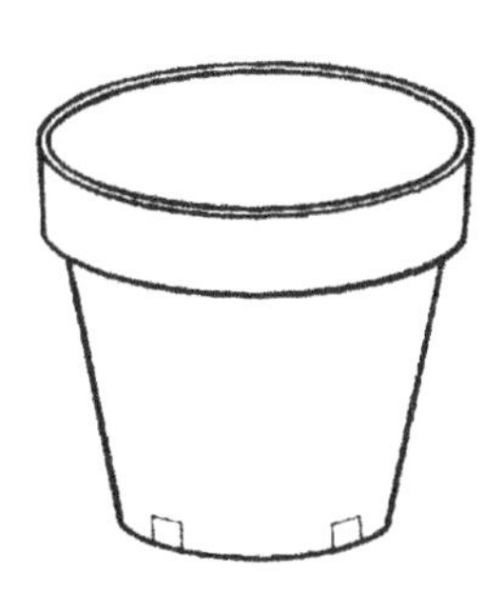

Directions:

- Put a little plaster of Paris powder into a small jar.
- Add a small amount of water and stir thoroughly.
- Keep adding water until you have a thick paste.
- Smear the paste thickly all around the outside of the flower pot.
- Gently push shells and small rocks into the paste while it is still wet.
- Leave the paste for one or two hours to harden.
- Paint with a clear varnish.

The way water passes through the sponge reminds us of how the disciples went in then out of prison.

(Day 3)

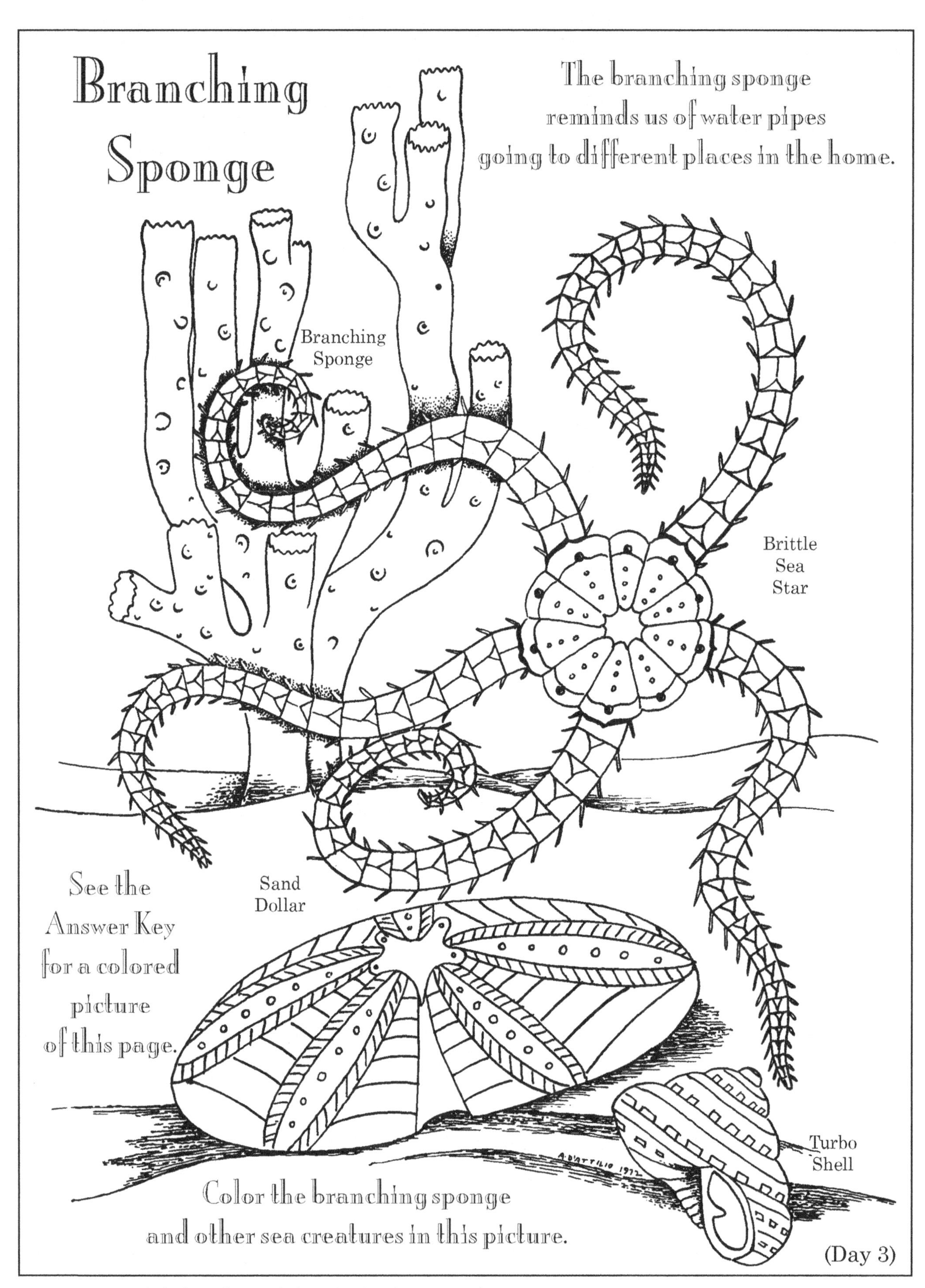
Branching Sponge
The branching sponge
reminds us of water pipes
going to different places in the home.
Branching Sponge
Brittle Sea Star
Sand Dollar
See the
Answer Key
for a colored
picture
of this page.
Turbo Shell
Color the branching sponge
and other sea creatures in this picture.
(Day 3)

Prisoners Gone

Read Acts 5:22-23
then answer the questions below.

What else did the officers report? Read Acts 5:25-26.
Who delivered the disciples?

(Day 4)

The Bodies of Sponges 3

Review today's lesson. Identify the sponge.
Find each item listed in the picture in an identification book.

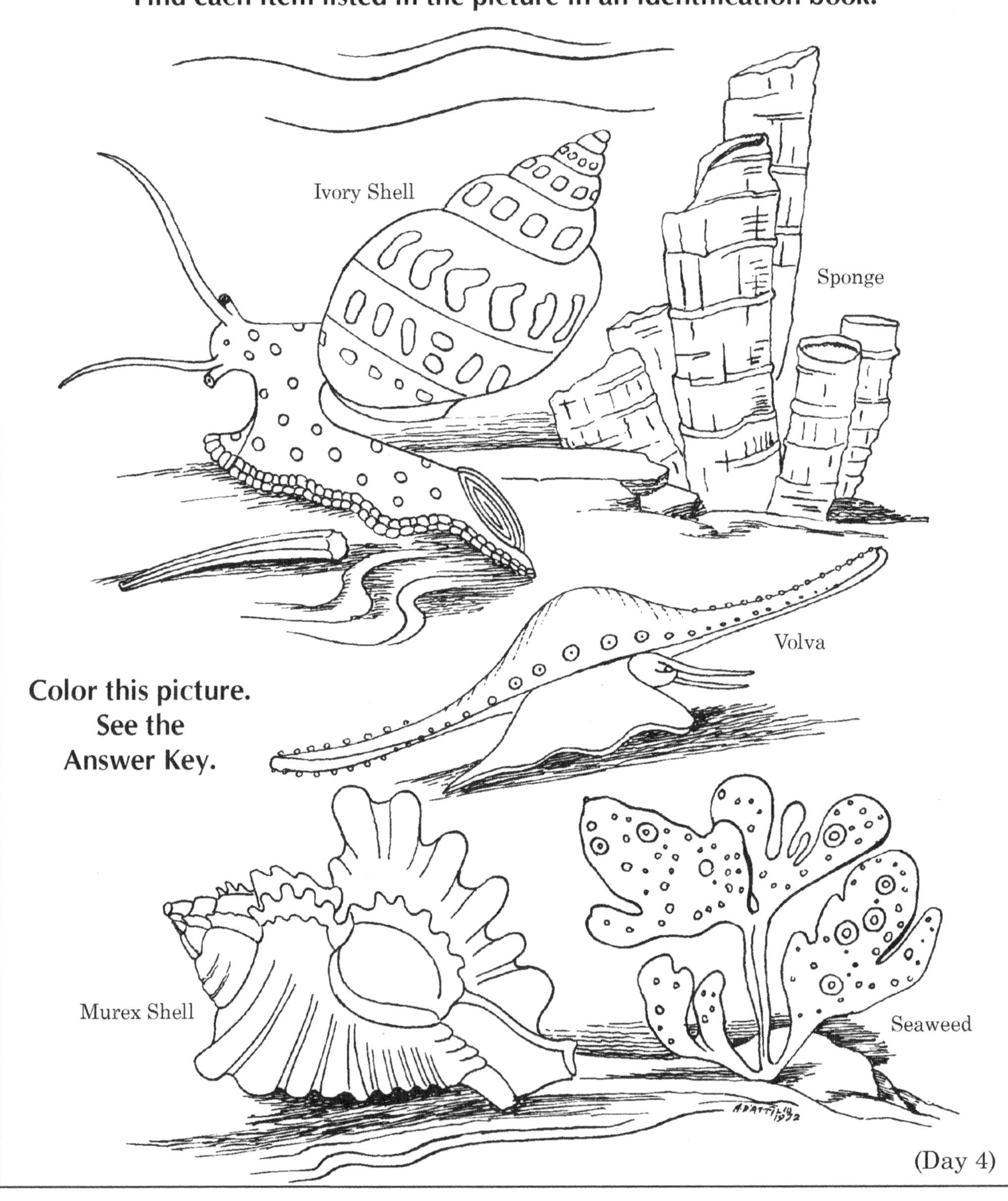

Color this picture.
See the
Answer Key.

(Day 4)

A Good Example

A boy was once tempted by some of his companions to pluck some ripe cherries from a tree which his father had forbidden him to touch.

"You need not be afraid, for if your father should find out that you had them, he is so kind that he will not hurt you."

"That is the very reason," replied the boy, "why I would not touch them. It is true, my father may not hurt me; yet my <u>disobedience</u>, I know, would hurt my father, and that would be worse to me than anything else."

Was not his an excellent reason?

(Day 4)

The Good Angels

Sister Lillie, can you tell
Where the holy angels dwell?
Is it very, very, high,
Up above the moon and sky?

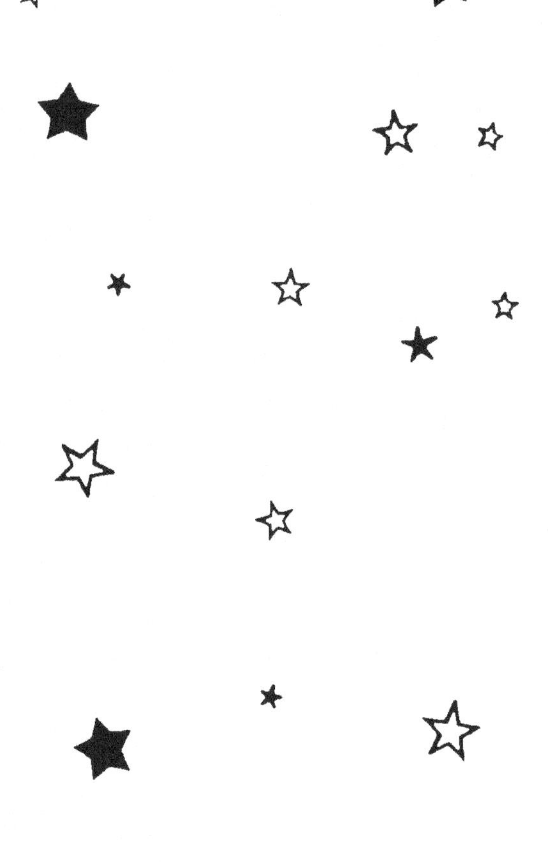

Holy angels, sister dear,
Dwell with little children here,
Every night and every day—
With the good they always stay.

Yet I never see them come,
Never know when they go home,
Never hear them speak to me,
Sister dear, how can it be?

Mary, did you never hear
Something whisper in your ear,
Don't be naughty, never cry,
God is looking from the sky?

Yes, indeed, and it must be
That's the way they talk to me;
Those are just the words they say,
Many times in every day.

And they kindly watch us too,
When the grass is wet with dew,
When we're tired and go to sleep
Angels then our slumbers keep.

(Day 4)

Every night and every day.
When we work and when we play,
God's good angels watch us still,
Keeping us from every ill.

When we're good, then they are glad;
When we're naughty, they are sad;
Should we very wicked grow,
Then away from us they'd go.

Oh! I would not have them go,
I do love the angels so;
I will never naughty be,
So they'll always stay with me.

—*Unknown*

A Sponge Lesson

Remember, the skeleton forms a framework
that supports and protects the body of the sponge.
Spicules may be grouped into bundles that form a strong structure.
In some sponges, many spicules grow around the osculum
which protects the sponge from animals that try to enter its body or eat it.

Read the information and color.

Our guardian angels guard over us each day.

Angels are sent to protect and help man.
An angel was sent to deliver the disciples from prison.
He also instructed them to continue to teach and they obeyed.
Where did the officers find the disciples?—not in prison!

(Day 4)

Gamaliel

Answer these questions using the key words.

Key Words

obey, disciples, Gamaliel, without violence, and nothing

1. What did the officers find in the prison?

____

2. Who was standing in the temple preaching?

____

3. How were the disciples arrested?

____

4. When asked why they did not cease from preaching what was the key word Peter used?

____

5. Who in the council gave sound advice?

____

Color the picture.

(Day 5)

Sponge Reproduction

Review today's Nature Lesson. Find the sponge below.

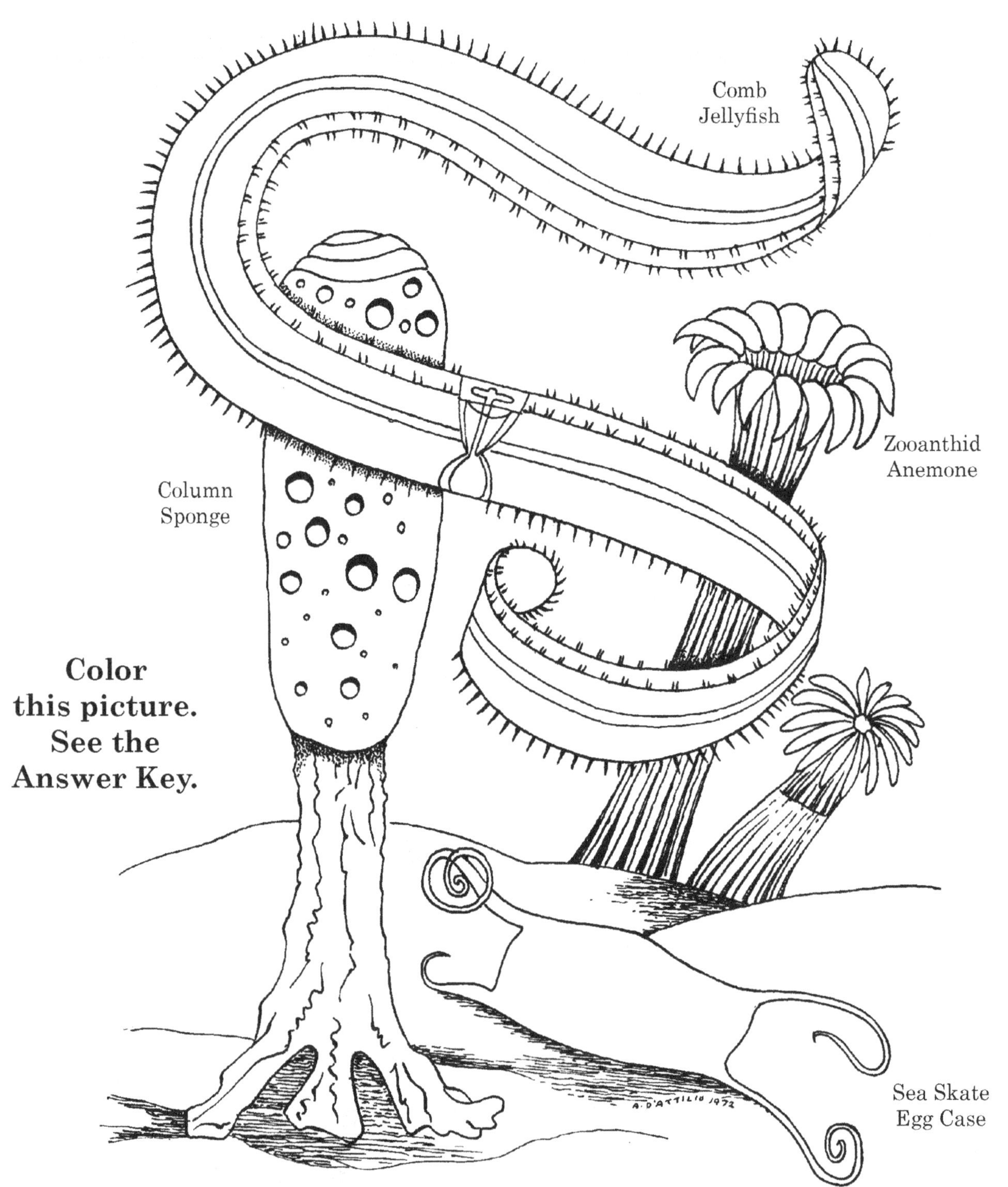

Color this picture. See the Answer Key.

Because the disciple's preaching was reproducing many new believers the Jewish leaders threatened them.

(Day 5)

Rejoicing

"And to him they agreed:
and when they had called the apostles,
and beaten them, they commanded that they should not
speak in the name of Jesus, and let them go."
Acts 5:40

"And daily in the temple,
and in every house,
they ceased not
to teach and preach
Jesus Christ."
Acts 5:42

Color these
words and pictures.

(Day 6)

Kinds of Sponges

Phylum–Porifers
(Pore-bearers)

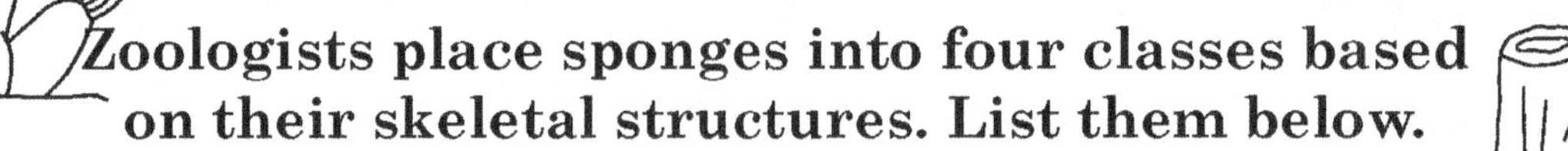

Zoologists place sponges into four classes based on their skeletal structures. List them below.

1. C _ _ _ _ _ _ _

2. H _ _ _ _ _ _ _ _ _ _ _ _ _ _

3. S _ _ _ _ _ _ _ _ _ _ _ _ _

4. D _ _ _ _ _ _ _ _ _ _ _

In the spiritual sense the skeleton (God's law) is what determines which of the two classes you are in.

5. R _ _ _ _ _ _ _ _

6. W _ _ _ _ _

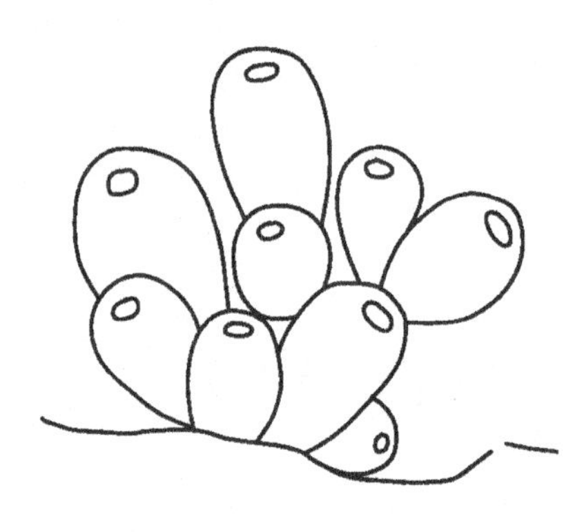

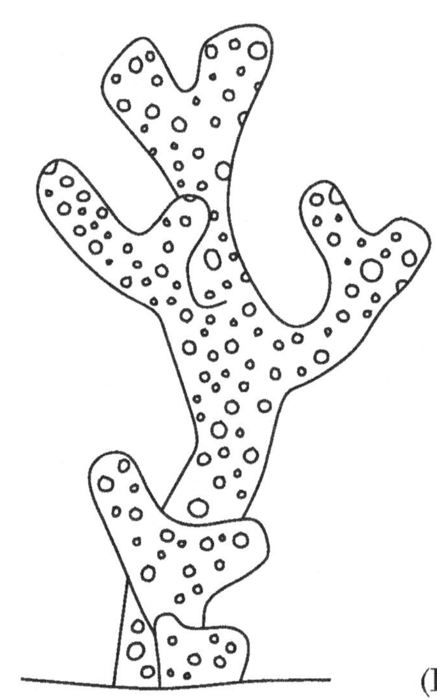

(Day 6)

The Opened Prison' Door

Two young Christian women were arrested in Leeuwarden, Holland, in 1549. One was put to death. The other, Hadewyck, was waiting in prison for trial.

As she was praying, a voice came to her and called, "Hadewyck!" Looking up and around, she perceived no one, and proceeded with her ardent prayer. She heard the voice a second time, and still seeing no one, persevered in her supplications, until the same voice a third time said to her, "Hadewyck, I tell you to depart!" Seeing the door open, she put on her cloak, and went out of the prison.

She knew not then where she would hide herself, and went, for the present, into the church, where she heard it said by those who were walking there, that the gates of the city were shut in consequence of a Christian woman having escaped from prison without its being known by what means, and as many suspicions were excited that it might be by means of witchcraft, great exertions were used everywhere to discover her.

Leaving the church, she immediately heard the drummer giving notice in the street that whoever should give information of her should receive a reward of a hundred guilders, but that whoever should conceal her should incur a fine of one hundred fifty guilders, which accordingly increased her alarms.

At last she found refuge in the garret of a Priest's house through a servant whom she had known, and by whom she sent a message to her brother-in-law, who came by boat to the steps at the rear of the house, on the canal, and took her away. She was spared to work for God many years, and died a natural death at Emden many years later.

Who opened those prison door?*

*Adapted from *The Hand That Intervenes*

(Day 6)

Prison

When they do talk of banishment,
Of death, and such like things,
Then to me God sends heart's content
That like a fountain springs.

God sometimes visits prisons more
Than lordly palaces,
He often knocketh at our door
When he their houses miss.

The truth and I were both here cast
Together, and we do
Lie arm in arm, and so hold fast
Each other; this is true.

This jail to us is as a hill
From whence we plainly see
Beyond this world, and take our fill
Of things that lasting be.

—*John Bunyan*
Written while in Prison

(Day 6)

9 – Stephen Stoned

Bible – Acts 6-7

Song – "Working, O Christ, With Thee"

Nature – Fish 1

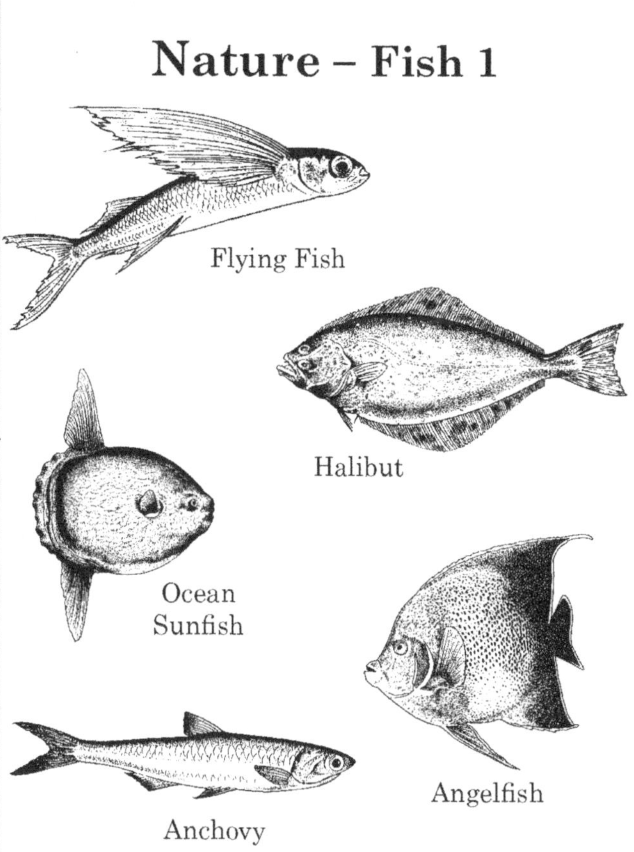

Character Quality

Helpfulness vs Hindrance
Helpfulness is to aid or assist another as if you were **helping** Jesus and thereby promoting a person's usefulness.

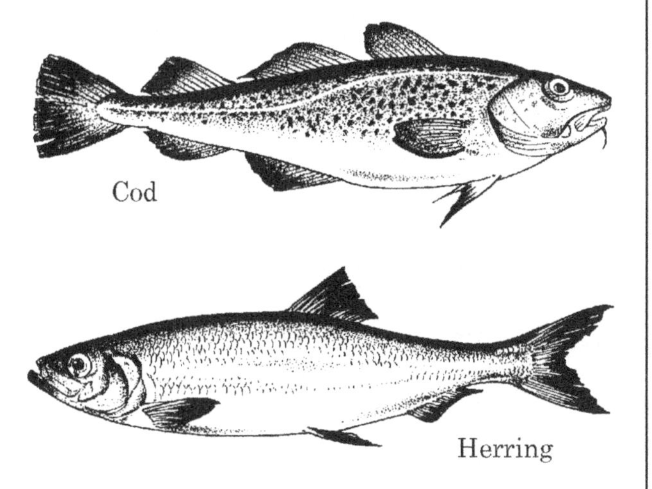

Memory Verse

"Fear none of those things which thou shalt suffer: behold, the devil shall cast some of you into prison, that ye may be tried; and ye shall have tribulation ten days: be thou faithful unto death, and I will give thee a crown of life." (Revelation 2:10).
Sing also Psalm 143:9-11.

Fish

The mighty manta ray is very large.
Yet this large fish eats nothing bigger than plankton!
Stephen had grown large in faith by eating (spiritually)
nothing more than the Word of God.
"Thy words were found, and I did eat them."

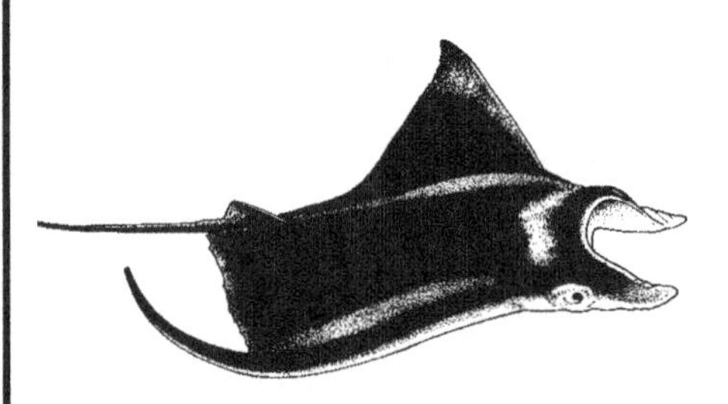

Draw or place a seal of a fish above
for each day this week
you study your lesson,
and say your memory verse.

Murmuring

Satan tries to cause discord through murmuring—
we must **help** one another not to grumble.

"Neither murmur ye, as some of them also murmured, and were destroyed of the destroyer."
I Corinthians 10:10

Grecian Man

Grecian Woman

Reread Acts 6:1

1. Color all the fish words orange.
2. Color all the murmuring words yellow.
3. Color all the water words blue.
4. Color all the **helpful** words green.
5. Write or read the words that are left in the lines below.

FISH	WATER	LET	TUNA	GRUM-BLE	SCHOOL	SHARK	TAIL
SURGEON FISH	SUNFISH	WAVE	CLOWN-TRIGGER FISH	SCALES	BROTHERLY	TRUNK-FISH	COMPLAIN
FAULT-FINDING	ANGEL-FISH	FINS	LAKES	SPOTTED-GOAT-FISH	OCEAN	TRUMPET-FISH	ASSIS-TANCE
BUTTER-FLY FISH	LOVE	HOGFISH	HELP-ING	DAMSEL-FISH	WHINE	FLAME-FISH	SCRAW-LED-FILE FISH
AIDING	HATCHET-FISH	RIVER	OARFISH	CONT-INUE	EEL	AID	PUFFER
BASS	HELPED	PERCH	HELPFUL-NESS	TROUT	STREAM	CATFISH	HELP."
STUR-GEON	CREEK	PADDLE-FISH	MURMURING	SALMON	USEFUL-NESS	RAIN	SILVER HATCHET-FISH

"____

____."

Hebrews 1:3

(Day 1)

Fish 1

Bean Bag Fish

The differences in fish reminds us of the differences in people,
various nationalities, that made up the early church
and our church today.

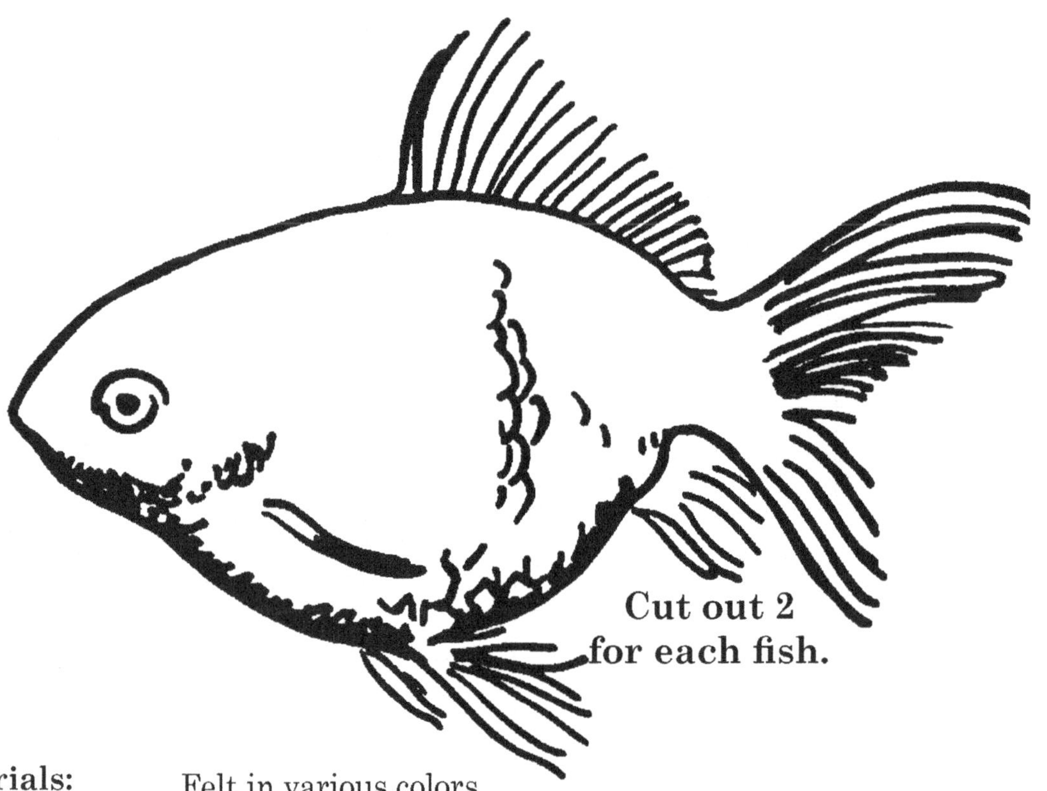

Materials:
Felt in various colors
Glue and yarn in different colors
Small beans
Squiggly eyes
Wastepaper basket

Directions:
Trace and cut out pattern
Make several different colors of fish.
Glue together around the edge leaving the mouth open.
Let dry. Or could sew with yarn.
Fill with small beans then glue or sew mouth.

Instructions:
Set your empty wastepaper basket a distance away and each time you throw a fish into the basket step back 1 step and repeat.
Excellent hand-eye coordination exercise.

(Day 1)

Seven Men Chosen

Deacons

Review today's Bible lesson.
Color this picture.

"...And they chose Stephen,
a man full of faith
and of the Holy Ghost,
and Philip, and Prochorus,
and Nicanor, and Timon,
and Parmenas, and Nicolas
a proselyte of Antioch."
Acts 6:5

"Whom they set
before the apostles:
and when they had prayed,
they laid their hands on them."
Acts 6:6

"And the word of God increased;
and the number of the disciples
multiplied in Jerusalem greatly;
and a great company of the priests
were obedient to the faith."
Acts 6:7

(Day 2)

Helpfulness vs Hindrance

Helpfulness and harm we may measure
By this simple rule alone:
Do we mind our neighbor's pleasure
Just as if it were our own?

Let us try to care for others,
Nor suppose ourselves the best;
We should all be friends and brothers;
'Twas the Saviour's last request.

His example we should borrow,
Who forsook His throne above,
And endured such pain and sorrow,
Out of tenderness and love.

When the poor are unbefriended,
When we will not pity lend,
Christ accounts Himself offended
Who is every creature's Friend.

Let us not be so ungrateful,
Thus His goodness to reward;
Hindrance, indeed, is hateful
In the followers of the Lord.

When a harmful thought would seize us,
And our resolution break,
Let us then remember Jesus,
And resist it for His sake.

—*Unknown*

(Day 2)

Fish 2

Read the following information. Color these pictures.

Usually fish will never attack
a human being.
A few that will, are certain sharks
(hammerhead and great white sharks),
barracudas, and moray eels may attack
if provoked.
Some fish that could harm humans
if they come in contact are stingrays
and stonefish,
because of their poisonous spines.

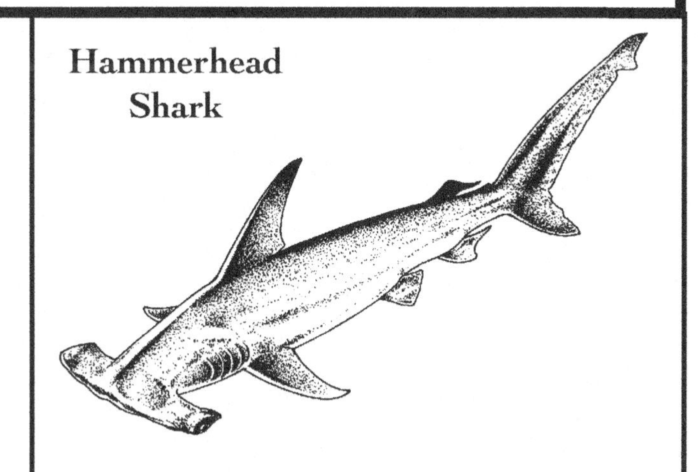

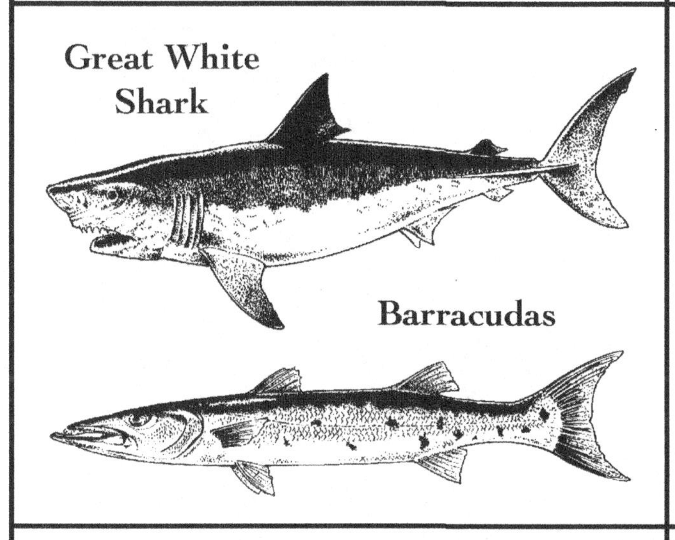

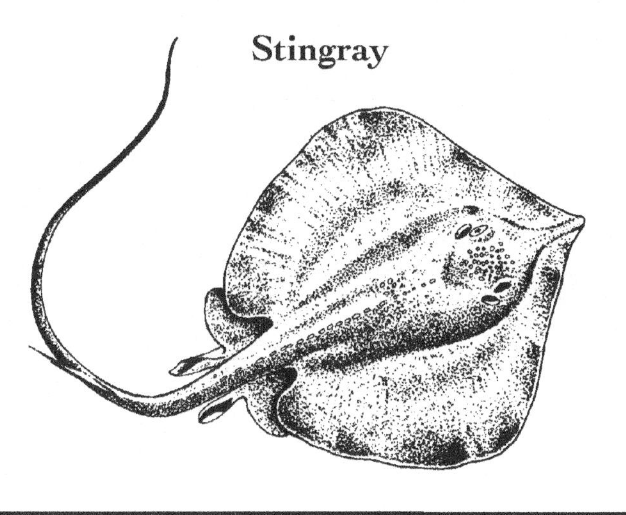

Satan was attacking the church
and trying to cause problems
among the members
but the Holy Spirit
gave helpful counsel.
The church work
was reorganized
so no one would
have their needs overlooked.
Murmuring words are poisonous.

(Day 2)

Sharks Are Dangerous

Read and color.

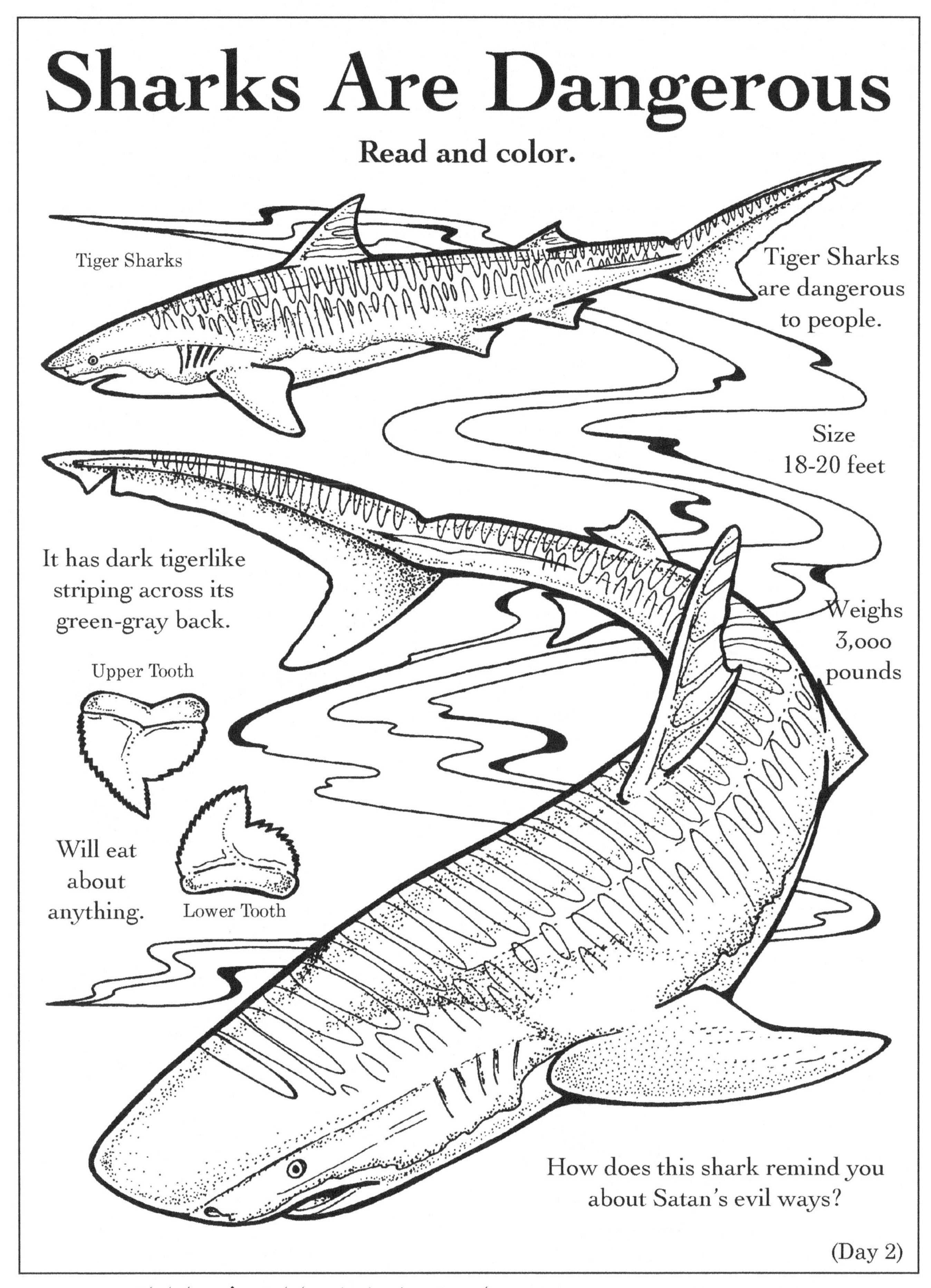

(Day 2)

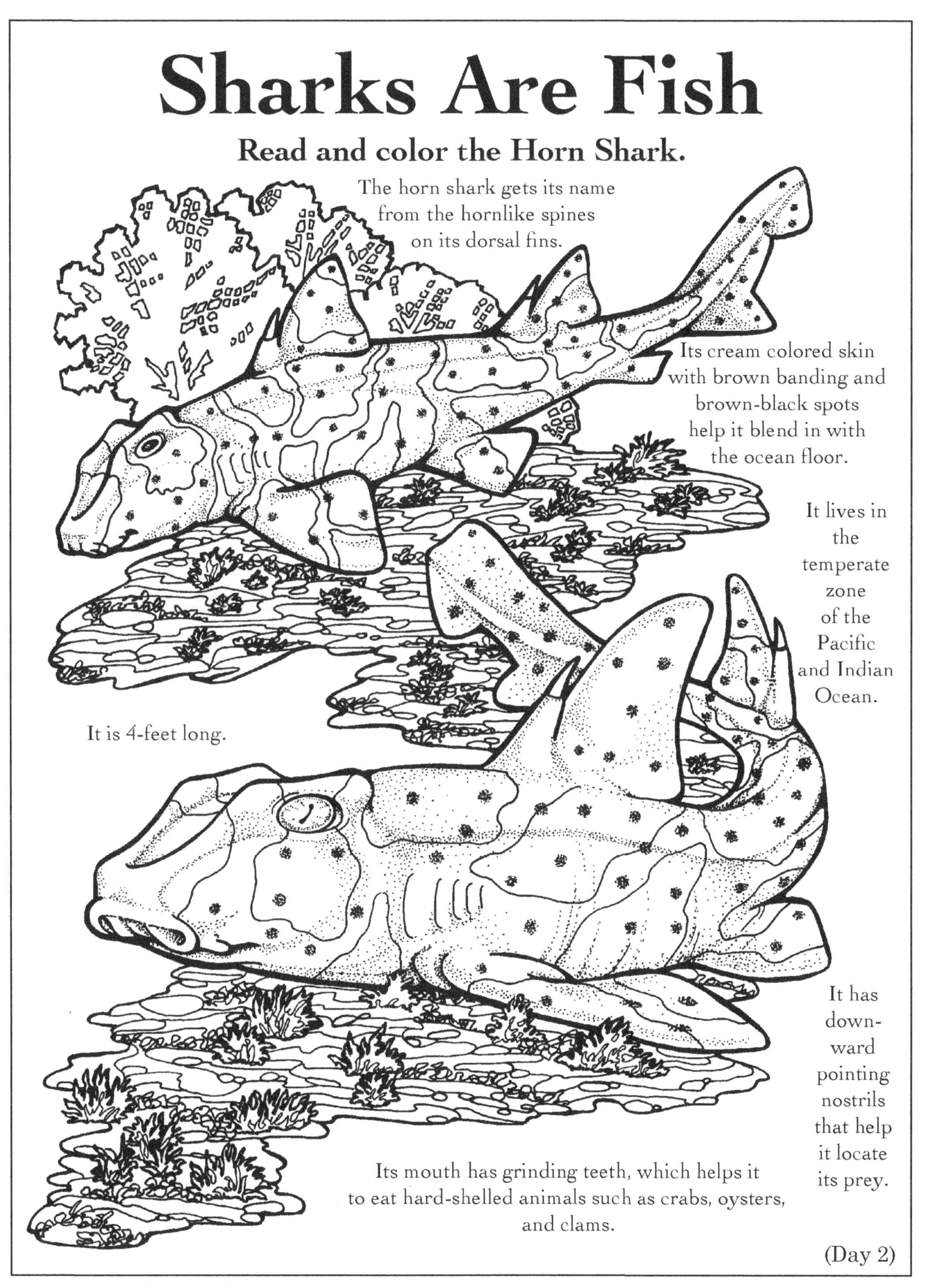
Sharks Are Fish
Read and color the Horn Shark.
The horn shark gets its name from the hornlike spines on its dorsal fins.
Its cream colored skin with brown banding and brown-black spots help it blend in with the ocean floor.
It lives in the temperate zone of the Pacific and Indian Ocean.
It is 4-feet long.
It has downward pointing nostrils that help it locate its prey.
Its mouth has grinding teeth, which helps it to eat hard-shelled animals such as crabs, oysters, and clams.
(Day 2)

Two Ways For Children

"I wish you would bring in an armful of wood, Della," said Mrs. Joy to her little girl. "Oh, I can't Mother," said she, beginning to cry: "I'm afraid some of the sticks will fall on my feet and hurt me;" and so the little girl displeased her Mother, and lost a chance to do good.

"Don't you clear off the table, Mother," said little Jane; "you sit right down to sewing, and I will wash the dishes, and do the work of the morning;" and so she did, though she was but six years old, about the same age as Della.

In this way, Jane is all the time doing things to lighten the labors of her Mother; and thus is not only very useful and happy, but makes sunshine all around her by her pleasant ways.

Now children, how happy you may make your parents and brothers and sisters by being industrious and **helpful.** This will be much the pleasanter way, even for you; for God is thus pleased, and will help such children, and be near them, if they love Him and pray to Him.

"While living in this world we are to be God's helping hand. Paul declared, *'Ye are God's husbandry, ye are God's building'* (I Corinthians 3:9). We are to cooperate with God in every measure that He desires to carry out. Are we fulfilling the purpose of the eternal God? Are we daily seeking to have the mind of Christ and to do His will in word and work?"

I Selected Messages 98

(Day 2)

7 7 7 Helpful Men 7 7 7 7

Use Acts 6:5 to find the names of 7
helpful men chosen to serve the church.

T	P	M	T	I	N	C	O	L	A	S	D
I	H	S	N	I	C	O	L	A	S	A	R
M	I	T	I	M	D	N	T	E	V	N	N
O	L	E	C	N	S	A	C	I	N	E	A
N	S	P	A	I	L	T	I	H	P	M	C
A	T	O	N	R	T	I	E	M	O	R	I
S	U	R	O	H	C	O	R	P	E	A	N
N	P	A	R	M	P	I	L	I	H	P	S
N	A	S	N	I	C	O	L	A	P	E	U
H	I	L	I	P	R	O	C	H	O	R	N

Answer these questions.

1. Who was formost of the seven deacons?
2. What kind of Christian was he?
3. Who came to his trial?

"And Stephen, full of faith and power,
did great wonders and miracles among the people."
Acts 6:8

(Day 3)

What is a Fish?

Fill in the blanks. Circle and color the true fish below.

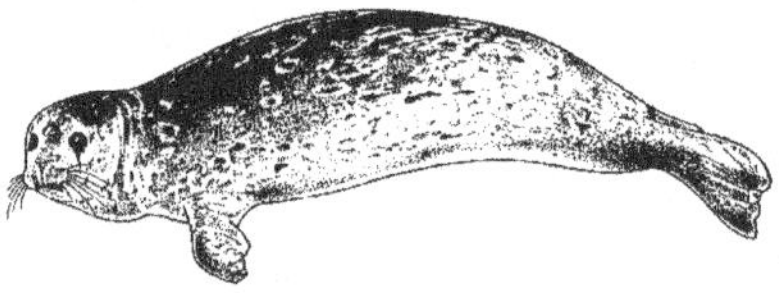

1. Fish have a _ _ _ _ _ _ _ _ _ _ _.
2. They breathe through _ _ _ _ _. 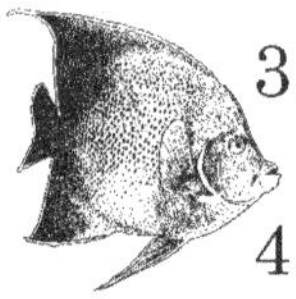
3. They are _ _ _ _–_ _ _ _ _ _ _ _ _ _ animals. 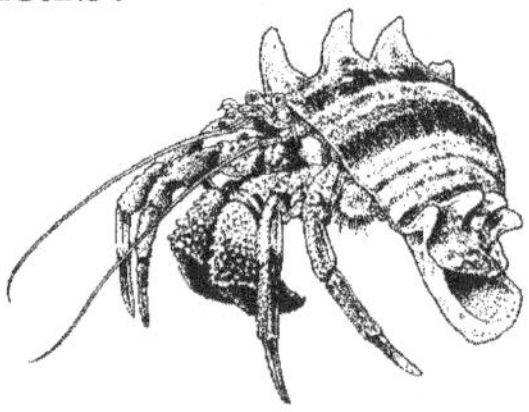
4. Many have _ _ _ _ and _ _ _ _ _ _ _ _ _.
5. There are about _ _, _ _ _ kinds of fish.
6. Scientists have ________ about that many kinds of fish. 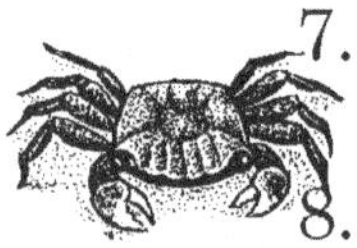
7. Scientists who study fish are called ________________.
8. They have divided fish into _______ main groups.
9. They are ____________ and ____________.

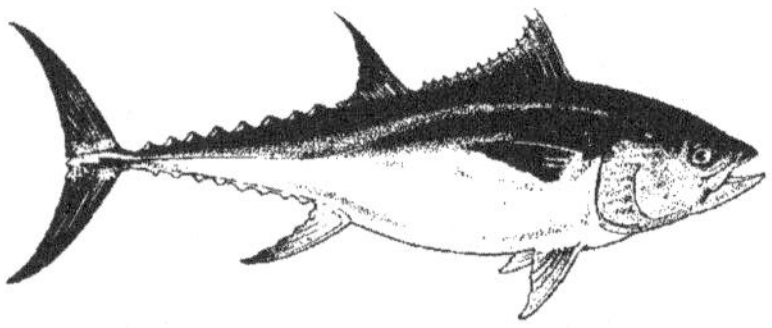

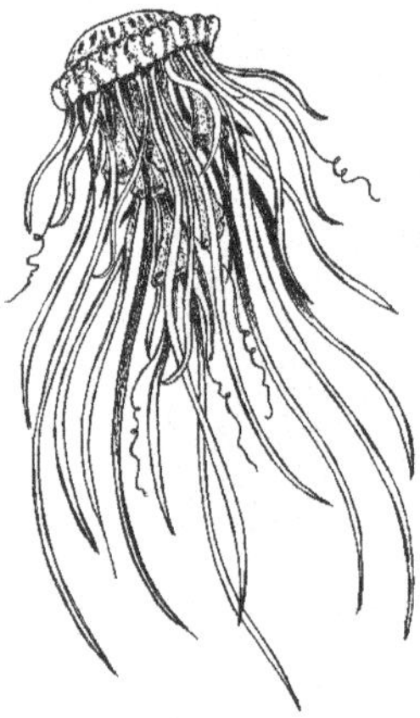

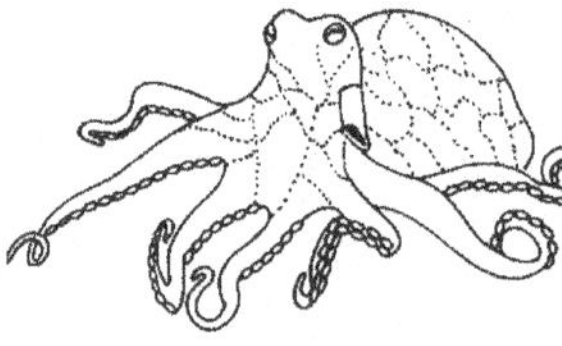

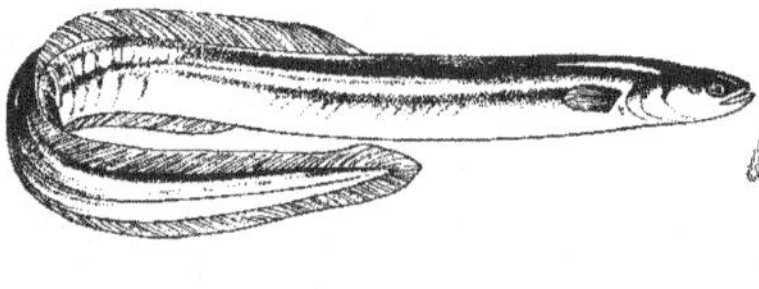

Who is a true follower of Christ?

(Day 3)

Stephen's Testimony

Review today's Bible Lesson by answering these questions.

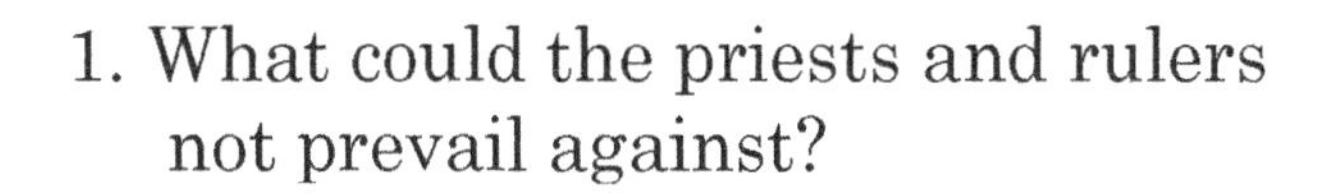

1. What could the priests and rulers not prevail against?

2. What did they determine to do? Why?

3. Who did they get to help them?

4. How did Stephen respond?

5. What did he say when questioned?

6. What alerted Stephen to the fact that he was giving his last testimony?

7. What was Stephen trying to do for these leaders?

8. Did they want his **help**?

9. What should you do when you have to answer for your faith?

Reread Acts 7:51-53.

(Day 4)

Kinds of Fish and Fins

Review today's Nature Lesson.

List the items in the Z letter. Notice the 2 fish. You may need to look at the Teacher's Key. Notice their fins.

Color each item as you say or learn its name.

Make a list of different fish from A through Z.
Look back at previous lessons or use an encyclopedia.

(Day 4)

The Good Samaritan

"But A Certain Samaritan...." Luke 10:33

Oberlin, the well-known man from Steinthal, while yet a candidate for the ministry, was traveling on one occasion from Strasburg, Germany. It was in the winter-time. The ground was deeply covered with snow, and the roads were almost impassable. He had reached the middle of his journey and was among the mountains, and by that time was so exhausted that he could stand up no longer.

He was rapidly freezing to death. Sleep began to overcome him; All power to resist it left him. He commended himself to God, and yielded to what he felt to be the sleep of death.

He knew not how long he slept, but suddenly became conscious of some one rousing him and waking him up. Before him stood a wagon-driver in his blue coat, and the wagon not far away. He gave him a little juice and food, and the spirit of life returned. He then **helped** him on the wagon, and brought him to the next village. The rescued man was profuse in his thanks, and offered money, which his benefactor refused.

"It is only a duty to **help** one another," said the wagoner. "And it is the next thing to an insult to offer a reward for such a service."

"Then," replied Oberlin, "at least tell me your name, that I may bring you in thankful remembrance before God."

"I see," said the wagoner, "that you are a minister of the gospel. Please tell me the name of the Good Samaritan."

"That," said Oberlin, "I cannot do, for it was not put on record."

"Then," replied the wagoner, "until you can tell me his name, permit me to withhold mine."

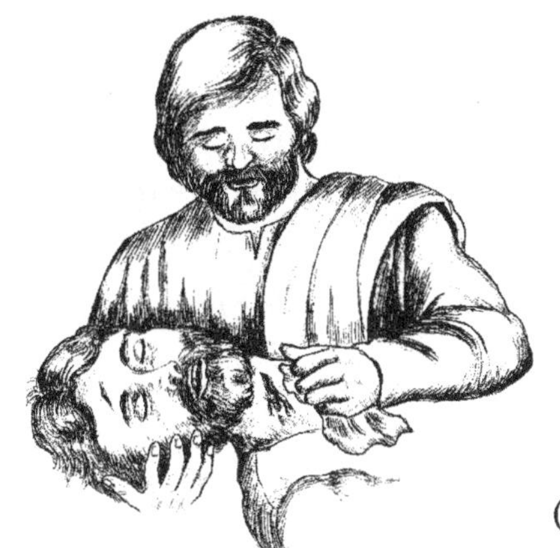

(Day 4)

Light Shining Out of Darkness

God moves in a mysterious way,
His wonders to perform;
He plants His footsteps in the sea,
And rides upon the storm.

Deep in unfathomable mines
Of never failing skill,
He treasures up His bright designs,
And works His sovereign will.

Ye fearful saints, fresh courage take,
The clouds ye so much dread
Are big with mercy, and shall break
In blessings on your head.

Judge not the Lord by feeble sense,
But trust Him for His grace;
Behind a frowning providence,
He hides a smiling face.

—*Unknown*

(Day 4)

Stephen Dies

"But he, being full of the Holy Ghost, looked up steadfastly into heaven,
and saw the glory of God,
and Jesus standing on the right hand of God,

"And said, Behold, I see the heavens opened,
and the Son of man standing on the right hand of God."
Acts 7:55-56

Fill in the blanks with the letters between the letters given.

Examples: rt = s or rst
–b = a

"It was through one who declared himself to be a 'brother, and companion in tribulation' (Revelation 1:9), that Christ revealed to His church the things that they must ______________ for His sake. Looking
rt tv eg eg df qs

down through long centuries of darkness and superstition, the aged exile saw ______________________________ ___________________________
ln tv km su hj su tv ce df rt rt tv eg eg df qs hj mo fh

________________________ because of their __________________ for the
ln -b qs su xz qs ce np ln km np uw df

______________ . But he saw also that He who sustained His early wit-
su qs tv su gi.

nesses would not forsake His faithful followers during the centuries of persecution that they must pass through ________________ the
ac df eg np qs df

______________ of ____________."
bd km np rt df su hj ln df **Read Revelation 2:10.**

The Acts of the Apostles 588

(Day 5)

The Stoning

"And he kneeled down, and cried with a loud voice, Lord, lay not this sin to their charge. And when he had said this, he fell asleep."

Acts 7:60

Color this picture.

(Day 5)

How Fish Breathe

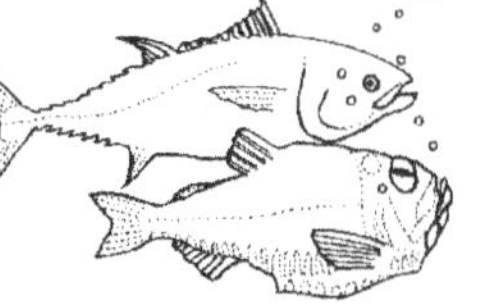

To stay connected with heaven you must have the breath of the Holy Spirit, like Stephen did.

Read about fish breathing.
Draw air bubbles above the fish below. Color the picture.

1. Fish need oxygen to live.
2. Fish breathe through their gills.
3. The blood inside the gills takes oxygen from the water.
4. The fish takes a big gulp of water then closes its mouth.
5. This pushes the water between the gills
6. After the blood takes the oxygen it carries it throughout the body.

Usually a foot and a half long, the saber squirrelfish has red scales with white margins.

(Day 5)

Winter Flounder

Learn about the flounder by reading the information and coloring the picture.
What spiritual lessons could you learn from this fish?

It is winter, and while other flatfish have headed into deeper, warmer seas, the winter flounder following its instinct, has come inland and lies half buried, along with many of its kind. It is so well camouflaged it is hard to decide <u>where the sand ends and flounder begins</u>. Its protruding <u>eyes</u>, both on the upper side of its head, move slightly as it surveys its surroundings hungrily for any passing shrimp or small fish it could catch for a meal. <u>Others should see Jesus in us and desire Him</u>!

(Day 5)

Death and Saul

"And cast him out of the city, and stoned him: and the witnesses laid down their clothes at a young man's feet, whose name was Saul."
Acts 7:58

Write these words in the crossword below after rereading *The Acts of the Apostles* page 101, paragraph 3.

KeY

martyrdom	minds	trial	Stephen
beholders	church	witnessed	testified
Saul	memory	truth	face
proclaimed	faith	words	death
glory	touched	sore	countenance

(Day 6)

Finding Their Way

A fish's 5 senses help them find their way. What are they:

1.______________________________

2.______________________________

3. ______________________________

4.______________________________

5.______________________________

Color the fish below, that you might keep in your aquarium.

The Holy Spirit can **help** you to be sensitive so that you might not sin.

(Day 6)

An Angry Mob

As a Methodist pioneer, Adam Clarke, of Ireland, traveled all about Ireland, England, and Wales, and to the Channel Islands. In those days Methodism met the opposition of the Established Church and of "society," and the irreligious mob felt itself doing respectable service in assailing the sect everywhere spoken against.

On one of these trips, Adam Clarke experienced so remarkable an interposition of Providence to save his life that he records it in his Commentary, as a note on the deliverance of Christ from the mob at Nazareth: found in Luke 4:30. Writing of himself in the third person, he says a certain missionary was called to preach in a place where there was much prejudice:

"About fifty people who had received impressions from the Word of God, assemble. He began his discourse, and after he had preached about thirty minutes, an outrageous mob surrounded the house armed with different instruments of death, and breathing the most terrible purposes. Some that were within, shut the door; and the missionary and his flock began to pray.

"The mob assailed the house, and began to hurl stones against the walls, windows, and roof; and in a short time almost every tile was destroyed, and the roof nearly uncovered, and before they quit the premises, scarcely left one square inch of glass in the five windows by which the house was enlightened.

"While this was going forward, a person came with a pistol to the window opposite to the place where the preacher stood (who was then exhorting his flock to be steady, to resign themselves to God, and trust in Him), presented it at him, and snapped it, but it only flashed in the pan.

"As the house was a wooden building, they began with crow bars and spades to destroy it, and take away its principal supports. The preacher then addressed his little flock to this effect: 'These outrageous people seek not you, but me; if I continue in the house, they will soon tear it down, and we shall all be buried in the ruins; I will therefore, in the name of God, go out to them, and you will be safe.' He then went toward the door; the poor people got around him, and entreated him not to venture out, as he might expect to be instantly killed. He went calmly forward, opened the door, at which a whole volley of stones and dirt was that instant discharge; but he received no damage.

"The people were in crowds in all the space before the door, and filled the road for a considerable way, so that there was no room to pass or repass.

"As soon as the preacher made his appearance, the savages became instantly as silent and as still as night; he walked forward, and they divided to the right and to the left, leaving a passage of about four feet wide, for himself and a young man who followed him, to walk in. He passed on through the whole crowd, not a soul of whom either lifted a hand or spoke one

(Day 6)

word, till he and his companion had gained the uttermost skirts of the mob. The narrator, who was present on the occasion, goes on to say:

" 'This was one of the most affecting spectacles I ever witnessed: an infuriated mob without any visible cause (for the preacher spoke not one word) became in a moment as calm as lambs. They seemed struck with amazement bordering on stupefaction; they stared and stood speechless; and after they had fallen back to right and left to leave him a free passage, they were as motionless as statues. They assembled with the full purpose to destroy the man who came to show them the way of salvation; but he, passing through the midst of them, went his way. Was not the God of missionaries in this work?' "

In the quietness that followed for a few minutes after the preacher disappeared, the people inside the church also went out and escaped. Then the mob awoke *"as from a dream,"* and broke the windows and otherwise vented their fury on the house.

The One who, passing through the midst of the mob at Nazareth, went His way, has promised the gospel worker, *"Lo, I am with you always, even unto the end of the world."**

In our lesson, Stephen was not saved from death but his death brought forth a new missionary to take his place whose name was Saul and later called Paul. We must always turn to God for **help**. He will do what is best for us.

Missionaries and Martyrs

"There are many who have given themselves to Christ,
yet who see no opportunity of doing a large work
or making great sacrifices in His service.
These may find comfort in the thought that it is not necessarily
the martyr's self-surrender which is most acceptable to God;
it may not be the missionary who has daily faced danger and death
that stands highest in heaven's records.
The Christian who is such in his private life,
in the daily surrender of self,
in sincerity of purpose and purity of thought,
in meekness under provocation, in faith and piety,
in fidelity in that which is least,
the one who in the home life represents the character of Christ—
such a one may in the sight of God be more precious
than even the world-renowned missionary or martyr."

Christ's Object Lessons 403

*Adapted from the book *The Hand That Intervenes*

9 – Stephen Stoned

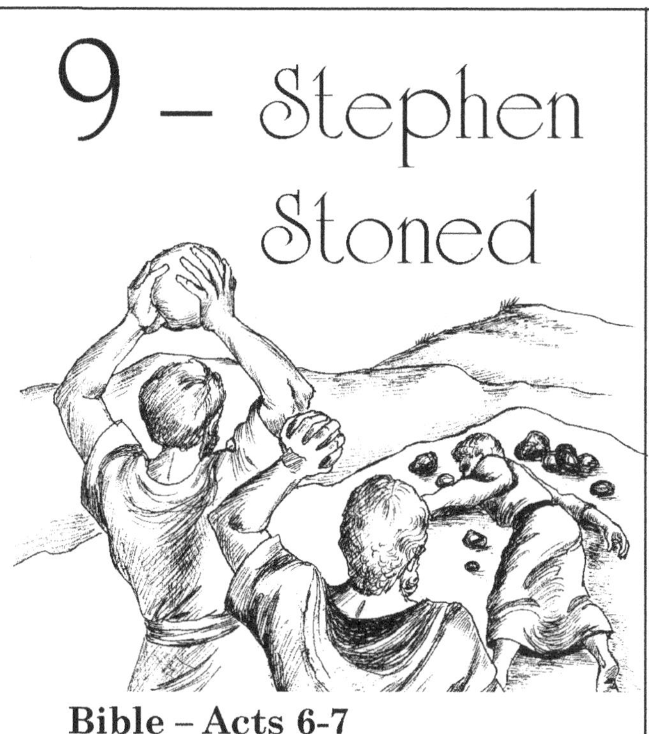

Bible – Acts 6-7

Song – "Working, O Christ, With Thee"

Nature – Fish

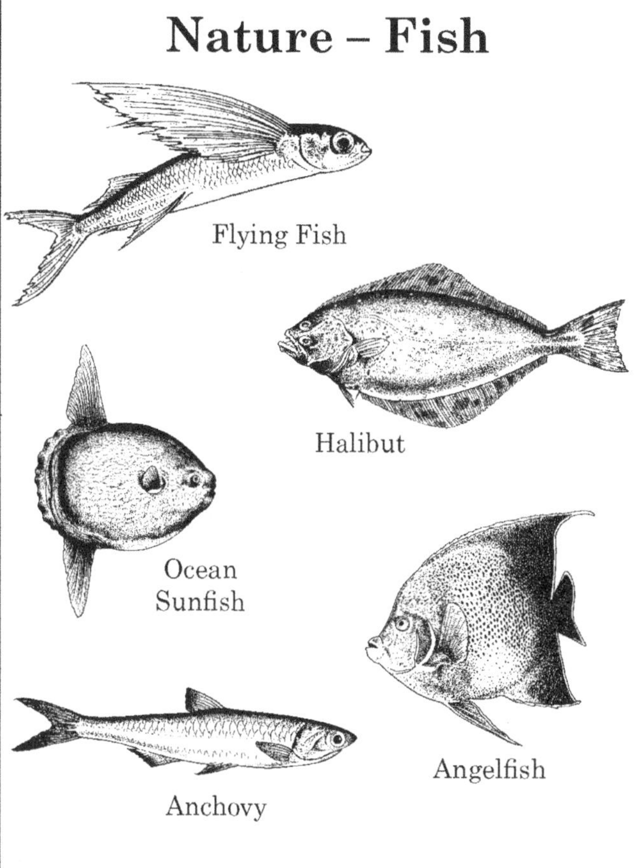

Character Quality

Helpfulness vs Hindrance
Helpfulness is to aid or assist another as if you were **helping** Jesus and thereby promoting a person's usefulness.

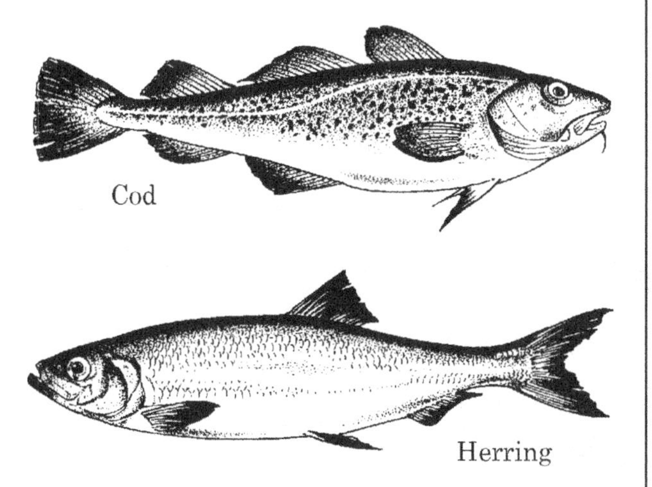

Memory Verse

"Fear none of those things which thou shalt suffer: behold, the devil shall cast some of you into prison, that ye may be tried; and ye shall have tribulation ten days: be thou faithful unto death, and I will give thee a crown of life."
Revelation 2:10

Fish

The mighty manta ray is very large.
Yet this large fish eats nothing bigger than plankton!
Stephen had grown large in faith by eating (spiritually)
nothing more than the Word of God.
"Thy words were found, and I did eat them."

Draw or place a seal of a fish above
for each day this week
you study your lesson,
and say your memory verse.

Grecian Man

Murmuring

Satan tries to cause discord through murmuring—
we must **help** one another not to grumble.

"Neither murmur ye, as some of them also murmured, and were destroyed of the destroyer."
I Corinthians 10:10

Grecian Woman

1. Color all the fish words orange.
2. Color all the murmuring words yellow.
3. Color all the water words blue.
4. Color all the **helpful** words green.
5. Write or read the words that are left in the lines below.

FISH	WATER	LET	TUNA	GRUM-BLE	SCHOOL	SHARK	TAIL
SURGEON FISH	SUNFISH	WAVE	CLOWN-TRIGGER FISH	SCALES	BROTHERLY	TRUNK-FISH	COMPLAIN
FAULT-FINDING	ANGEL-FISH	FINS	LAKES	SPOTTED-GOAT-FISH	OCEAN	TRUMPET-FISH	ASSIS-TANCE
BUTTER-FLY FISH	LOVE	HOGFISH	HELP-ING	DAMSEL-FISH	WHINE	FLAME-FISH	SCRAW-LED-FILE FISH
AIDING	HATCHET-FISH	RIVER	OARFISH	CONT-INUE	EEL	AID	PUFFER
BASS	HELPED	PERCH	HELPFUL-NESS	TROUT	STREAM	CATFISH	HELP."
STUR-GEON	CREEK	PADDLE-FISH	MURMURING	SALMON	USEFUL-NESS	RAIN	SILVER HATCHET-FISH

"____

____."

Hebrews 1:3

(Day 1)

Fish 1

Bean Bag Fish

The differences in fish reminds us of the differences in people (various nationalities) that made up the early church and our church today.

Materials:

Felt in various colors
Glue and yarn
Small beans
Squiggly eyes
Wastepaper basket

Directions:

Trace and cut out pattern
Make several different colors of fish.
Glue together around the edge leaving the mouth open.
Let dry. Or could sew with yarn.
Fill with small beans then glue or sew mouth.

Instructions:

Set your empty wastepaper basket a distance away and each time you throw a fish into the basket step back 1 step and repeat. Excellent hand-eye coordination exercise.

(Day 1)

Seven Men Chosen

Deacons

Review today's Bible lesson.
Color this picture.

"...And they chose Stephen,
a man full of faith
and of the Holy Ghost,
and Philip, and Prochorus,
and Nicanor, and Timon,
and Parmenas, and Nicolas
a proselyte of Antioch."
Acts 6:5

"Whom they set
before the apostles:
and when they had prayed,
they laid their hands on them."
Acts 6:6

"And the word of God increased;
and the number of the disciples
multiplied in Jerusalem greatly;
and a great company of the priests
were obedient to the faith."
Acts 6:7

(Day 2)

<u>Helpfulness</u> vs Hindrance

Helpfulness and harm we may measure
By this simple rule alone:
Do we mind our neighbor's pleasure
Just as if it were our own?

Let us try to care for others,
Nor suppose ourselves the best;
We should all be friends and brothers;
'Twas the Saviour's last request.

His example we should borrow,
Who forsook His throne above,
And endured such pain and sorrow,
Out of tenderness and love.

When the poor are unbefriended,
When we will not pity lend,
Christ accounts Himself offended
Who is every creature's Friend.

Let us not be so ungrateful,
Thus His goodness to reward;
Hindrance, indeed, is hateful
In the followers of the Lord.

When a harmful thought would seize us,
And our resolution break,
Let us then remember Jesus,
And resist it for His sake.

—*Unknown*

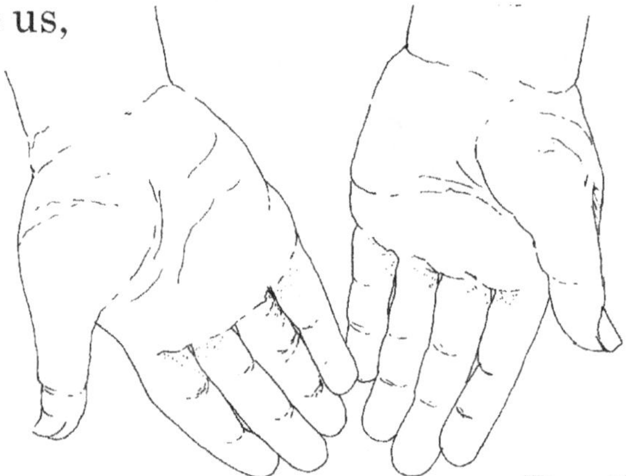

(Day 2)

Fish 2

Read the following information. Color these pictures.

Usually fish will never attack
a human being.
A few that will, are certain sharks
(hammerhead and great white sharks),
barracudas, and moray eels may attack
if provoked.
Some fish that could harm humans
if they come in contact are stingrays
and stonefish,
because of their poisonous spines.

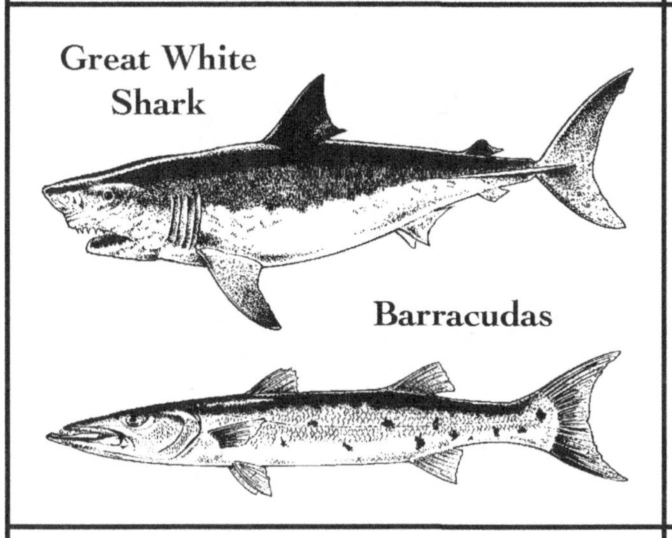

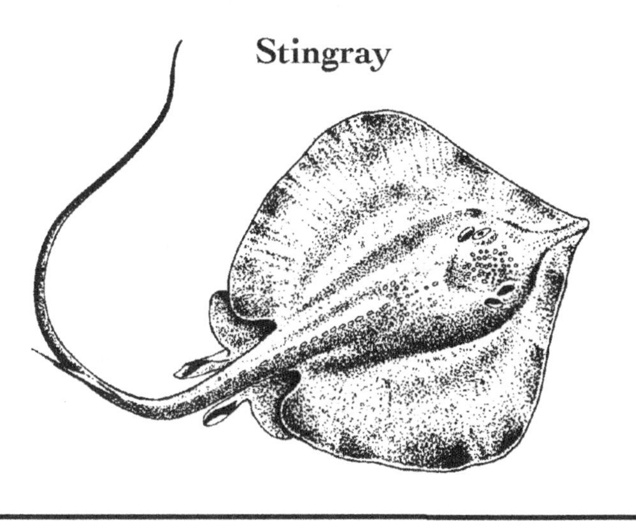

Satan was attacking the church
and trying to cause problems
among the members
but the Holy Spirit
gave helpful counsel.
The church work
was reorganized
so no one would
have their needs overlooked.

(Day 2)

Sharks Are Dangerous

Read and color.

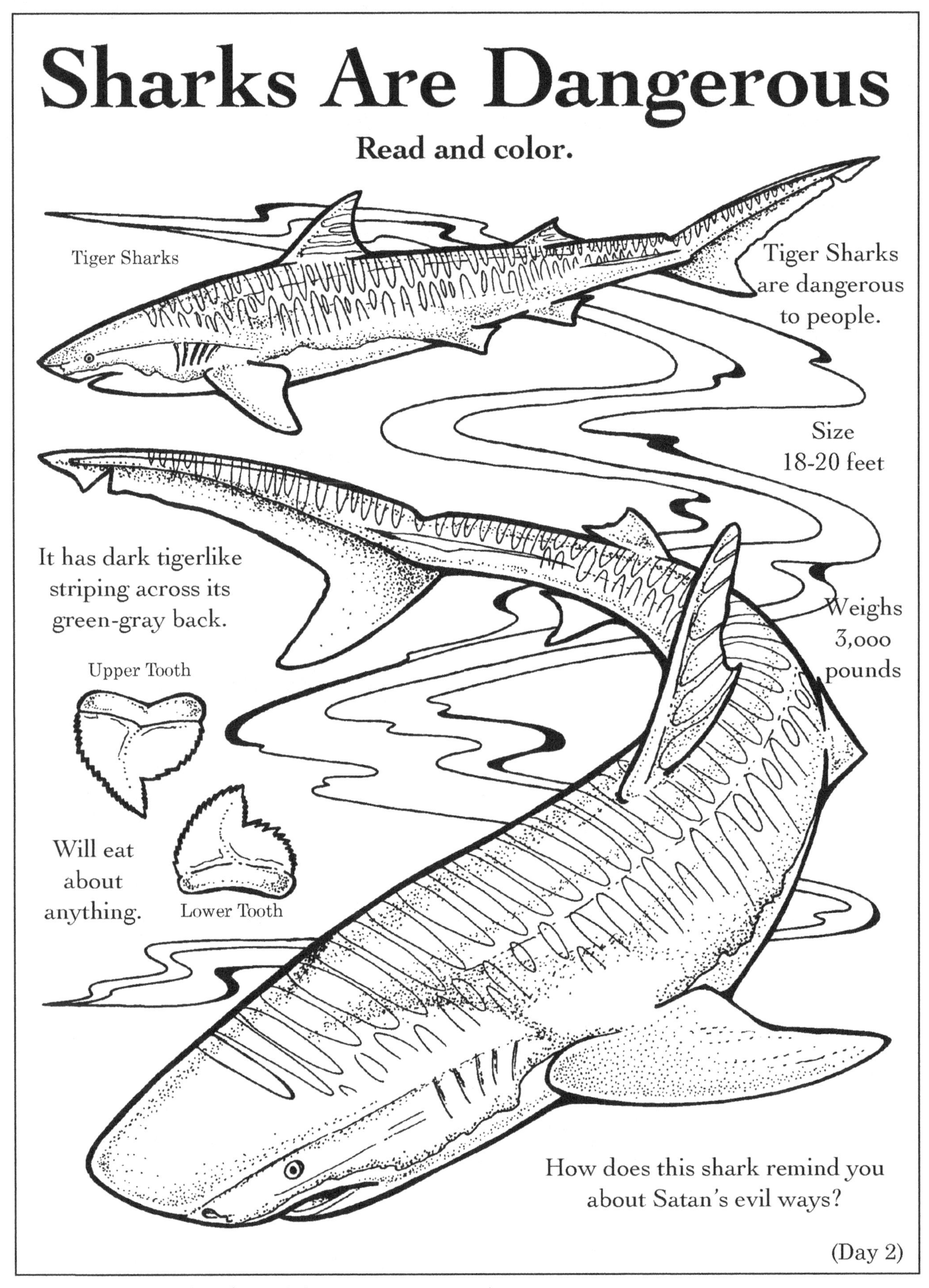

(Day 2)

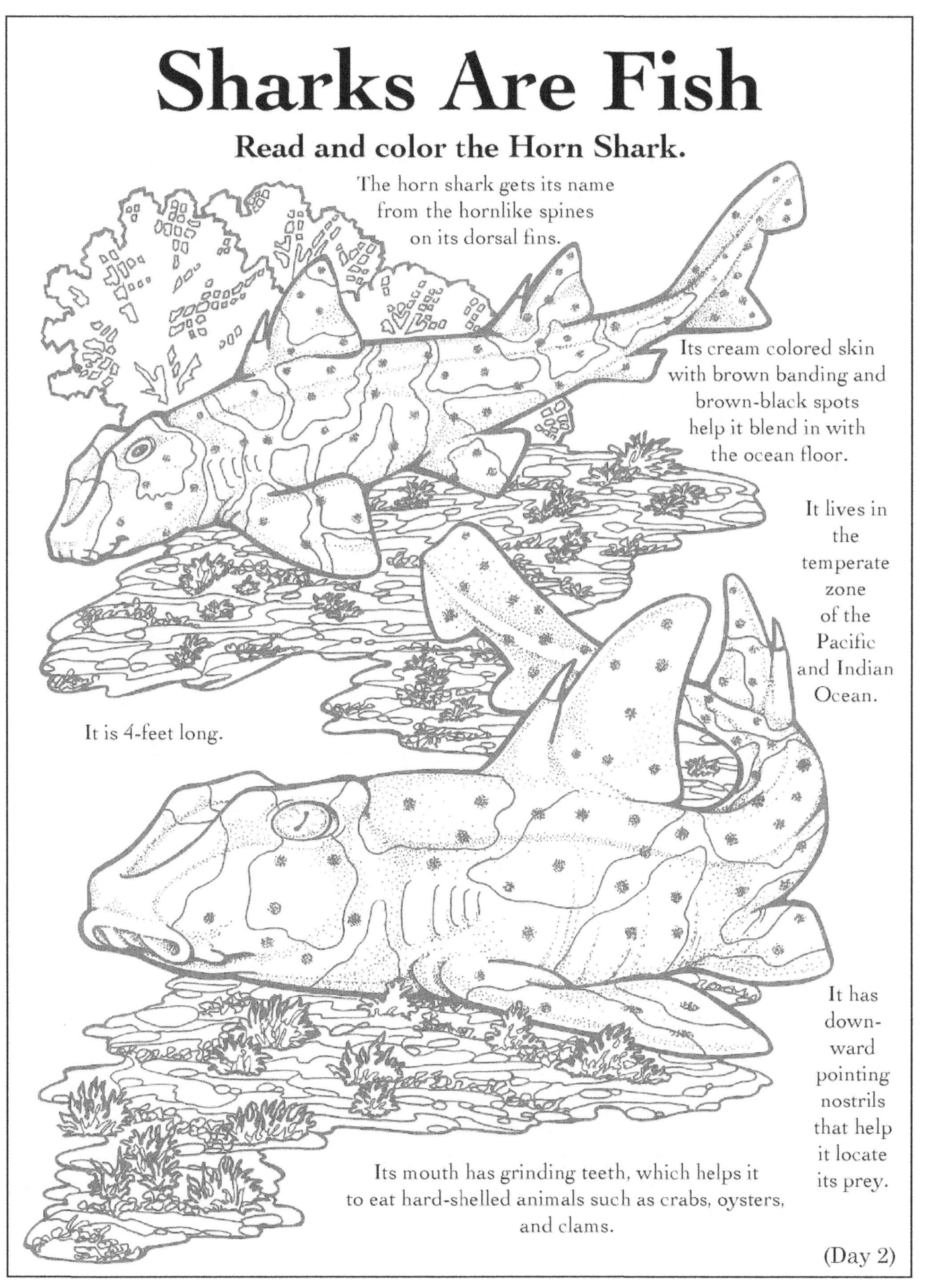
Sharks Are Fish
Read and color the Horn Shark.
The horn shark gets its name from the hornlike spines on its dorsal fins.
Its cream colored skin with brown banding and brown-black spots help it blend in with the ocean floor.
It lives in the temperate zone of the Pacific and Indian Ocean.
It is 4-feet long.
It has downward pointing nostrils that help it locate its prey.
Its mouth has grinding teeth, which helps it to eat hard-shelled animals such as crabs, oysters, and clams.
(Day 2)

Two Ways For Children

"I wish you would bring in an armful of wood, Della," said Mrs. Joy to her little girl. "Oh, I can't Mother," said she, beginning to cry: "I'm afraid some of the sticks will fall on my feet and hurt me;" and so the little girl displeased her Mother, and lost a chance to do good.

"Don't you clear off the table, Mother," said little Jane; "you sit right down to sewing, and I will wash the dishes, and do the work of the morning;" and so she did, though she was but six years old, about the same age as Della.

In this way, Jane is all the time doing things to lighten the labors of her Mother; and thus is not only very useful and happy, but makes sunshine all around her by her pleasant ways.

Now children, how happy you may make your parents and brothers and sisters by being industrious and **helpful.** This will be much the pleasanter way, even for you; for God is thus pleased, and will help such children, and be near them, if they love Him and pray to Him.

"While living in this world we are to be God's helping hand. Paul declared, *'Ye are God's husbandry, ye are God's building'* (I Corinthians 3:9). We are to cooperate with God in every measure that He desires to carry out. Are we fulfilling the purpose of the eternal God? Are we daily seeking to have the mind of Christ and to do His will in word and work?"

I Selected Messages 98

(Day 2)

7 7 7 Helpful Men 7 7 7 7

Use Acts 6:5 to find the names of 7
<u>helpful</u> men chosen to serve the church.

T	P	M	T	I	N	C	O	L	A	S	D
I	H	S	N	I	C	O	L	A	S	A	R
M	I	T	I	M	D	N	T	E	V	N	N
O	L	E	C	N	S	A	C	I	N	E	A
N	S	P	A	I	L	T	I	H	P	M	C
A	T	O	N	R	T	I	E	M	O	R	I
S	U	R	O	H	C	O	R	P	E	A	N
N	P	A	R	M	P	I	L	I	H	P	S
N	A	S	N	I	C	O	L	A	P	E	U
H	I	L	I	P	R	O	C	H	O	R	N

Answer these questions.

1. Who was formost of the seven deacons?
2. What kind of Christian was he?
3. Who came to his trial?

"And Stephen, full of faith and power,
did great wonders and miracles among the people."
Acts 6:8

(Day 3)

What is a Fish?

Fill in the blanks. Circle and color the true fish below.

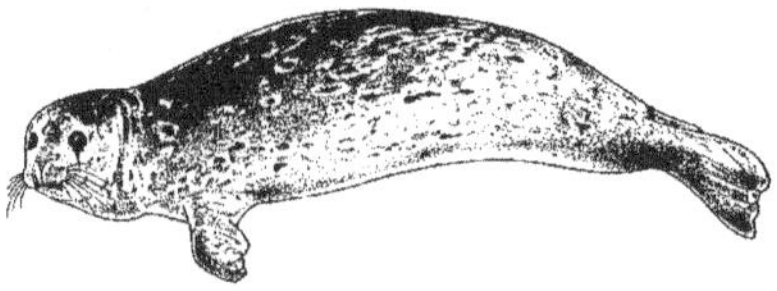

1. Fish have a _ _ _ _ _ _ _ _ _ _ _.
2. They breathe through _ _ _ _ _ _. 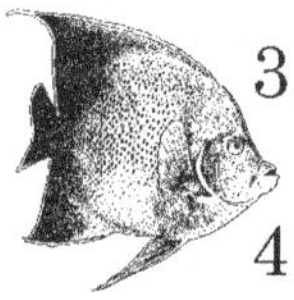
3. They are _ _ _ _–_ _ _ _ _ _ _ _ _ _ _ animals. 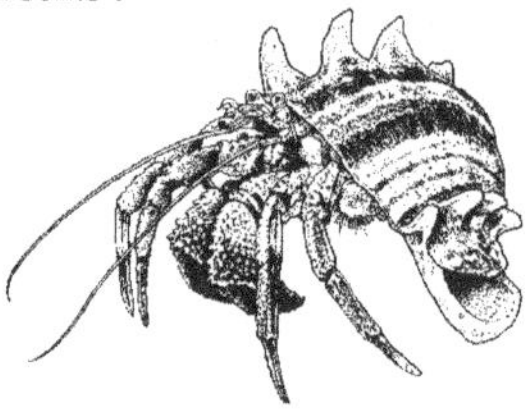
4. Many have _ _ _ _ _ and _ _ _ _ _ _ _ _ _.
5. There are about _ _, _ _ _ _ kinds of fish.
6. Scientists have ________ about that many kinds of fish. 
7. Scientists who study fish are called _________________.
8. They have divided fish into _______ main groups.
9. They are ____________ and ____________.

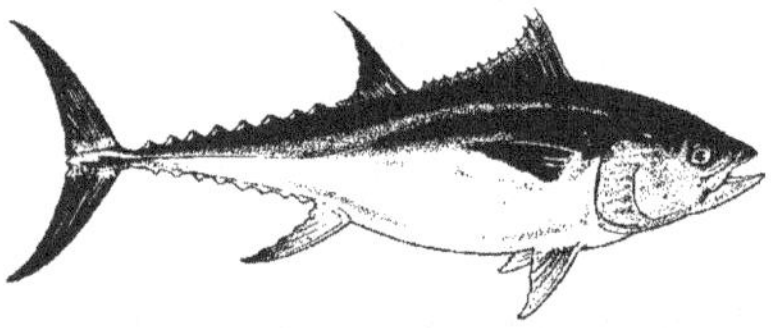

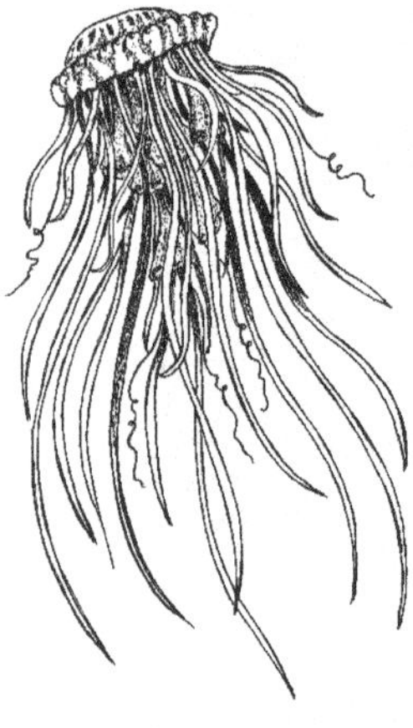

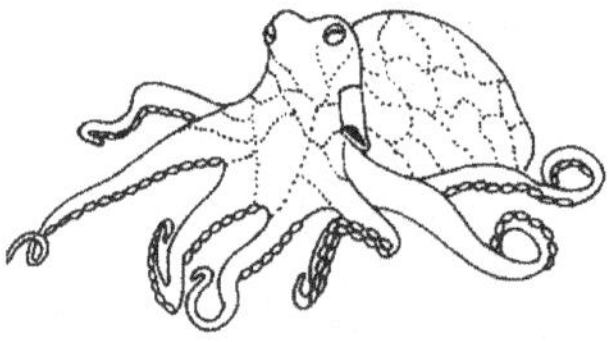

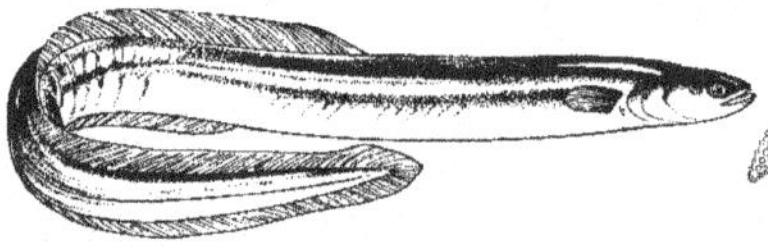

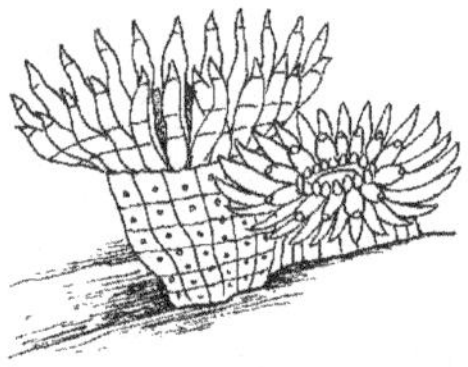

Who is a true follower of Christ?

(Day 3)

Stephen's Testimony

Review today's Bible Lesson by answering these questions.

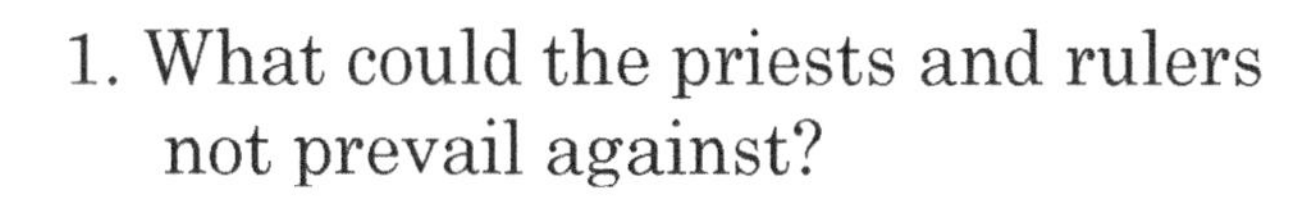

1. What could the priests and rulers not prevail against?

2. What did they determine to do?

3. Who did they get to help them?

4. How did Stephen respond?

5. What did he say when questioned?

6. What alerted Stephen to the fact that he was giving his last testimony?

7. What was Stephen trying to do for these leaders?

8. Did they want his **help**?

9. What should you do when you have to answer for your faith?

(Day 4)

Kinds of Fish

Review today's Nature Lesson.

List the items in the Z letter. Notice the 2 fish. You may need to look at the Teacher's Key.

Color each item as you say or learn its name.

Make a list of different fish from A through Z.

(Day 4)

The Good Samaritan

"But A Certain Samaritan...." Luke 10:33

Oberlin, the well-known man from Steinthal, while yet a candidate for the ministry, was traveling on one occasion from Strasburg, Germany. It was in the winter-time. The ground was deeply covered with snow, and the roads were almost impassable. He had reached the middle of his journey and was among the mountains, and by that time was so exhausted that he could stand up no longer.

He was rapidly freezing to death. Sleep began to overcome him; All power to resist it left him. He commended himself to God, and yielded to what he felt to be the sleep of death.

He knew not how long he slept, but suddenly became conscious of some one rousing him and waking him up. Before him stood a wagon-driver in his blue coat, and the wagon not far away. He gave him a little juice and food, and the spirit of life returned. He then **helped** him on the wagon, and brought him to the next village. The rescued man was profuse in his thanks, and offered money, which his benefactor refused.

"It is only a duty to **help** one another," said the wagoner. "And it is the next thing to an insult to offer a reward for such a service."

"Then," replied Oberlin, "at least tell me your name, that I may bring you in thankful remembrance before God."

"I see," said the wagoner, "that you are a minister of the gospel. Please tell me the name of the Good Samaritan."

"That," said Oberlin, "I cannot do, for it was not put on record."

"Then," replied the wagoner, "until you can tell me his name, permit me to withhold mine."

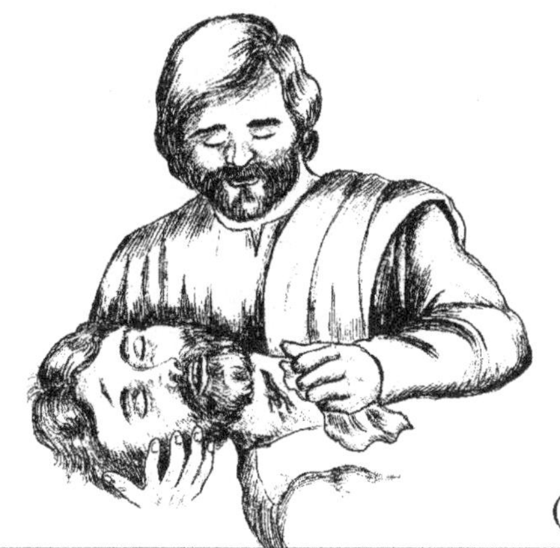

(Day 4)

Light Shining Out of Darkness

God moves in a mysterious way,
His wonders to perform;
He plants His footsteps in the sea,
And rides upon the storm.

Deep in unfathomable mines
Of never failing skill,
He treasures up His bright designs,
And works His sovereign will.

Ye fearful saints, fresh courage take,
The clouds ye so much dread
Are big with mercy, and shall break
In blessings on your head.

Judge not the Lord by feeble sense,
But trust Him for His grace;
Behind a frowning providence,
He hides a smiling face.

—*Unknown*

(Day 4)

Stephen Dies

"But he, being full of the Holy Ghost, looked up steadfastly into heaven,
and saw the glory of God,
and Jesus standing on the right hand of God,

"And said, Behold, I see the heavens opened,
and the Son of man standing on the right hand of God."
Acts 7:55-56

Fill in the blanks with the letters between the letters given.

Example: rt = s or rst

"It was through one who declared himself to be a 'brother, and companion in tribulation' (Revelation 1:9), that Christ revealed to His church the things that they must ____________ for His sake. Looking
rt tv eg eg df qs

down through long centuries of darkness and superstition, the aged exile saw ____________________ ____________________
ln tv km su hj su tv ce df rt rt tv eg eg df qs hj mo fh

____________________ because of their ______________ for the
ln -b qs us xz qs ce np ln km np uw df

____________ . But he saw also that He who sustained His early wit-
su qs tv su gi.

nesses would not forsake His faithful followers during the centuries of persecution that they must pass through ______________ the
ac df eg np qs df

____________ of ___________."
bd km np rt df su hj ln df **Read Revelation 2:10.**

The Acts of the Apostles 588

(Day 5)

The Stoning

"And he kneeled down, and cried with a loud voice, Lord, lay not this sin to their charge. And when he had said this, he fell asleep."
Acts 7:60

Color this picture.

(Day 5)

How Fish Breathe

To stay connected with heaven you must have the breath of the Holy Spirit, like Stephen did.

Read about fish breathing then color this fish.
Draw air bubbles above the fish below. Color the picture.

1. Fish need oxygen to live.

2. Fish breathe through their gills.

3. The blood inside the gills takes oxygen from the water

4. The fish takes a big gulp of water then closes its mouth.

5. This pushes the water between the gills.

6. After the blood takes the oxygen it carries it throughout the body.

(Day 5)

Winter Flounder

Learn about the flounder by reading the information and coloring the picture. What spiritual lessons could you learn from this fish?

It is winter, and while other flatfish have headed into deeper, warmer seas, the winter flounder following its instinct, has come inland and lies half buried, along with many of its kind. It is so well camouflaged it is hard to decide where the sand ends and flounder begins. Its protruding eyes, both on the upper side of its head, move slightly as it surveys its surroundings hungrily for any passing shrimp or small fish it could catch for a meal. Others should see Jesus in us!

(Day 5)

Death and Saul

"And cast him out of the city, and stoned him: and the witnesses laid down their clothes at a young man's feet, whose name was Saul."
Acts 7:58

Write these words in the crossword below after rereading *The Acts of the Apostles* page 101, paragraph 3.

Key				
K	martyrdom	minds	trial	Stephen
e	beholders	church	witnessed	testified
Y	Saul	memory	truth	face
	proclaimed	faith	words	death
	glory	touched	sore	countenance

(Day 6)

Finding Their Way

A fish's 5 senses help them find their way. What are they:

1.________________________________

2.________________________________

3. ________________________________

4.________________________________

5.________________________________

Color the fish below that you might keep in your aquarium..

The Holy Spirit can **help** you to be sensitive so that you might not sin.

(Day 6)

An Angry Mob

As a Methodist pioneer, Adam Clarke, of Ireland, traveled all about Ireland, England, and Wales, and to the Channel Islands. In those days Methodism met the opposition of the Established Church and of "society," and the irreligious mob felt itself doing respectable service in assailing the sect everywhere spoken against.

On one of these trips, Adam Clarke experienced so remarkable an interposition of Providence to save his life that he records it in his Commentary, as a note on the deliverance of Christ from the mob at Nazareth. In Luke 4:30. Writing of himself in the third person, he says a certain missionary was called to preach in a place where there was much prejudice:

"About fifty people who had received impressions from the Word of God, assemble. He began his discourse, and after he had preached about thirty minutes, an outrageous mob surrounded the house armed with different instruments of death, and breathing the most terrible purposes. Some that were within, shut the door; and the missionary and his flock began to pray.

"The mob assailed the house, and began to hurl stones against the walls, windows, and roof; and in a short time almost every tile was destroyed, and the roof nearly uncovered, and before they quit the premises, scarcely left one square inch of glass in the five windows by which the house was enlightened.

"While this was going forward, a person came with a pistol to the window opposite to the place where the preacher stood (who was then exhorting his flock to be steady, to resign themselves to God, and trust in Him), presented it at him, and snapped it, but it only flashed in the pan.

"As the house was a wooden building, they began with crow bars and spades to destroy it, and take away its principal supports. The preacher then addressed his little flock to this effect: 'These outrageous people seek not you, but me; if I continue in the house, they will soon tear it down, and we shall all be buried in the ruins; I will therefore, in the name of God, go out to them, and you will be safe.' He then went toward the door; the poor people got around him, and entreated him not to venture out, as he might expect to be instantly killed. He went calmly forward, opened the door, at which a whole volley of stones and dirt was that instant discharge; but he received no damage.

"The people were in crowds in all the space before the door, and filled the road for a considerable way, so that there was no room to pass or repass.

"As soon as the preacher made his appearance, the savages became instantly as silent and as still as night; he walked forward, and they divided to the right and to the left, leaving a passage of about four feet wide, for himself and a young man who followed him, to walk in. He passed on through the whole crowd, not a soul of whom either lifted a hand or spoke one

(Day 6)

word, till he and his companion had gained the uttermost skirts of the mob. The narrator, who was present on the occasion, goes on to say:

" 'This was one of the most affecting spectacles I ever witnessed: an infuriated mob without any visible cause (for the preacher spoke not one word) became in a moment as calm as lambs. They seemed struck with amazement bordering on stupefaction; they stared and stood speechless; and after they had fallen back to right and left to leave him a free passage, they were as motionless as statues. They assembled with the full purpose to destroy the man who came to show them the way of salvation; but he, passing through the midst of them, went his way. Was not the God of missionaries in this work?' "

In the quietness that followed for a few minutes after the preacher disappeared, the people inside the church also went out and escaped. Then the mob awoke *"as from a dream,"* and broke the windows and otherwise vented their fury on the house.

The One who, passing through the midst of the mob at Nazareth, went His way, has promised the gospel worker, *"Lo, I am with you always, even unto the end of the world."**

In our lesson, Stephen was not saved from death but his death brought forth a new missionary to take his place whose name was Saul and later called Paul. We must always trust in God to do what is best for us.

Missionaries and Martyrs

"There are many who have given themselves to Christ,
yet who see no opportunity of doing a large work
or making great sacrifices in His service.
These may find comfort in the thought that it is not necessarily
the martyr's self-surrender which is most acceptable to God;
it may not be the missionary who has daily faced danger and death
that stands highest in heaven's records.
The Christian who is such in his private life,
in the daily surrender of self,
in sincerity of purpose and purity of thought,
in meekness under provocation, in faith and piety,
in fidelity in that which is least,
the one who in the home life represents the character of Christ—
such a one may in the sight of God be more precious
than even the world-renowned missionary or martyr."

Christ's Object Lessons 403

*Adapted from the book *The Hand That Intervenes*

10 – Philip, the Missionary

Bible – Acts 8

Song – " 'Tis So Sweet To Trust In Jesus"

Nature – Fish 2

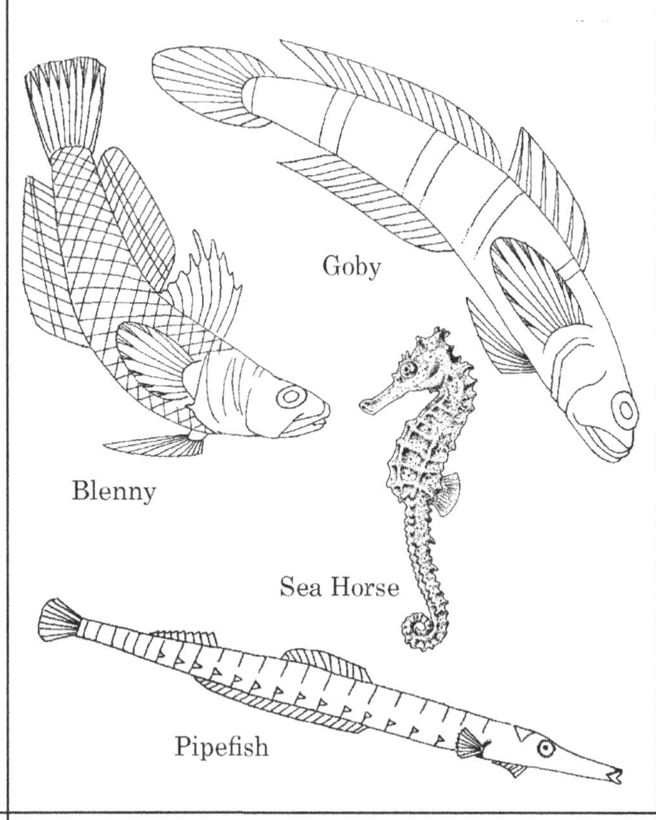

Character Quality

Encouragement vs Discouragement
Encouragement means to fill with courage or strength by the power of the Holy Spirit with purpose to follow Christ no matter what the consequences.

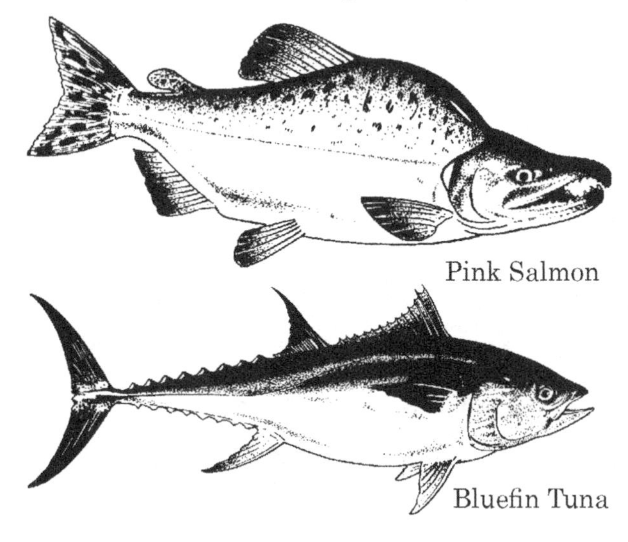

Memory Verse

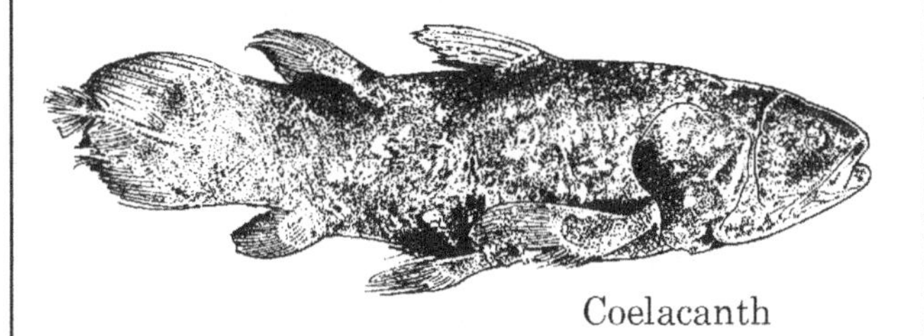

Coelacanth

"But ye shall receive power, after that the Holy Ghost is come upon you: and ye shall be witnesses unto me both in Jerusalem, and in all Judaea, and in Samaria, and unto the uttermost part of the earth."
Acts 1:8

Fish

**Most fish have a protective covering of scales.
There are several patterns of scales.
The early believers had the protection of angels
and the Holy Spirit, as we also have today.**

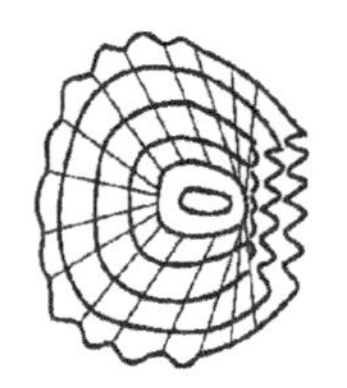

Ctenoid Scale

Cycloid Scale

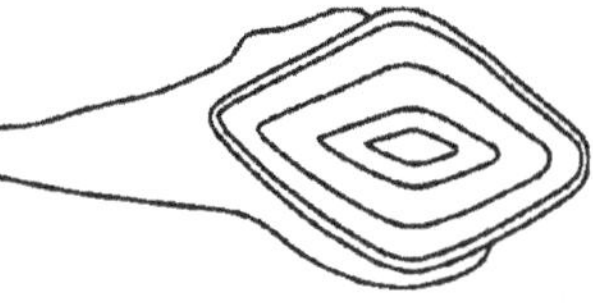

Ganoid Scale

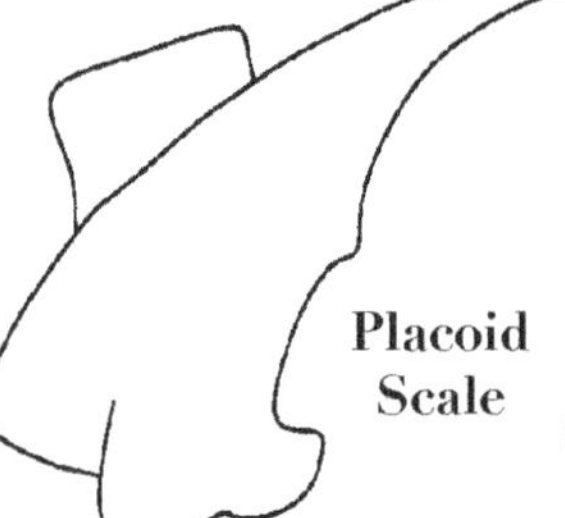

Placoid Scale

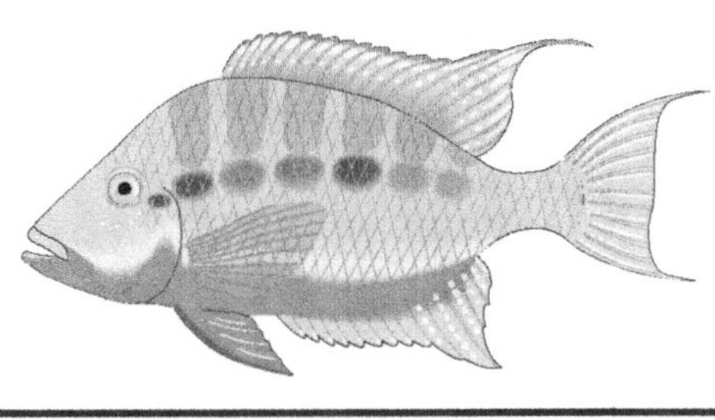

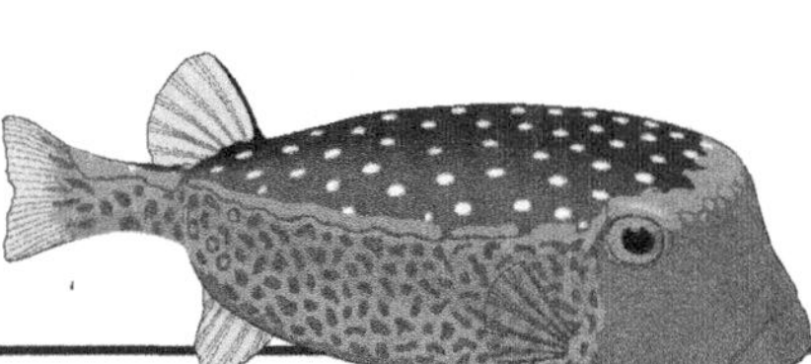

**Draw a scale pattern above
for each day this week
you study your lesson,
and say your memory verse.**

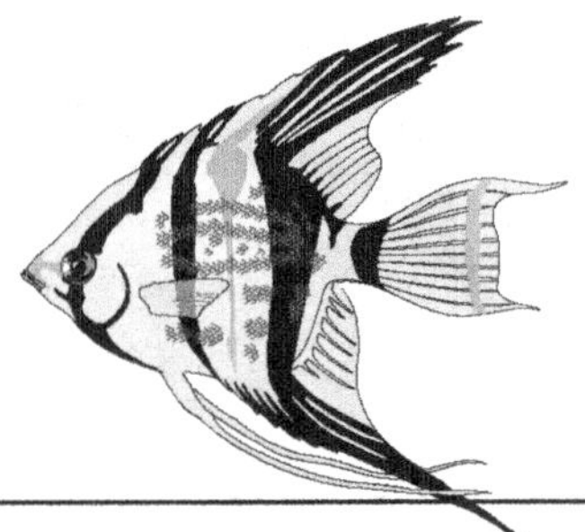

Persecution

Read and color these words.

"As for Saul,
he made havoc of the church,
entering into every house,
and haling men and women
committed them to prison."
Acts 8:3

(Day 1)

Shapes of Fish

What kind of <u>shape</u> was the early church in?
Use Acts 8:1-3 to find the answer for 1-5 and the Nature Lesson for 6-11.

1. S _ _ _ _ _ _ _ _ _   _ _ _ _ _ _ _
2. H _ _ _ _ _ to _ _ _ _ _ _ _
3. _ _ _ _ A and _ _ _ _ _ _ _ _
4. P _ _ _ _ _ _ _ _ _ _ _
5. _ _ _ E _ _ _ _ _   _ _ _ _ _ _ _   _ _ _ _ _ _ _

6. Some fish are shaped like rocks in the bottom of the sea.

7. Fish with flattened bodies.

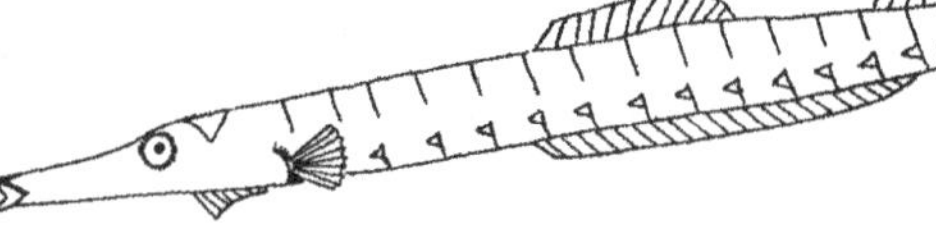

Pipefish

8. Fish come in a _______________ of different shapes.

9. A fast swimming fish with a torpedo-like shape.

10. The shape of the fish's body is made _______________ for swimming.

11. This fish looks like a weed.

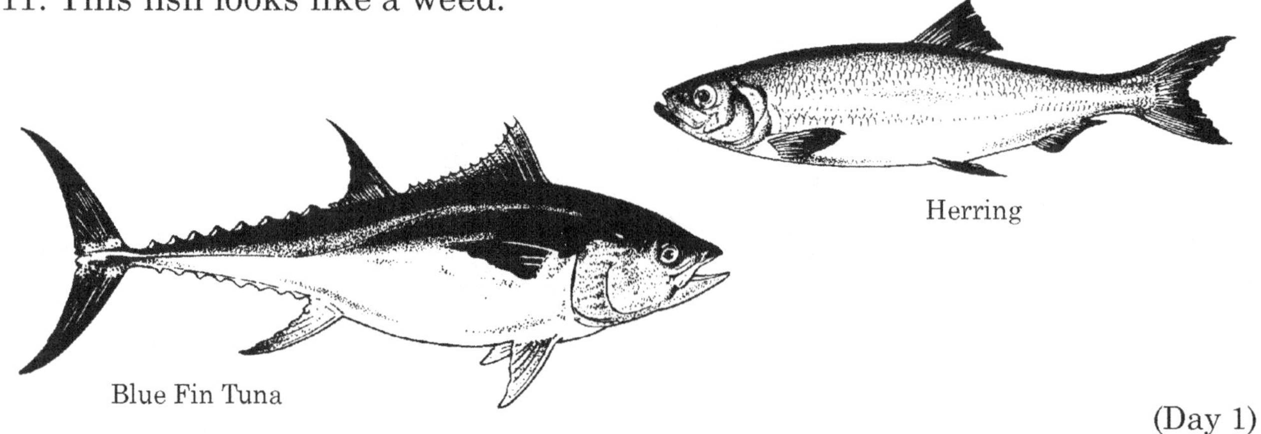

Herring

Blue Fin Tuna

(Day 1)

Ocean Sunfish

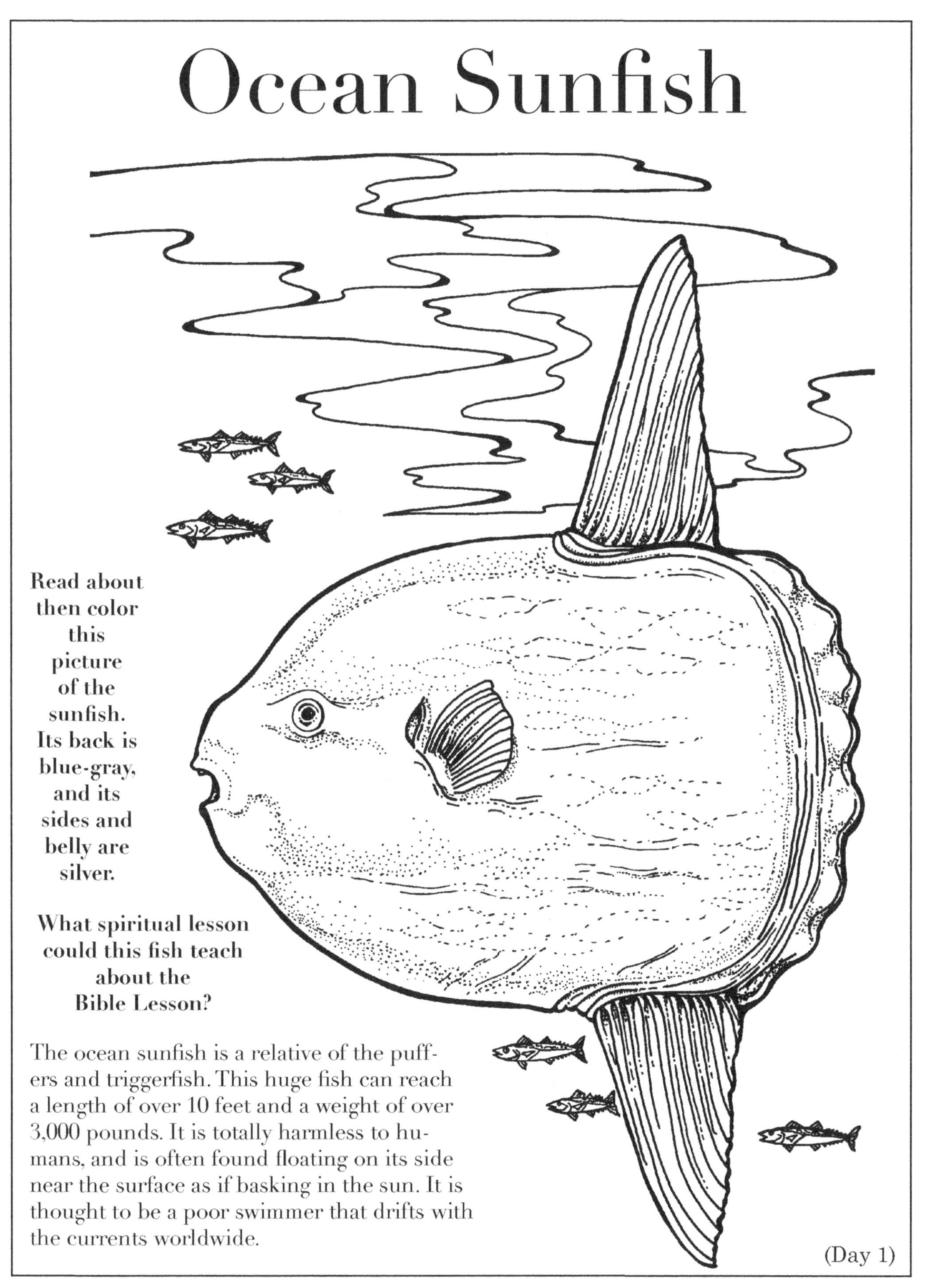

Read about then color this picture of the sunfish. Its back is blue-gray, and its sides and belly are silver.

What spiritual lesson could this fish teach about the Bible Lesson?

The ocean sunfish is a relative of the puffers and triggerfish. This huge fish can reach a length of over 10 feet and a weight of over 3,000 pounds. It is totally harmless to humans, and is often found floating on its side near the surface as if basking in the sun. It is thought to be a poor swimmer that drifts with the currents worldwide.

(Day 1)

Deep Sea Anglers

Read then color this picture.

Living at depths of 3,000-12,000 feet, these brown or black 2 1/2–4 inch anglers are truly deep-see fishermen. It reminds us how Philip went out to fish for men and bring them to Christ. In each species, part of the dorsal fin on the front of the head enables the fish to use it like a rod and lure to attract prey. In most species the rod glows with a blue-green light produced by bacteria in its cells.

(Day 1)

Philip in Samaria

1. Who was Philip?

2. What kind of gospel work did Philip do in Samaria?

3. Would you say Philip's work was successful or not successful?

4. What did he have to do?

5. What do these words mean in Acts 1:8?

"But ye shall receive power after that the Holy Ghost is come upon you: and ye shall be witnesses unto me both in Jerusalem, and in all Judea, and in Samaria, and unto the uttermost part of the earth." Acts 1:8

Memorize these words:

"He sent his word and healed them, and delivered them from their destructions."

Psalm 107:20

(Day 2)

The Skin of Fish

Review today's Nature Lesson then color these pictures.

**The color of most fish matches that of their surroundings.
Some fish change colors to match color changes
in their environment.
In Samaria the people changed "colors"
from unbelievers to believers for they saw the truth.**

Triger Fish

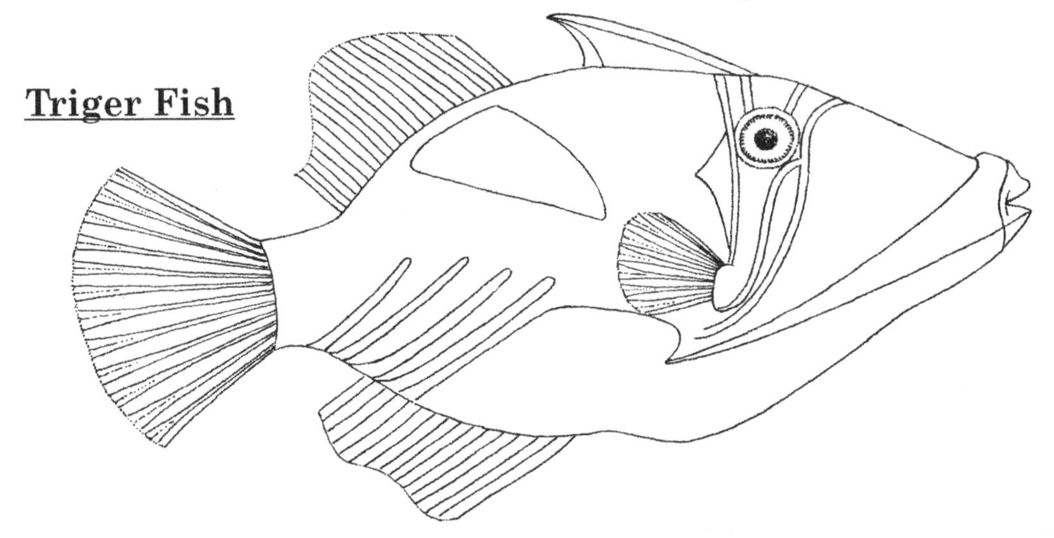

The stonefish lives among the rocks where it is camouflaged.

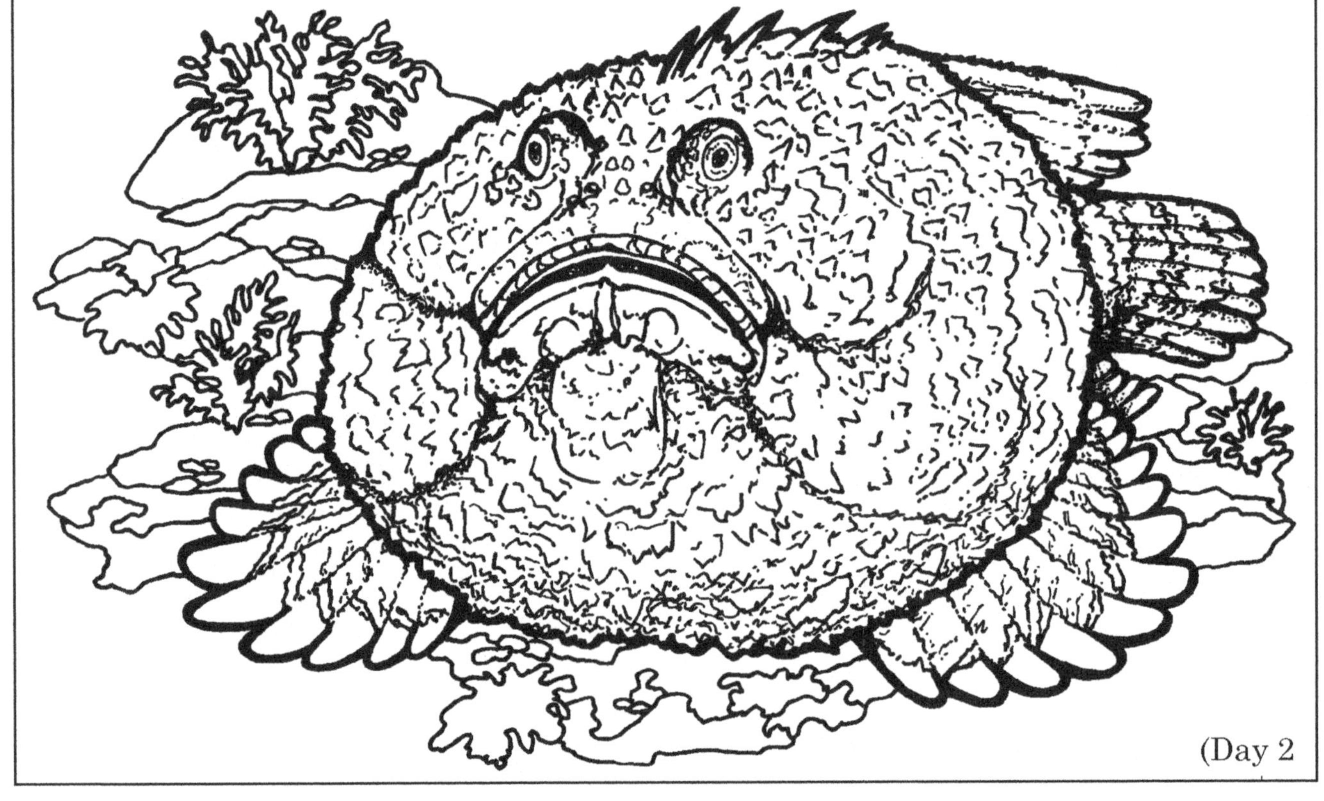

(Day 2

Ornate Wobbegong

Color this picture.

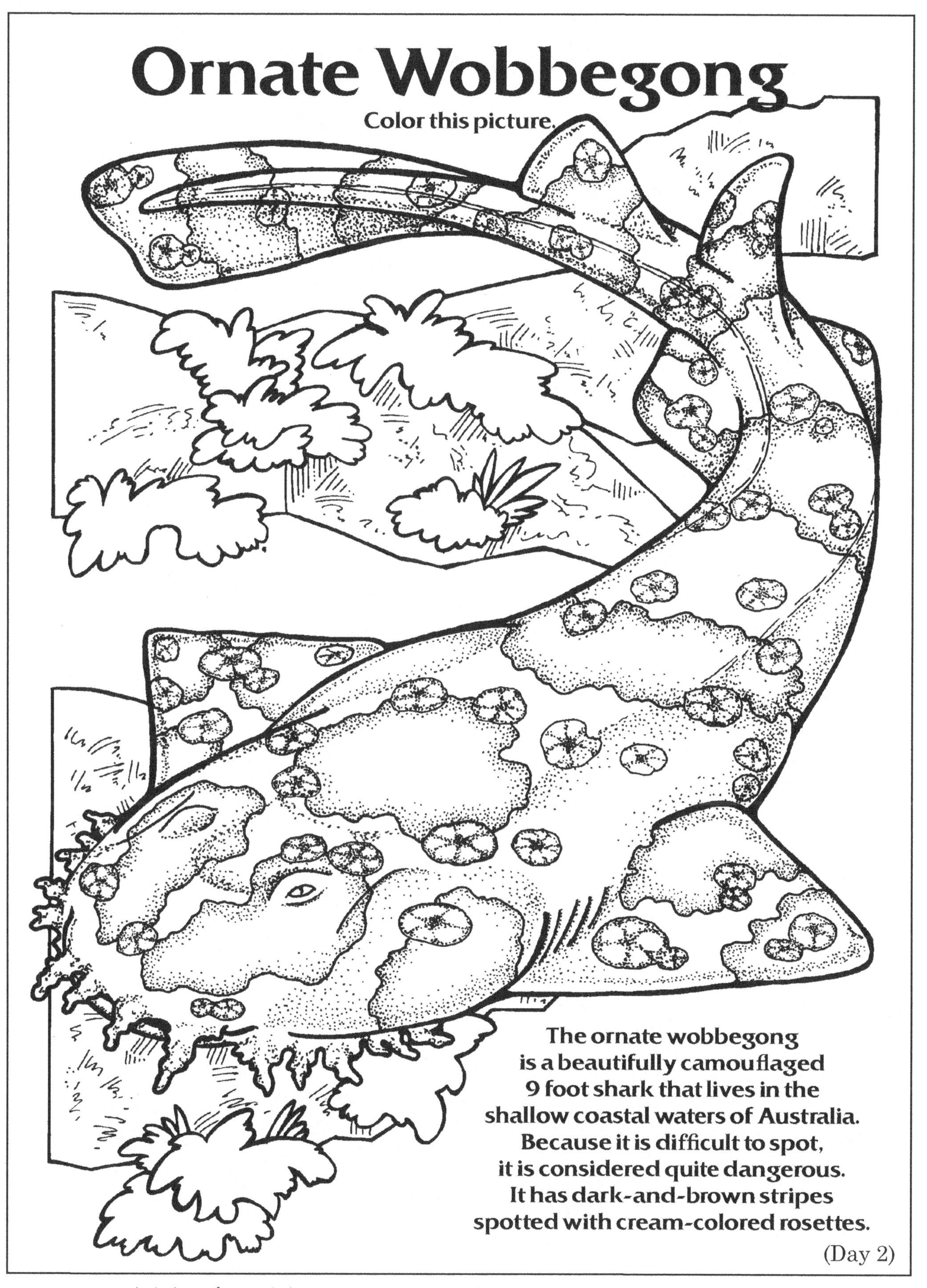

The ornate wobbegong
is a beautifully camouflaged
9 foot shark that lives in the
shallow coastal waters of Australia.
Because it is difficult to spot,
it is considered quite dangerous.
It has dark-and-brown stripes
spotted with cream-colored rosettes.

(Day 2)

Butterfly fish to Color

Where is the spot found on this fish that looks like an eye? (Day 2)

Encouragement to Make The Perfect Copy

"Always busy at your drawing, Edwin?" said his elder brother, Henry, as he entered the schoolroom one morning.

Edwin looked up for a moment with a smile, and then went on tracing, with evident pleasure, the outline of a face. His brother came behind him, and looked over his shoulder. Edwin listened to his remarks, though without ceasing to draw.

"You are taking pains, I see," said Henry, at last, in a kindly tone; "but I am afraid that you will have to use your eraser here, and here; these lines, you may perceive, are not in good drawing."

"I don't see much wrong in them," replied Edwin, suspending his pencil, with something of anger in his tone, for he had expected nothing but praise.

"If you compare them with your study, you will perceive that all this outline is incorrect."

"Where is the study?" asked Henry, looking in vain for it on the table.

"Oh! its somewhere upstairs," said Edwin. I remember very well what it is like, and can go on without looking at it every minute."

"Would you oblige me by bringing it?" said his brother, who perceived that as long as Edwin merely drew from memory, he would not see the faults in his sketch.

Edwin went upstairs, rather unwillingly, and soon brought down a beautiful study: a face most perfect in form and expression.

Henry silently put the two pictures together. Edwin gazed with bitter disappointment on his own copy, which but a few minutes before he had thought so good. Not a feature was really alike; the whole looked crooked and cramped; even his partial eye could not but see a thousand faults in his sketch.

(Day 2)

"I shall never get it right!" Edwin exclaimed, in a burst of frustration; and, snatching up the drawing, he would have torn it in pieces, had he not been prevented by his brother.

"My dear Edwin, you have doubly erred; first in being too easily satisfied, and then in being too easily discouraged."

"I shall never make it like that beautiful face!" cried the disheartened boy.

"You need patience, you need help, you need, above all, to look often at your copy," his brother **encouragingly** said. "A perfect resemblance you may never have, but you may succeed in getting one which will do credit both to you and your master."

Edwin took up the pencil which he had flung down, and carefully and attentively studied the picture. He found very much in his copy to change, very much to erase; but at last he completed a very fair sketch, which he presented, with a little hesitation, to his brother.

"I shall have this framed, and hung up in my room," said Henry.

"Oh! it is not worth that!" exclaimed Edwin, coloring with pleasure his surprise.

"Not in itself, perhaps," replied Henry, "but it will serve to often remind us both of an important truth, which was suggested to me when I saw you laboring at your copy."

Edwin looked in surprise at his brother, who thus proceeded to explain his words:

"We, dear Edwin, as Christians, all have one work set before us: to copy into our lives the example set us by a Heavenly Master. It is in the Bible that we behold the features of a character perfect and pure. But how many of us choose rather to imagine for ourselves what a Christian should be like! We aim low; we are content with little progress; we perhaps please ourselves with the thought of our own wisdom and goodness, while everyone but ourselves can see that our copy is wretched and worthless."

"What are we to do?" asked Edwin.

"We must closely examine the Example [or study] set us in the Bible; we must compare our lives with God's law; and we shall then soon find enough of the meekness and gentleness of Christ. We shall be ashamed of our own passion and pride when we find how holy was our great Example; we shall be grieved to think how unlike to him we are."

"We can never make a good copy," sighed Edwin: "we may just give up the attempt at once."

"You judge as you did when you wished to tear up your picture in despair, as soon as you saw how imperfect it was. No, no, my dear boy; I say to you now, as I said to you then, you need patience, you need help, help from the Holy Spirit of God: and, above all, you need to look often at your study, to keep the character and work of your Lord ever before your eyes."

"All who long

to bear the likeness

of the character

of God

shall be satisfied."

The Desire of Ages 302

"The trials

of life

are God's Workmen,

to remove

the impurities

and roughness

from our character."

Mount of Blessings 10

Encouragement For Little Children

God is so good that He will hear
  Whenever children humbly pray;
He always lends a gracious ear
  To what the youngest child can say.

His own most holy book declares
  He **encourages** children kind,
He lovingly condescends to own
  A good, meek, and lowly mind.

This is an offering we may bring,
  However small our store;
The poorest child, the greatest king,
  Can give Him nothing more.

—Adapted from Unknown

(Day 2)

Philip's Work

Find the memory verse by following the path.

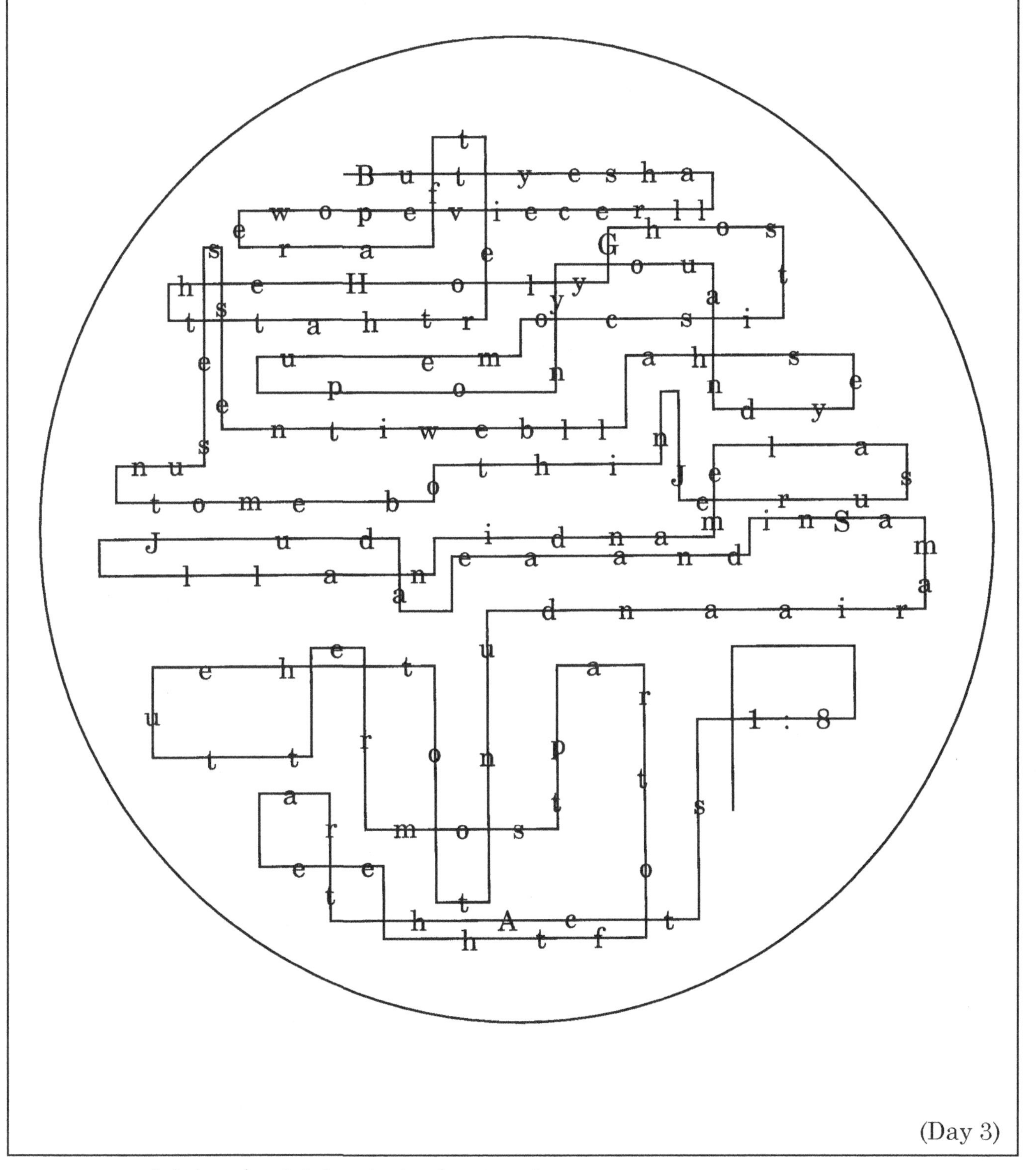

(Day 3)

Scales and fins

Skin and scales are a protection for fish.
The early believers had the protection of angels
and the Holy Spirit as we also have today.
Read this information sheet.

The following fish have these types of scales:

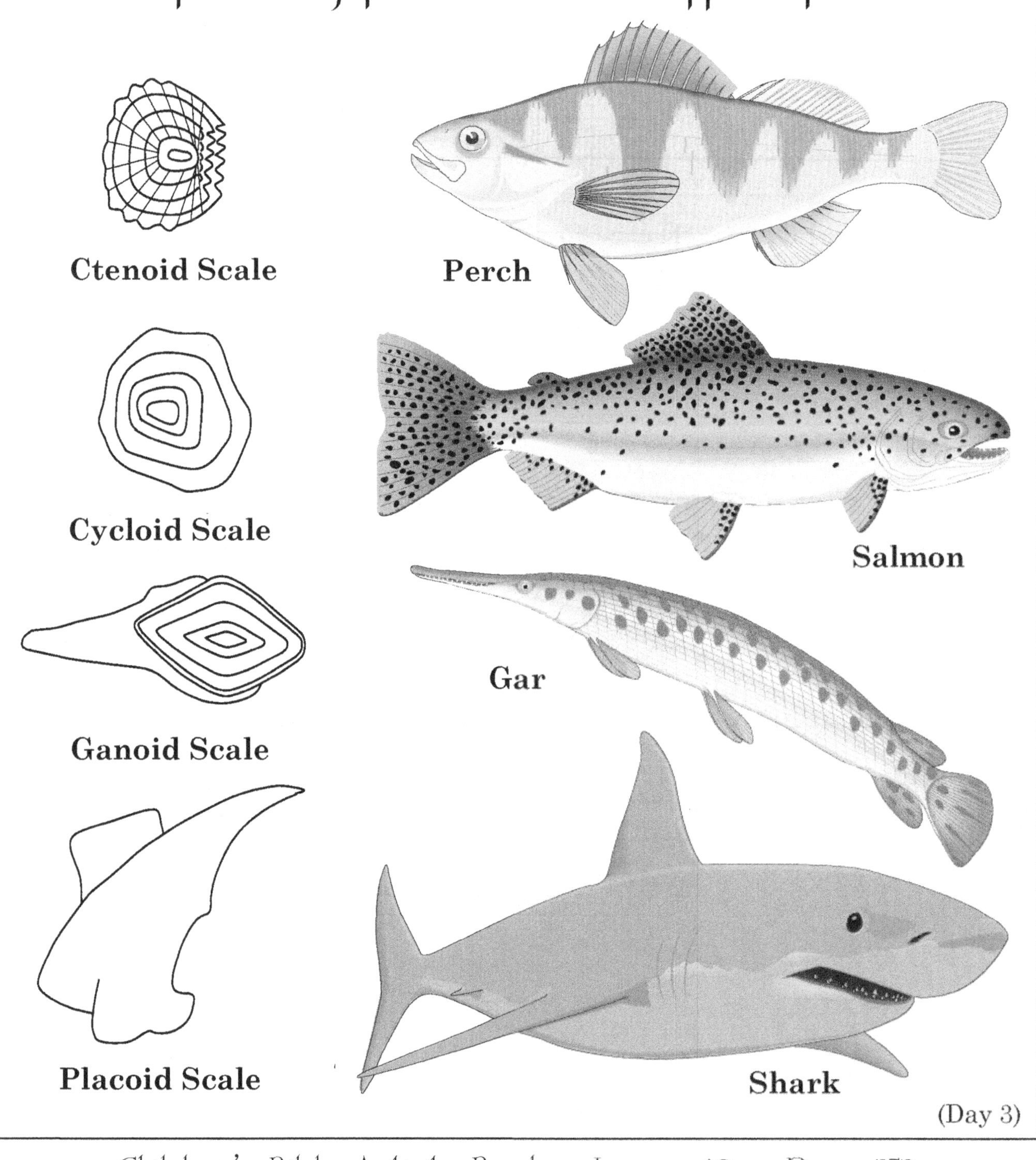

(Day 3)

"Go...Unto Gaza...."

Answer these questions.

1. Philip was directed by a ___________ ___________ to go toward the south.

2. Philip, the _________, was to go unto _________.

3. Who was the Ethiopia?

4. Where had the Ethiopian just come from?

5. What was he doing there?

6. What question did the Ethiopian have.

7. What did God see in his future?

It was not the salvation
of only one soul
that was involved as we shall see.
It was only the beginning of a link
in a long chain of influence.
So we may be encouraged
that each time we act
under God's direction
the results for good will
be far-reaching.

(Day 4)

Fish Reproduction

Read this information.

Bitterling Nest

The bitterling chooses one of the most unusual places to lay her eggs. At spawning time in late spring, the female bitterling grows a long tube known as an ovipositor, through which she lays her eggs into the body cavity of the freshwater mussel, a shellfish living in lakes and slow rivers. The male bitterling releases his sperm nearby and the mussel sucks this in as it filter feeds. The male may then stand guard as the eggs develop and young hatch out to swim free from their shellfish nursery a month later.

Mussels

Each spring the male makes a rough nest of gravel, roots, and other pieces of plant, usually in a swampy part of his lake or river home. Females lay eggs in the nest; the male fertilizes the eggs and then guards them until the larvae hatch. The larvae attach themselves to the nest by glue-glands on their heads, feeding off their yolk sacs until they can swim freely.

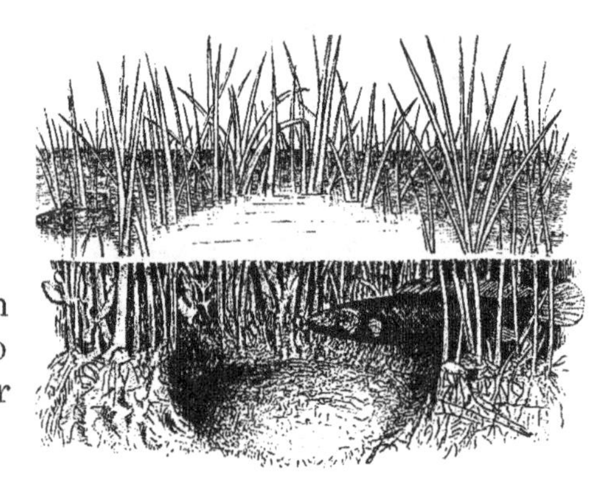

Eggs

Draw and color small round circles below in the square and color some black for beluga sturgeon eggs and some red for salmon eggs.

Egg Cases

Chimaera Egg Case

Port Jackson Shark Egg Case

Spotted Ray Egg Case

Egg cases vary according to the type of fish that lays them. The chimaera produces a long tadpole like case; the bottom-dwelling Port Jackson shark from Australia has a distinctive corkscrew-shaped case; while the spotted ray's case is more like the common "mermaid's purse."

(Day 4)

"Encouragement That's enough for Me?"

"What do you do without a Mother to tell all your troubles to?" asked a child who had a Mother, of one who had none for her Mother was dead.

"Mother told me who to go to before she died," answered the little orphan. "I go to the Lord Jesus. He was my Mother's friend, and He's mine."

"Jesus Christ is up in the sky. He is away off, and has a great many things to attend to in Heaven. It is not likely He can stop to pay attention to you."

"I do not know any thing about that," said the orphan. "All I know, He says He will; and that's enough for me."

What a beautiful answer that was! And what was enough for this child is enough for all.

Are you tired of carrying the burden of sin? *"Come unto me, all ye that labor and are heavy laden, and I will give you rest."* But I am unworthy of His forgiving love. Never mind that. "He says he will; and that's enough for me." Take the Lord Jesus Christ at His word, for the forgiveness of your sins and for peace to your souls. *"My peace I give unto you,"* He says. Will he? Oh! His peace is very precious. Will He give us His peace? "He says He will; and that's enough for me." Trust Him. His word never fails.

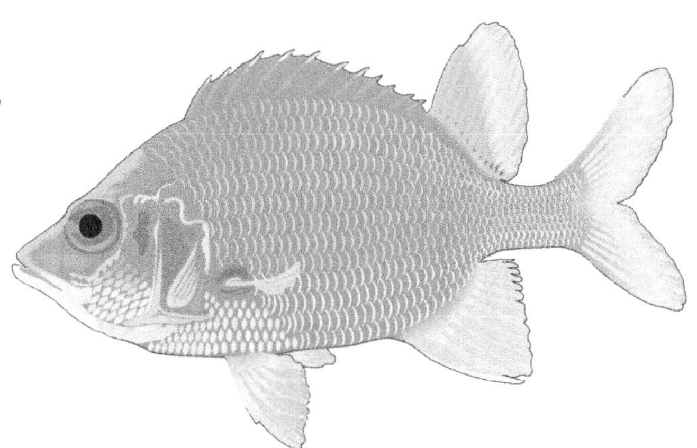

**God cares for the fish
in the great oceans, lakes, rivers, and streams,
and He cares for me!**

(Day 4)

God is in Heaven

God is in heaven—can He hear
A feeble prayer like mine?
Yes, little child, thou need not fear,
He listens to thine.

God is in heaven—can He see
When I am doing wrong?
Yes, that He can—He looks at thee,
All day and all night long.

God is in heaven—would He know
If I should tell a lie?
Yes, If thou said it very low,
He'd hear it in the sky.

God is in heaven—can I go
To thank Him for His care?
Not yet—but love Him here below,
And thou shall praise Him there.

—Unknown

(Day 4)

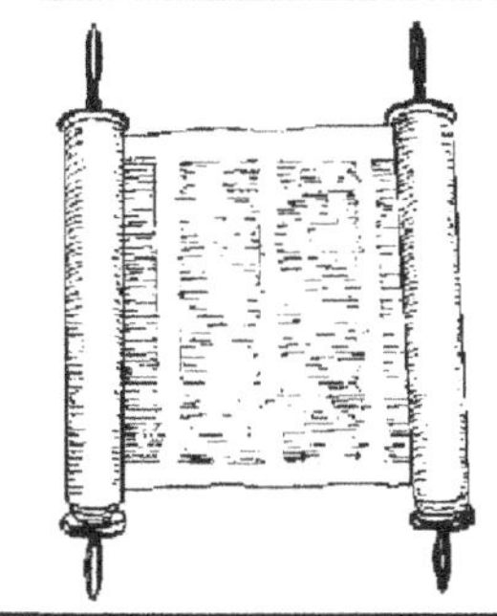

The Ethiopian

Encouragement

Fill in the missing words.

1. "_____________ of God were attending this ______________ for light, and he was being ___________ to the Saviour."

2. "By the ministration of the ________ _________ the Lord brought him into _________with one who could lead him to the _________."

3. "__________ was directed to go to the ________________ and __________ to him the ____________ that he was _____________."

(Day 5)

Fish Eggs

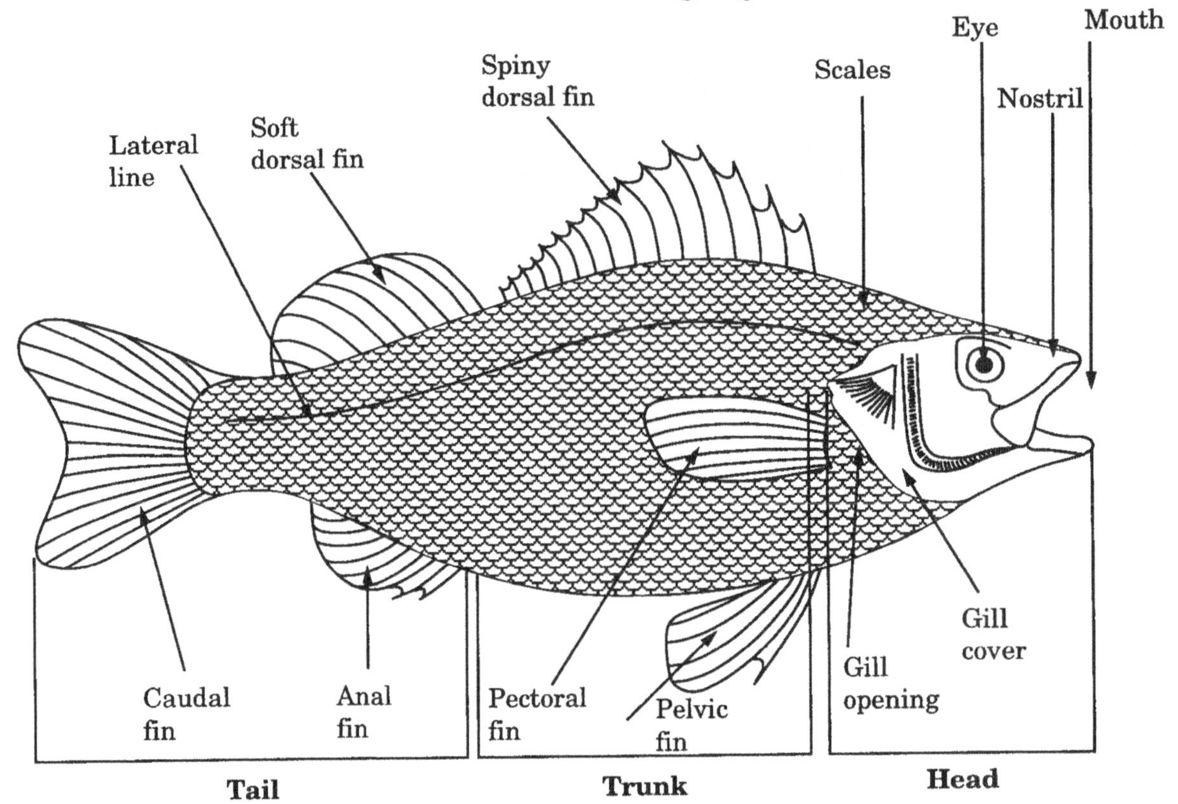

Fish Anatomy

Answer these questions.
Study this picture then turn the page
and fill in what you can remember.

1. Most fish lay lots of very small eggs. What happens to the eggs?

2. Describe how a fish develops. One spiritual lesson to this is__________.

3. Give an example of a fish laying a large egg.

4. Does a guppy lay eggs? Explain.

5. What does a sharks do?

6. Male tilapias carry eggs__________________.

(Day 5)

Do You Remember?

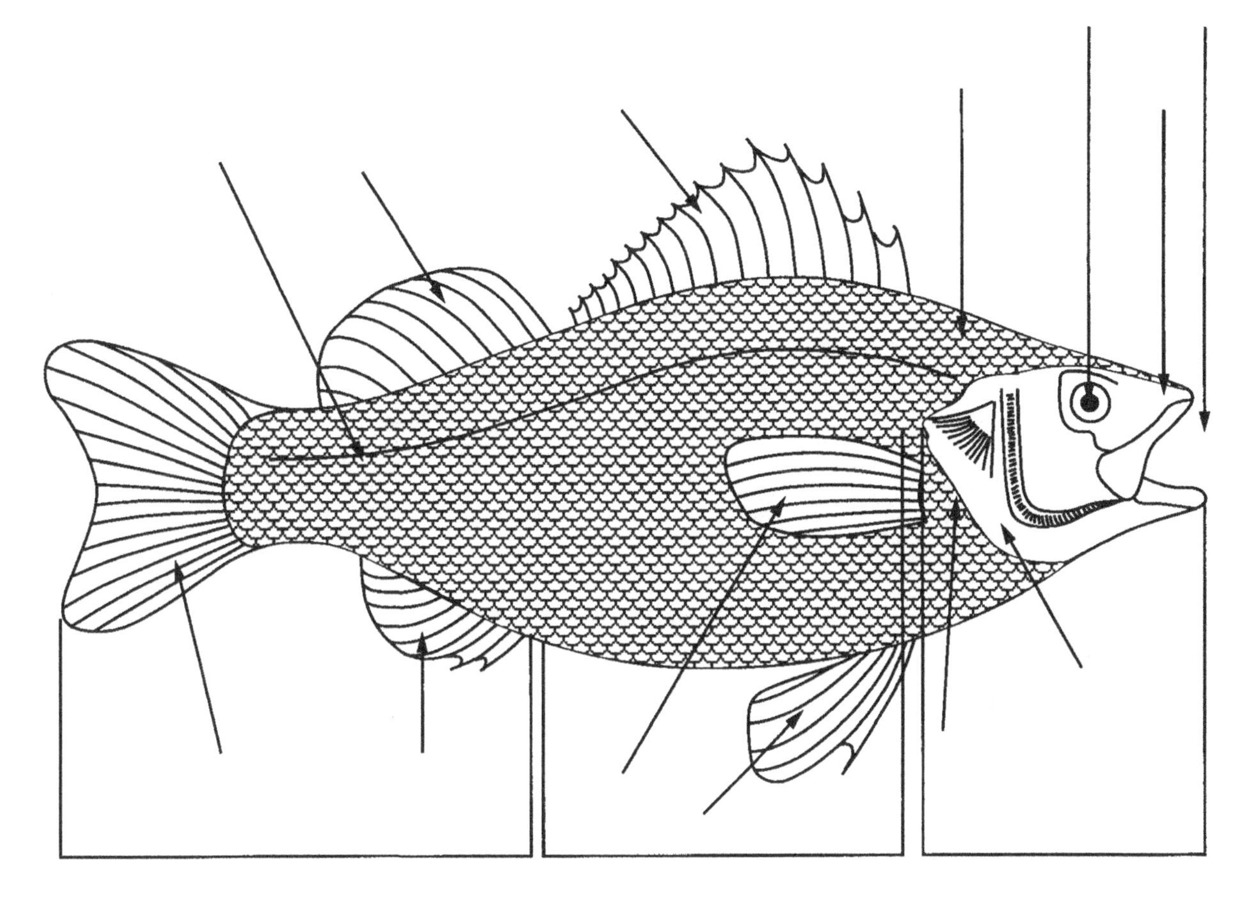

7. The spiritual lesson is_________________________.

8. Describe how some male fish get the attention of the female fish.
   The spiritual lesson is _______________________.

9. What are some unusual nests made of?

10. Do you know a spiritual lesson
    for the previous question?

Moonfish

(Day 5)

G is for ____________ and ____________

Name the two Fish in the letter G.
What other things are found in the letter from nature?

(Day 5)

Baptism

Fill in the squares below, using the next letter of the alphabet above each square. (+ = A)

" ... R D D , G D Q D H R

V + S D Q ; V G + S

C N S G G H M C D Q

L D S N A D

A + O S H Y D C ?"

Acts 8:36

(Day 6)

Seahorse

The seahorse has parts like which animals below? Circle them.

The Horses of the Sea

Because the seahorse changes color according to its surroundings, color these seahorses bright colors like their backgrounds might be.

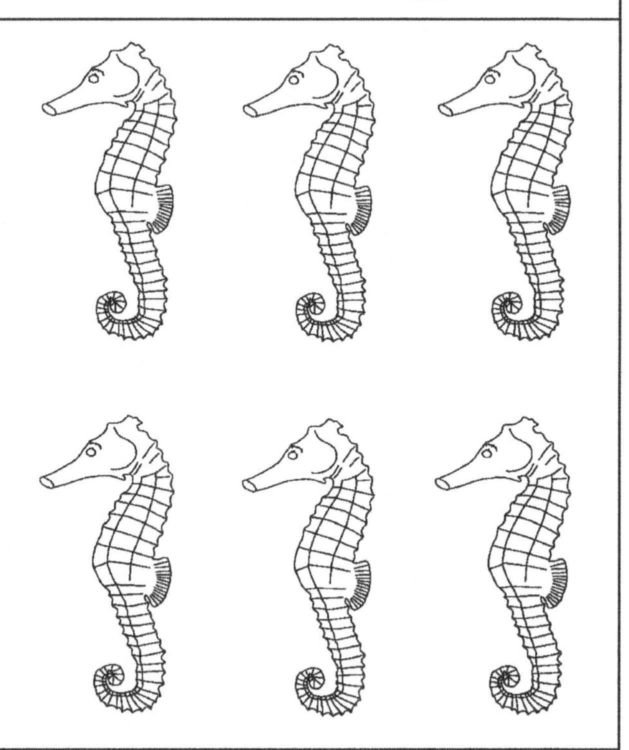

Seahorses are protected by a covering of tough armour. The Ethiopian was a protector of the queen of Ethiopia's money. What lesson does the "birth" of a seahorse remind us about? Describe how seahorse eggs are cared for and how they finally develop.

(Day 6)

Orange Seahorses

Color these orange seahorses in the eelgrass.

Japanese Seahorse
(Light Blue)

Fringed Australian Reef Seahorse
(Yellow-Light orange)

(Day 6)

S is for Sea Horse
Color these seahorses
in the Gorgonian Coral.
(Day 6)

Little Horses of the Sea

"For my thoughts are not your thoughts, neither are your ways my ways, saith the LORD."
Isaiah 55: 8

When God made fish, how did He come to think of a sea horse? No human mind could have put together such a unique creature. Unlike conventional fish, we think it odd-shaped and strange, but really, is it?

God combined a colt's head, an arching neck, a pigeon's bosom, an insect's shell=like body, a kangaroo's pouch, the grasping tail of a monkey with the color-changing power of a chameleon. Eyes that turn independently enable the creature to see in all directions, up, down, right, or left at the same time.

Forty kinds of sea horses show God's love for variety. They range from tiny one-inch pygmies to the one-foot species found in Australia and Japan. Although most are dark gray or black, some are golden yellow, bright green, brown, red, or orange. Some are splattered with pink, yellow, blue, or white, camouflaged like the seaweeds in which they live. Some grow filaments that resemble antlers or seaweed strands on the head, body and tail. They swim standing straight up, looking like little statues. They are propelled slowly through the water by a fluttering, fan-like fin on their back, tiny vibrating flaps on each side of the head, and a bit of fin tissure just below the abdominal bulge. To go upwards the sea horse straightens out, to lower itself it kinks up. Because of its bony, brittle, prickly plates of armor, it is left alone to eat tiny animal and plant life. Thus God's wisdom is again shown in providing a means of protection for this slow-moving, defenseless fish.

God taught the female to transfer from 200 to 600 tiny eggs to her husband's pouch, where he fertilizes and nourishes them by blood vessels within the pouch. When father sea horse ejects a herd of tiny colts about the size of a comma, they look like him except that they have transparent bodies. Color comes when they are larger.

God's thoughts are much higher and greater than ours. In wonder we can only ask, "How did You combine so much in such a tiny creature? Thank You, Lord, for thinking of me and planning for me in a much greater, more personal way than You do for even the sea horses."*

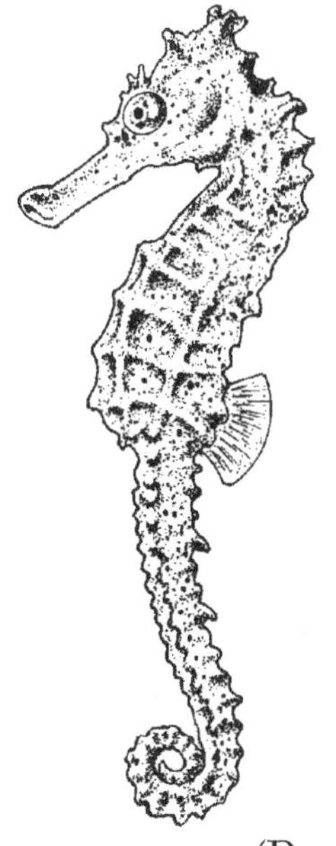

(Day 6)

**Stop Look and Listen* 198

A Strange Seahorse

The **Leafy Seadragon** is an odd, foot-long relative of the seahorse and looks more like a plant than a fish. Its camouflage makes it hard to distinguish from the kelp beds where it lives, in the warm coastal waters of Australia. It is a very rare fish, not often sighted; there are currently none in any public aquarium, and only a few dried specimens in museums. It is thought that the female breeds by attaching her eggs to a brood patch on the underside of the male's tail.

Color this picture of the Leafy Seadragon

(Day 6)

11 – Saul–Paul

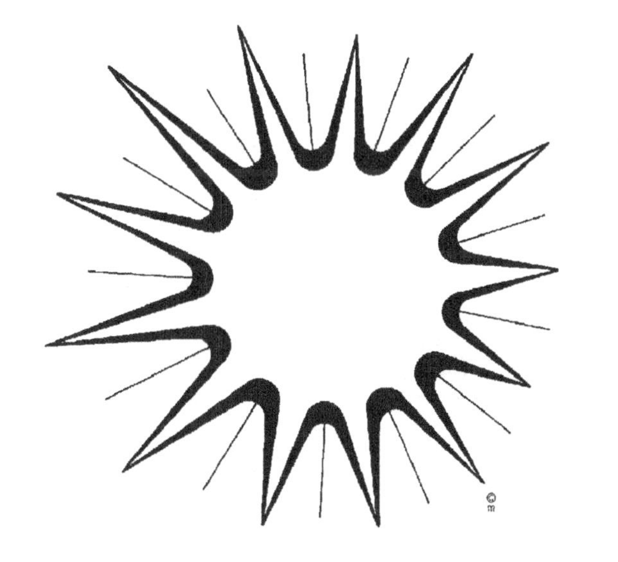

Bible – **Acts 9:1-31**

Song – **"All To Jesus I Surrender"**

Nature – Fish 3

Electric Eel

Anchovy

Morish Idol

Bluefish

Character Quality

Humbleness vs Pride
Humbleness is depending upon God and His will in every decision and letting Him and others take the credit for any successes in your life.

Memory Verse

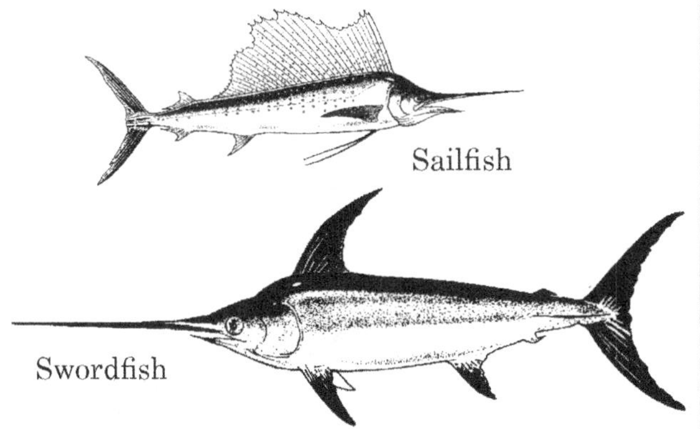

"And he trembling and astonished said, Lord, what wilt thou have me to do? And the Lord said unto him, Arise, and go into the city, and it shall be told thee what thou must do."
Acts 9:6

Fish

**As the oceans teams with fish so the world is teaming with people.
Yet, God sees and calls each individual in different ways
as he called Saul on the road to Damascus.
He also knows your name and your needs.**

**Draw or place a fish seal in the fish bowl
for each day this week
you study your lesson.
and say your memory verse.**

"Preaching" & "Threatenings"

Connect these words by going from one to the next to put together this Bible verse. Use a ruler to make straight lines.

Start

"Deliver
unto
me
the
not
over
will
for
of
mine
false
enemies:
witnesses
are
risen
against
up
me,
and
such
as
breathe
out
cruelty."

End

(Day 1)

How Fish Eat

What do fish eat? Discuss.
Circle what fish eat then color the picture.
What does the shape of a fish's mouth tell you? ____________________

____

Fish killing and eating one another reminds us how Saul was threatening and destroying the disciples of Christ.

(Day 1)

Parrotfish

Among the most colorful of fishes that abound on shallow tropical reefs, parrotfish are so named. Find and then look at a picture of a parrot and then color these fish.

Parrotfish are like cows grazing in a field as they spend their days scraping algae and coral from rocks using their strong beak-like mouths. Each day the disciples of Christ "*preached the word*" among the cities feeding the people spiritually.

(Day 1)

Atlantic Herring

These herring feed on plankton
that concentrates near the surface of the water.
Color this picture

(Day 1)

Going to Damascus

Answer the questions and color this picture.

1. When Saul and his companions came within full view of Damascus what did they see?
2. How did this affect them?
3. While they gazed with admiration on the fruitful plain and the fair city below what happened?
4. Who fell to the ground?
5. What was the result?
6. How bright was the light?
7. How does falling down help us?

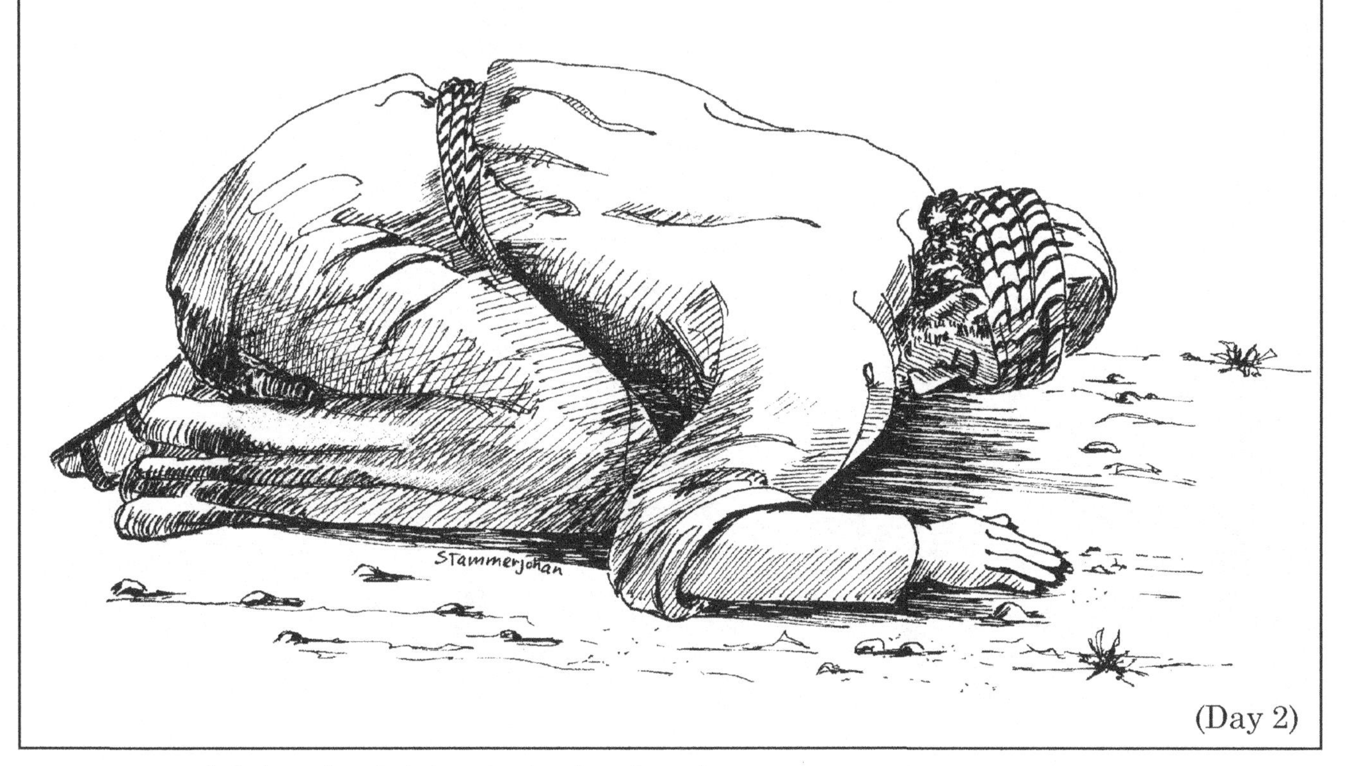

(Day 2)

Eating

Review today's Nature Lesson. Read the information. Color.

The swordfish has a longer nose extension than any of the so-called billfishes, sometimes amounting to one-third of its total length. The sword functions primarily as a cutwater for high-speed swimming and perhaps secondarily as a weapon used to strike broadside and stun or kill schooling prey. Found throughout warm temperate seas worldwide and frequently observed at the surface, they are capable of descending to depths below 2,000 feet where they feed on squid.

Saul went out to capture Christians.

The world-record swordfish measured 15 feet and weighed 1,182 pounds.

(Day 2)

Great Barracuda

Read and then color.

Remember, the Barracudas have razor-sharp teeth, which they use to tear the flesh of their victims. Saul was planning to tear the disciples of Christ away from Damascus and take them bound to Jerusalem.

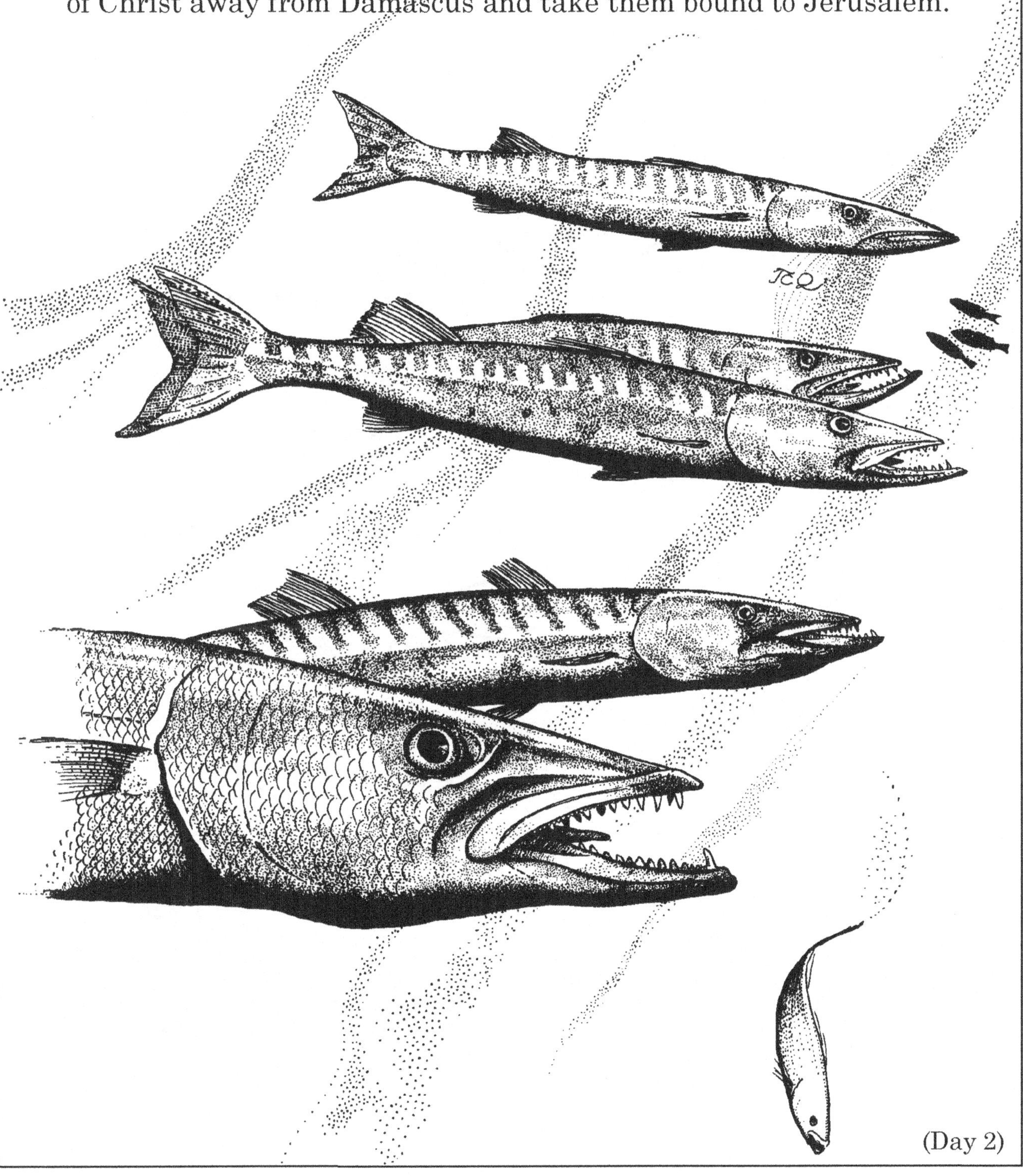

(Day 2)

Electric Eel & Torpedo

Read and color.

Though not related, the electric eel (olive-green with yellow-orange on the underside of its head) and the Atlantic torpedo (black or dark brown) are both dangerous because of the electric charge they can produce.

Electric eels and other fish with electric-producing organs use them to stun their prey with an electrical shock. God shocked Saul with the bright light of His presence to gain his attention.

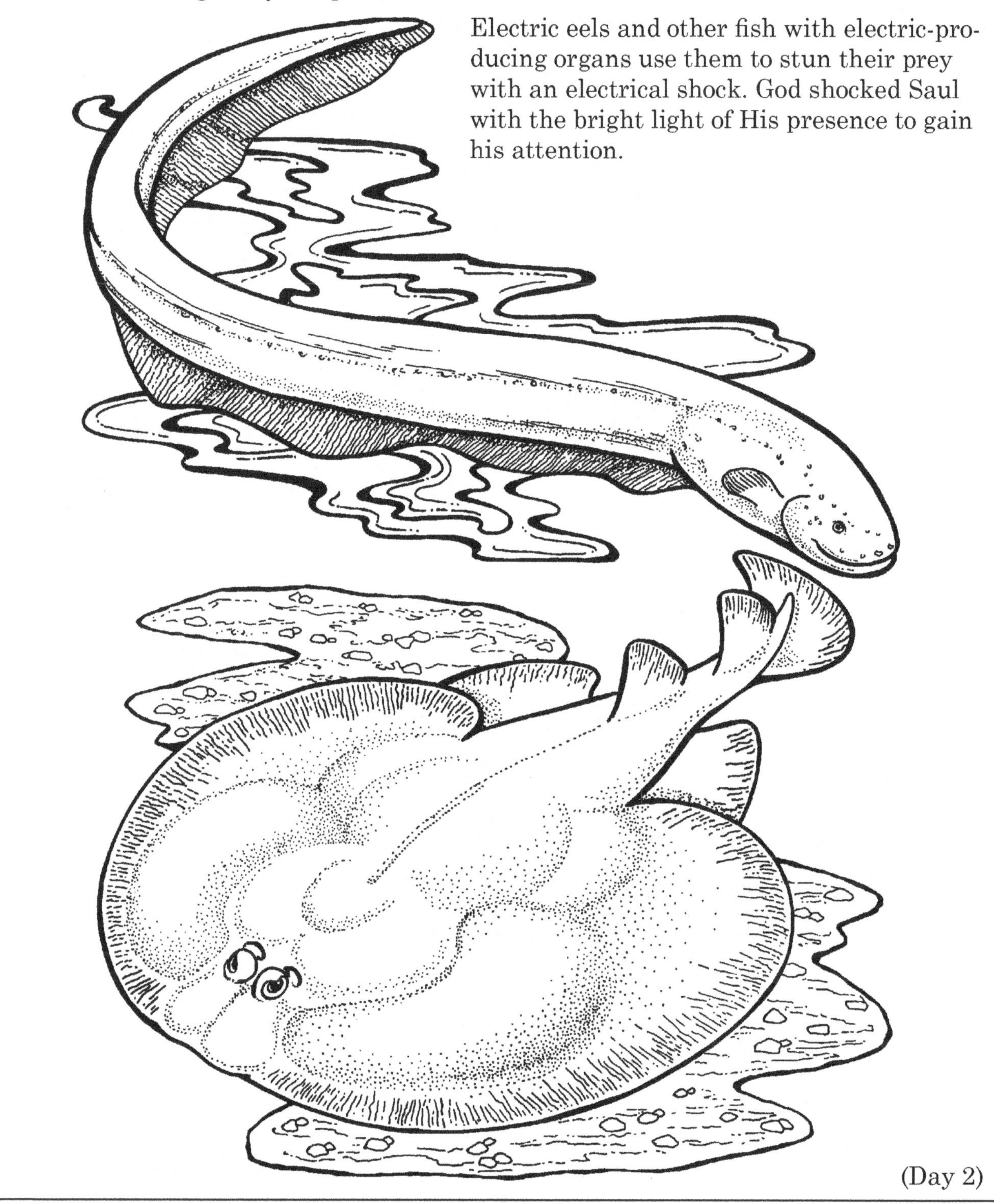

(Day 2)

B is for Butterflyfish

Read and color.

(Day 2)

The Jungle Boy

If you never saw a jungle, you might like to know what it is.

A jungle is a thicket or forest, in which there are large and tall trees. Wild plants and flowers twist about them like ropes, and climb to the top of the high boughs. In some parts of India, the jungle is so thick that no one can walk through it; but in other places it is more open, and people live here and there in it. Many of these people do not know the true God, but pray to idols.

Many years ago a lady went to Burmah, where there are also some of these jungles, to teach the people the truths of the Bible. One day she sat in the front of her house, with a book in her hand. There was a sweet shrub, full of lovely little buds, growing by her side, and its scent filled the air. On one of its rich, white flowers was a beetle, with wings of green and gold. Not far away, the birds were very busy among the high grass. And still further out was a jungle.

By the side of the house a schoolroom had been built; but it was not such a schoolroom as you see in this land. It was made of poles; the roof was formed of large leaves; and there were no walls. From this spot there came the sound of the little dark-faced boys and girls who were being taught to read.

While the lady was sitting at the door of her house now, looking at her book, and then turning her eyes to the jungle, she saw a boy coming out from among the trees of the wood. All the dress he wore was a dirty piece of cloth thrown over him. His hair hung down his back, and he looked as fierce as one of the wild beasts of the wood.

When he saw the lady, he ran to her, and said, almost out of breath, “Does Jesus Christ live here?” And then, he fell down at her feet.

“What do you want with Jesus Christ?” she asked.

“I want to see him. I want to confess my sin to him,” said the poor boy.

“Why, what have you been doing that you want to confess your sin to him?” said the lady.

“Doing! why, I tell lies, I steal, I do many things that are bad. I am afraid I shall go to hell. But does Jesus Christ live here? I want to see him; for I heard a man say he can save me. Oh, tell me where I can find him.”

“But he does not save people from sin, if they will go on in sin,” the lady said; for she wished him to know that he must give up all evil ways.

(Day 2)

"I want to keep from doing sin," said the jungle boy; "but I do not know how to stop. The evil thoughts are in me, and the bad deeds come of evil thoughts."

"You cannot see Jesus now as he was here on earth," said the lady, and the boy began to cry. "But," said the lady, "I am his **humble** friend, and He has sent me to teach those who wish to flee from sin how they may do so."

The boy looked glad at these words, and he cried, "Oh, tell me. Only ask your friend, Jesus Christ, to save me, and I will be your slave for life. Do not be angry. Do not send me away. I want to be saved."

The lady was not likely to be angry, nor did she wish to take him for a slave. She told him of the love of Jesus in coming into this world, what He did when he was here, how he saves from the guilt and power of sin, and that He will not cast away any who go to him in faith. She said He was in Heaven, but could still hear our prayer, and help us.

The next day this wild boy of the jungle was seated in the school, that he might hear this kind lady speak again of Jesus Christ.

Ten years passed, and that pious lady died. But there was a man who lived in the jungle, lying on a bed, and turning from side to side in great pain. He was dying. But there was a smile on his dark face, and his eyes were bright, for he was happy. Then his sight became dim, and he could see no more, not speak nor smile. He was dead. It was he who was once the wild jungle boy. He had found Jesus Christ. He had given him his heart, and had been saved from sin. He had grown to be a pious young man, an he died trusting that Jesus would save him.

Dear young friend, are you seeking to find Jesus Christ with as much care as the poor heathen boy did? Do you believe in Him, and love Him? Do you wish to give up all sin? If not, learn a lesson from the jungle boy. If you would go to Heaven, you must now find Jesus; you must pray to God to forgive you all sin, for Jesus' sake, and you must ask for the Holy Spirit to create within you a clean heart, and to lead you to live a **humble**, holy life.

For a Child Who Feels He Has a Wicked Heart

What is there, Lord, a child can do,
  Who feels with guilt oppressed?
There's evil that I never knew
  Before, within my breast.

My thoughts are vain; my heart is hard;
  My temper apt to rise;
And, when I seem upon my guard,
  It takes me by surprise.

Whenever to thy commands I turn,
  I find I've broken them;
And in Thy holy Scriptures learn,
  That God will sin condemn.

And yet if I begin to pray,
  And lift my feeble cry,
Some thought of folly or of play,
  Prevents me when I try.

On many Sabbaths, though I've heard
  Of Jesus and of heaven,
I've scarcely listened to Thy Word,
  Or prayed to be forgiven!

O look with pity in thine eye
  Upon a heart so hard!
Thou will not slight a feeble cry,
  Or show it no regard.

The work I cannot undertake,
  I leave to Thee alone;
And pray Thee for Thy mercy's sake,
  To change this heart of stone.

—*Unknown*

(Day 2)

Saul Meets Jesus

Review today's Bible Lesson.
Color this picture

(Day 3)

Saul

Find as many words as you can in the letters below. Go from left to right. The first word is done for you.

SAULIGHTSHINEDOWNVOICEPERSECUTEST EYESAWOPENEDAMASCUSLEDHAND

1. SAUL
2. ______
3. ______
4. ______
5. ______
6. ______
7. ______
8. ______
9. ______
10. ______
11. ______
12. ______
13. ______
14. ______
15. ______
16. ______
17. ______
18. ______

"Then opened he their understanding, that they might understand the Scriptures."
Luke 24:45

(Day 3)

Fish of Costal Waters and Open Ocean

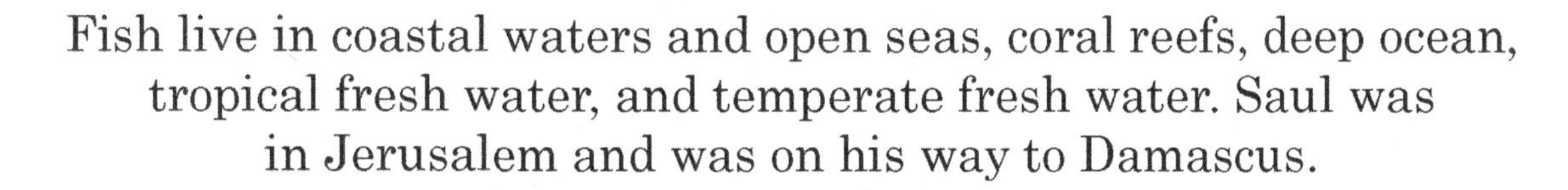

Fish live in coastal waters and open seas, coral reefs, deep ocean, tropical fresh water, and temperate fresh water. Saul was in Jerusalem and was on his way to Damascus.

Make fish in the ocean below by pressing your thumb on an ink pad or color the end of your thumb with a felt-tip marker. Press your thumb on the paper to make the body. Draw the mouth, eye, fins, and tail.

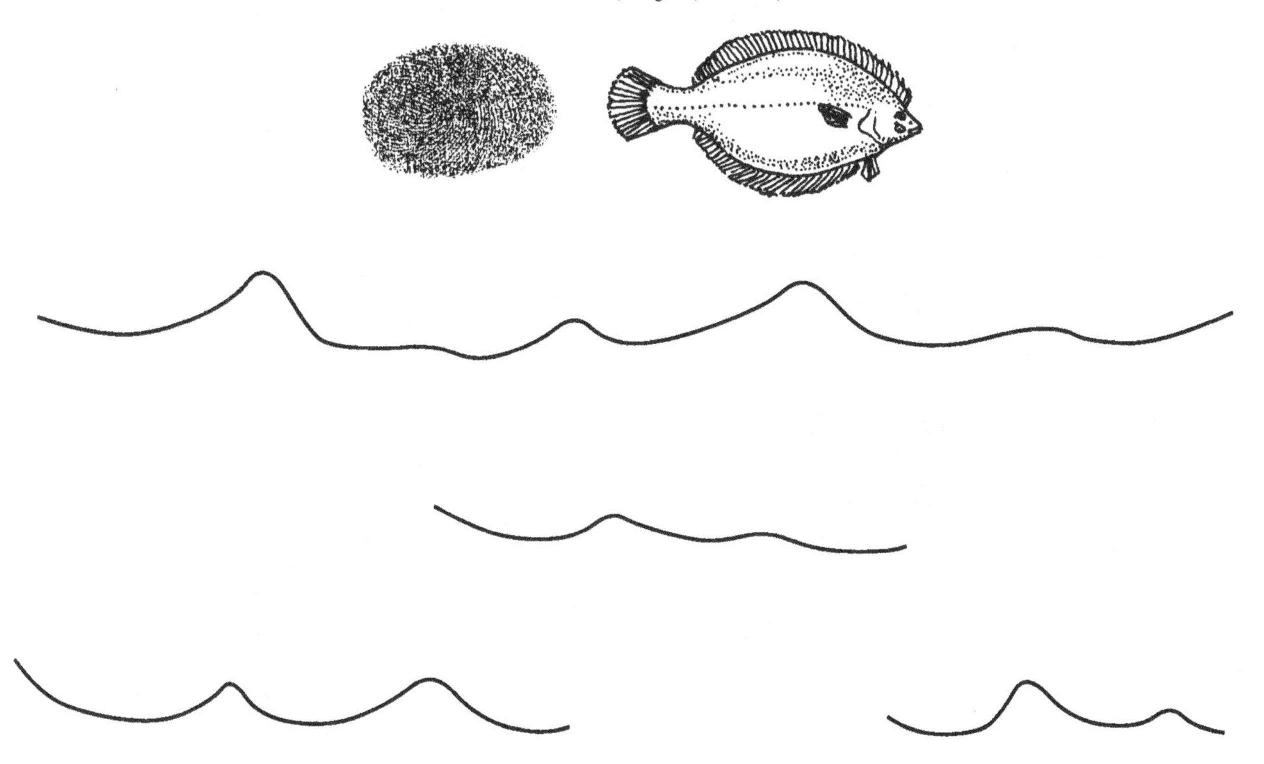

(Day 3)

Bluefish

Read and color.

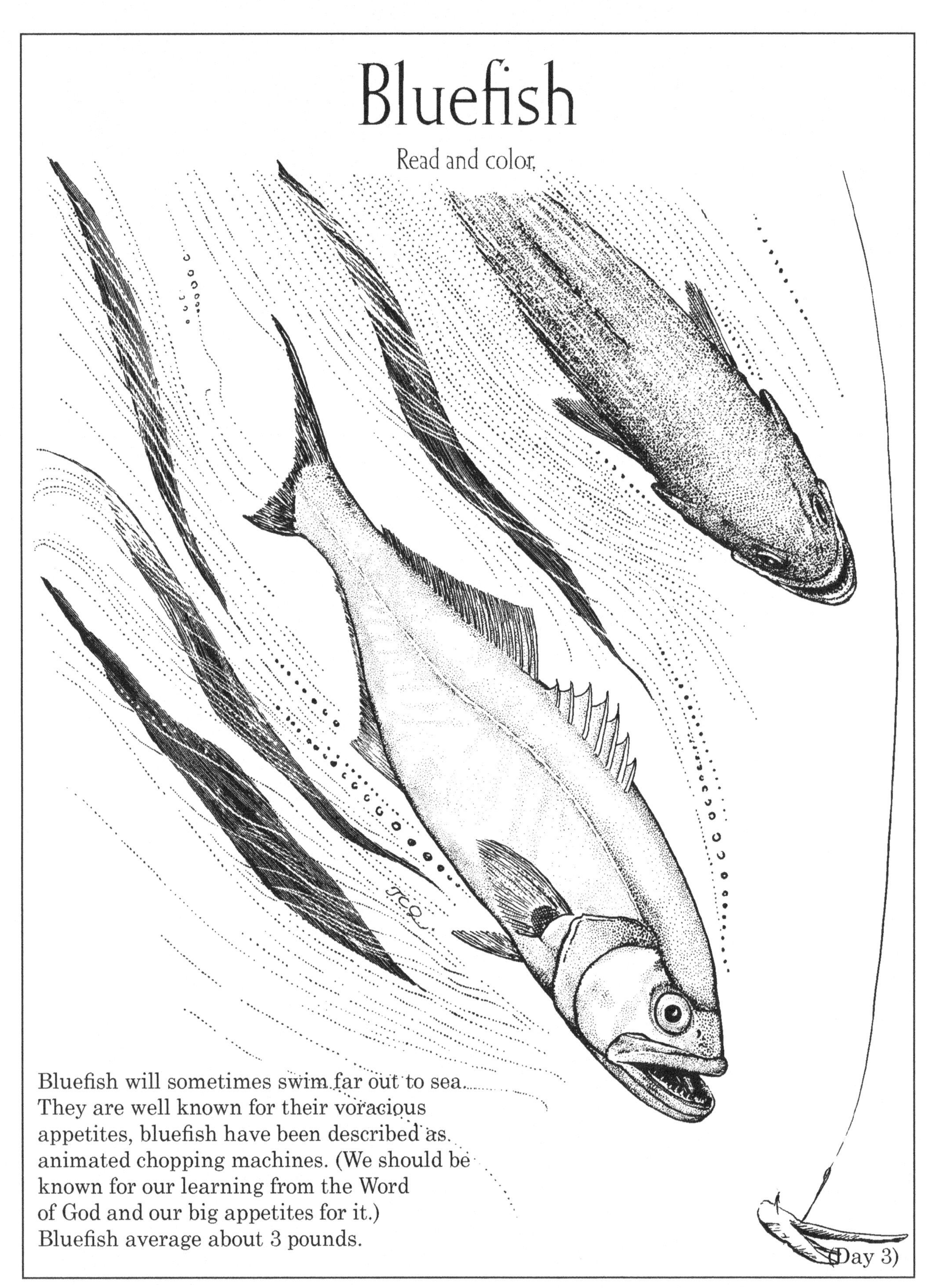

Bluefish will sometimes swim far out to sea. They are well known for their voracious appetites, bluefish have been described as animated chopping machines. (We should be known for our learning from the Word of God and our big appetites for it.) Bluefish average about 3 pounds.

(Day 3)

Ananias

Answer these questions.

1. How did Saul enter Damascus? Whose home did he seek out? What was the name of the street?

2. What did he do there?

3. Who appeared unto a disciple at Damascus?

4. Who did God send to heal Saul? What did He tell him?

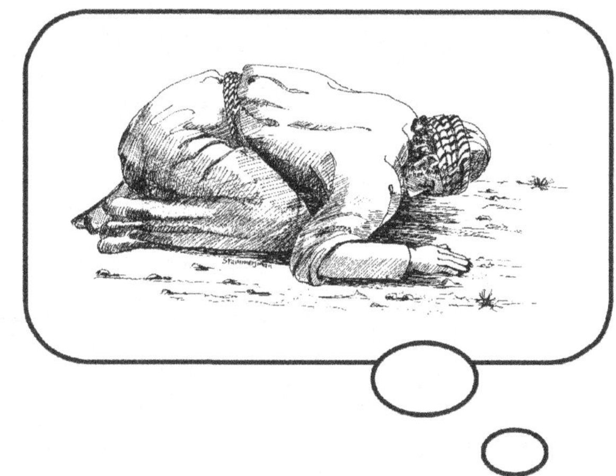

5. How did he respond? Why?

6. Did he obey God's directions? What did Ananias do for Saul?

7. What did Ananias call Saul? What happened next?

8. How did the Lord teach Saul **humbleness**?

(Day 4)

Fish in the Deep Ocean

Oarfish

In the deep ocean there are fish most unusual and there is not much known about them. Many have very large eyes, big mouths, fang-like teeth, and light organs that flash on and off. The unusual fish in the deep sea with their big eyes reminds us of the unusual way Saul's eyes were healed. Most fish that live in the deep sea hardly ever come up to the surface, and, because of its shape, looks like a "sea serpent" if it breaks the surface.

The oarfish has surely been the inspiration for many sea-serpent stories. Normally found in deep waters, it will occasionally come near the surface. It is 20-30 feet long. Its spectacular fins are bright red and its body is translucent blue-gray with dark stripes.

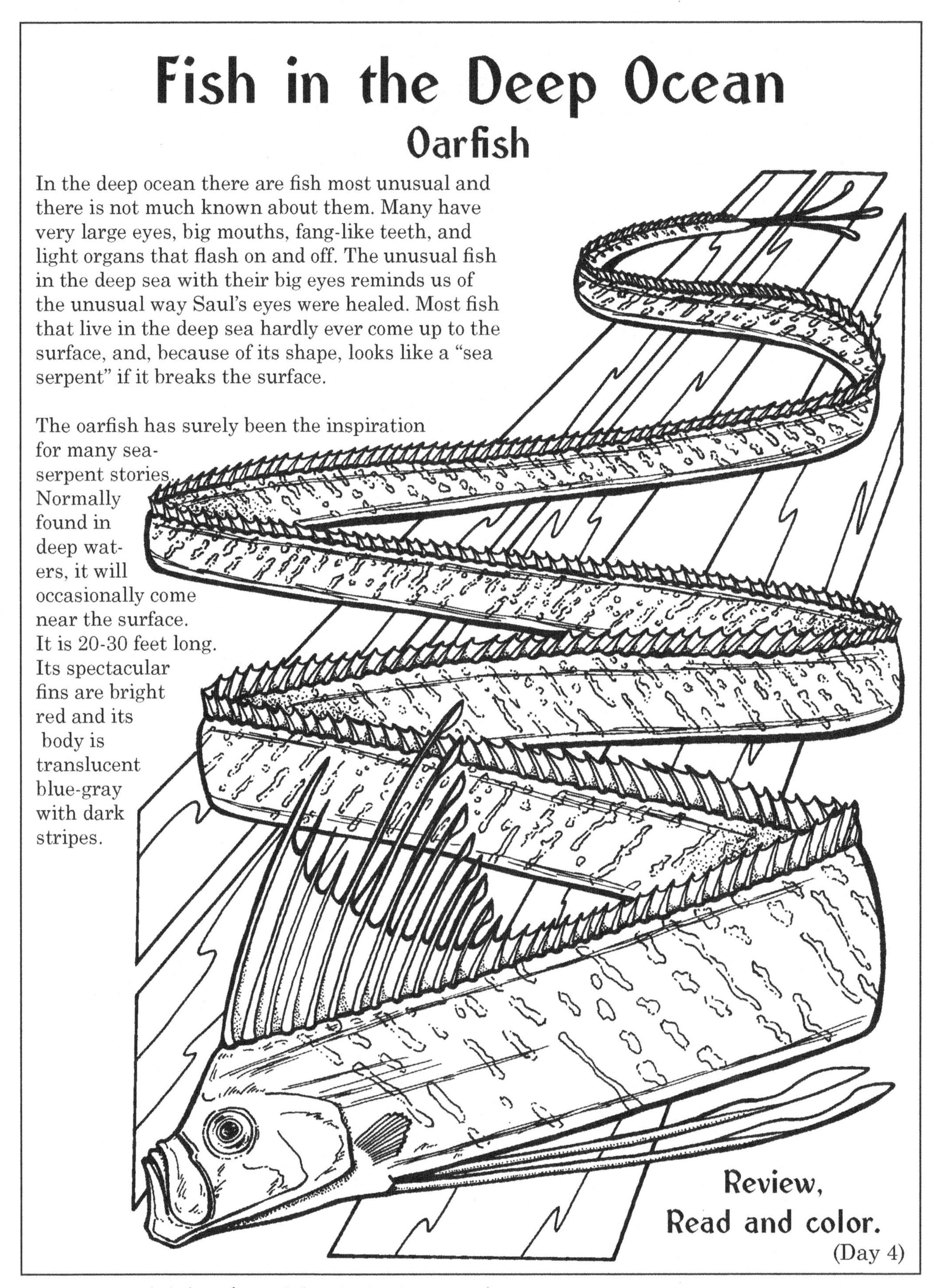

Review, Read and color.

(Day 4)

Humbleness and Honor

Little Charlie Foster was playing with his ball in the schoolyard one morning before school began. Presently the ball slipped out of his hand sooner than he intended and went through the window with a crash. The window was broken to fragments and the ball rolled away into a corner of the school-room.

Charlie was frightened. He was a timid boy, and the teacher, Mr. Trumbull, seemed to him very big and very stern. But Charlie had been taught to love the truth, and stick to it at all times. He did not think for a moment of trying to hide what was done. So, blushing and trembling with **humiliation**, he ran as fast as he could down the road along which the teacher usually came to school, to tell him all about it. Before long he met the teacher walking rapidly towards the school and so busy thinking that he did not seem to see the little boy who was trying to get his attention.

"Mr. Trumbull! Mr. Trumbull! Stop a moment, please," said he.

"Oh, Charlie! Good morning. Why, what's the matter now, my little man?"

"I broke your window, sir, but I didn't mean to. I'm very sorry for it. I did it with my ball, and the ball is in the schoolroom now."

"Poor child," said the teacher, who saw his eyes filled with tears and a look of great distress on his face. "So you ran all the way to tell me, did you? You've begun right, Charlie, my boy. Whatever mischief you do, never be afraid or ashamed to tell of it."

Then, with a light heart, Charlie ran back to the school. None of the boys knew that Charlie had told the teacher about it. They had collected together and were talking about the broken window and what the teacher would say, as boys like to do under such circumstances.

(Day 4)

After awhile, a little fellow named Johnny Thompson found the ball with C. F.—the initials of Charlie Foster's name—marked on it. He guessed at once who had done the mischief. He was not himself in the habit of confessing when he had done wrong, and, judging Charlie by himself, he supposed that the teacher knew nothing about who was to blame for the accident; so he held up his hand to show that he wished to speak. "Well, Johnny, what have you to say?" asked Mr. Trumbull.

"Please, sir, I've found out who broke that there window," said Johnny, in a way which showed how easy it was for him to break the rules of grammar if he didn't break the window.

"So have I, and a very honorable person broke it."

"A very honorable person!" That made Charlie feel very comfortable. And then the teacher told all the boys how Charlie had **humbly** come himself to tell all about it. He spoke in high terms of him as a boy to be trusted and of the honor he had gained in this way. Then he showed how different it would have been if he had denied it and told a lie to hide it. He would have been found out sooner or later, and then he would have been covered with shame and disgrace.

"Deliver my soul, O Lord, from lying lips."

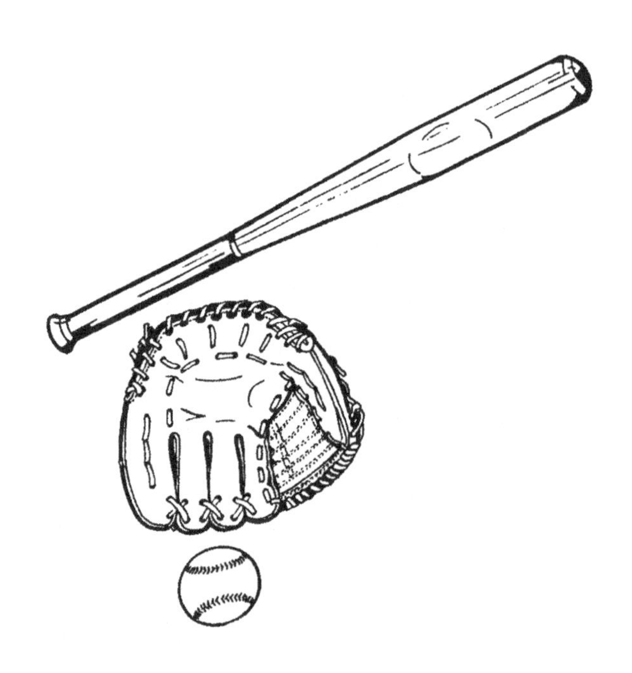

(Day 4)

A Broken and Contrite Heart

Though God preserves me every hour,
And feeds me day by day,
I know it is not in my power
His goodness to repay.

The poorest child, the greatest king,
Alike must **humbly** own,
No worthy present they can bring
To offer at His throne.

For we, and all our treasures too,
Are His who reigns above;
Then is there nothing I can do,
To prove my grateful love?
A broken heart He'll not despise,
For 'tis His chief delight.

This is a **humble** sacrifice,
Well-pleasing in His sight

Though treasures brought before His throne
Would no acceptance find,
He kindly condescends to own
A meek and lowly mind.

This is an offering we may bring,
However small our store;
The poorest child, the greatest king,
Can give Him nothing more.

—Unknown

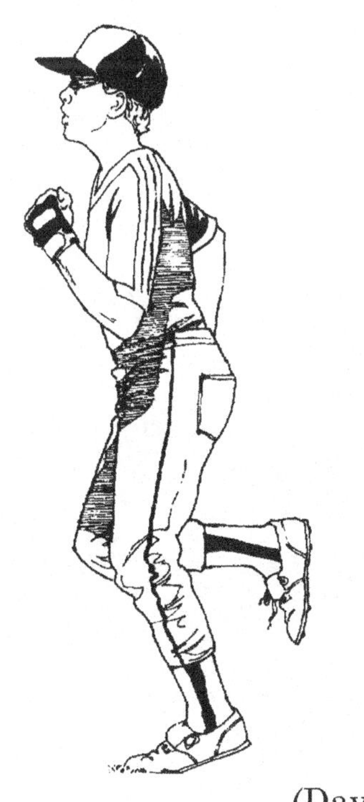

(Day 4)

Remember the Ocean Depths

Remember how the ocean depths are silent
But the shallow waves may roar?
Humility is in the under currents—
While pride crashes on the shore.

—Unknown

(Day 4)

Damascus

When Saul entered Damascus it was quite different than he had planned.

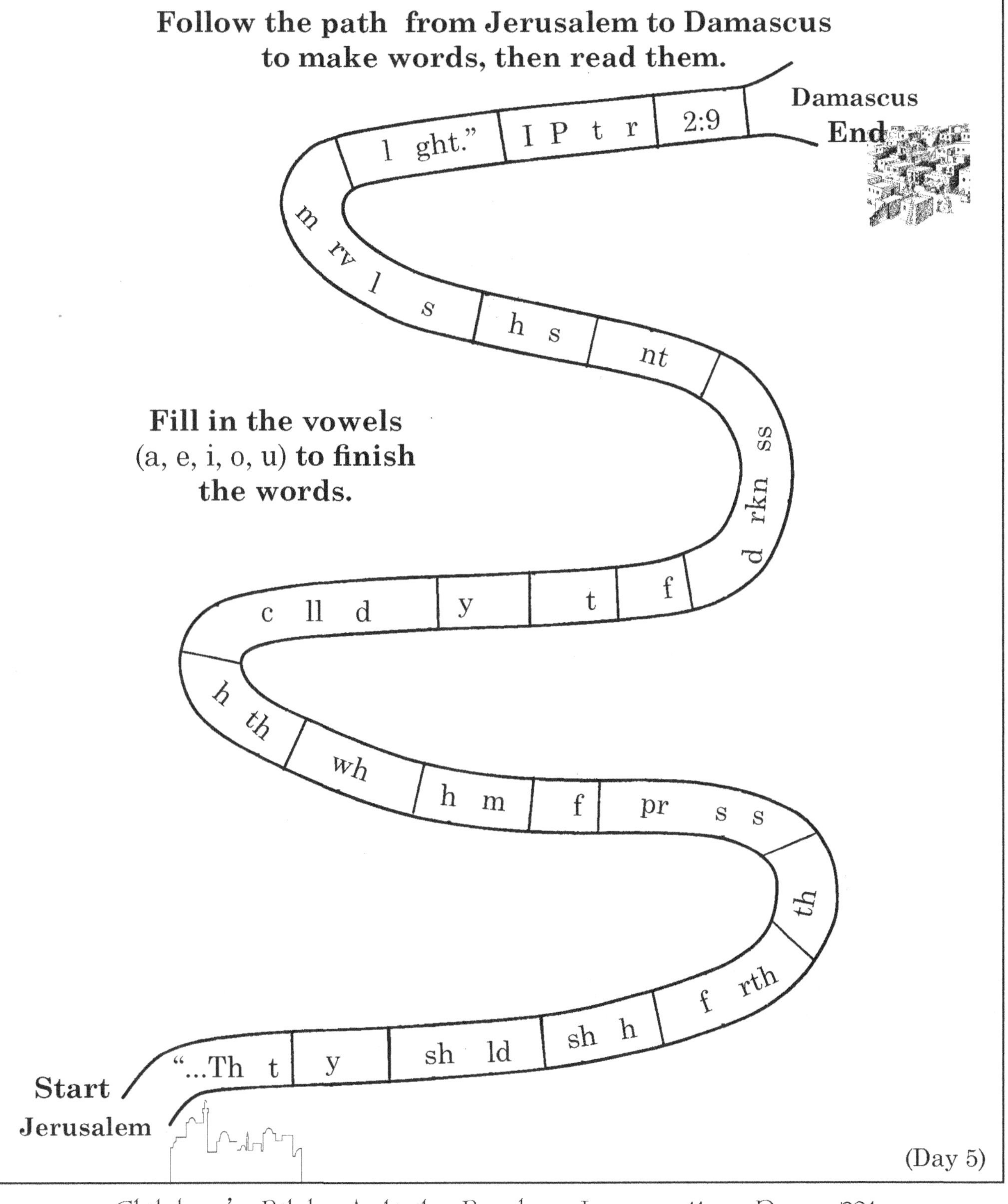

(Day 5)

Eels Are Fish

The common eel changes several times during its life.
Paul had changes in his life.

Fill in the letters to the words that explain the stages of the common eel.

Eel Cycle

1. _ _ _ _

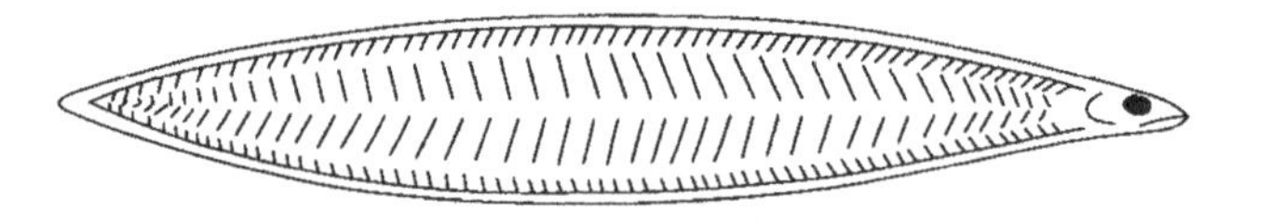

2. _ _ _ _ _ _

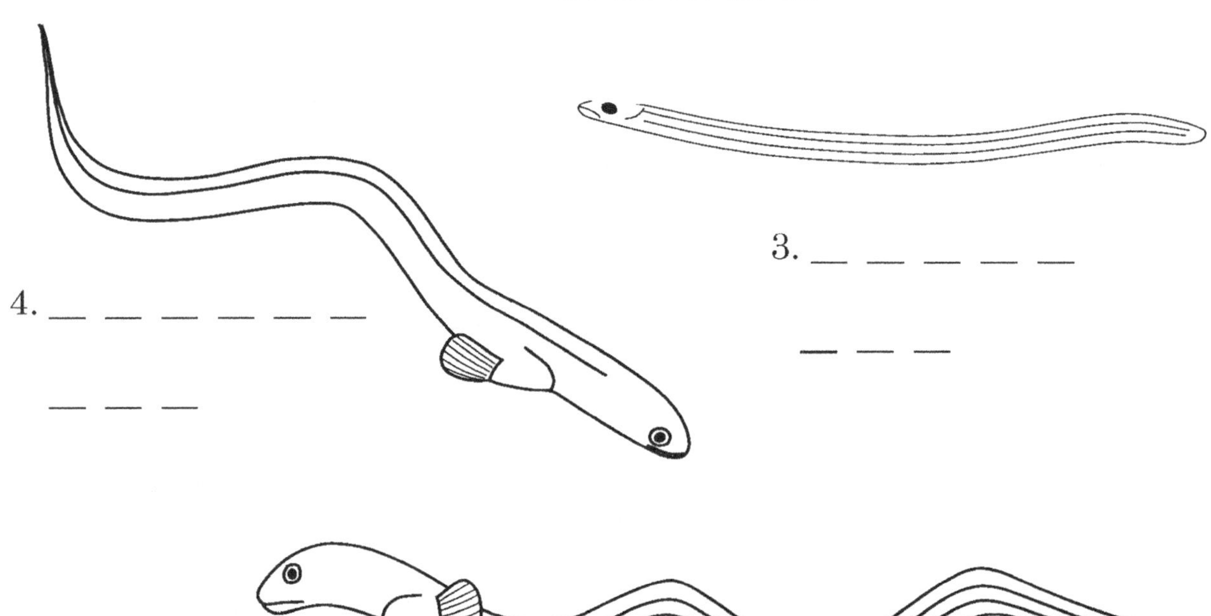

3. _ _ _ _ _ _ _ _ _

4. _ _ _ _ _ _ _ _ _ _

5. _ _ _ _ _ _ _ _ _ _

(Day 5)

Yellow-edge Moray Eel
This eel
grows
to eight feet
in length.
Color this moray
dark brown with
yellow edges
on its fins.
(Day 5)

Spotted Moray Eel

Covered with dark patches, the Spotted Moray Eel hides away during the day and hunts for food at night. Color.

(Day 5)

Escape

Write the right word in the squares to finish the verses.

"Then the ☐ *took him by* ☐ ,

and let him down by the wall in a ☐ *."*

"And he spake boldly in the name of the ☐

☐ *, and disputed against the Grecians: but they went*

about to ☐ *him."*

"Which when the brethren knew, they brought him down to

☐ *, and sent him forth to* ☐ *."*

Acts 9:25, 29-30

Jesus	Caesarea	disciples	slay
basket	Lord	Tarsus	night

(Day 6)

Eels Are Not Snakes!

Finish drawing these eels.

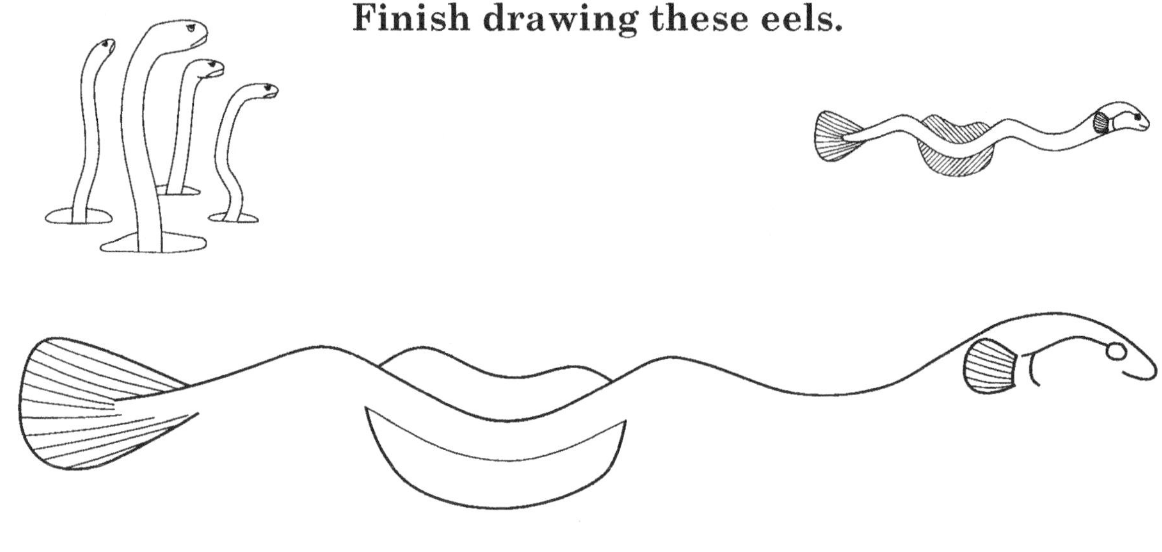

Eels swim (wiggle) through the water to keep safe, and Paul had to leave Damascus and Jerusalem to other regions for safety.
(Day 6)

Electric Eels & Garden Eels

The electric eel gives shocks to kill or stun its prey. It has special organs that run down the sides of its body and produce electricity. The Jewish leaders were shocked to hear Saul - Paul had become a Christian.

Reviewing today's lesson.

The black ribbon eel is a beautiful fish that lives in cracks and caves in the reef. When a meal passes it darts out like a snake to catch it with its toothy jaws. Many times the early Christians had to hide and only came forth to share Christ then dart away again.

Garden eels live in colonies and spend most of their lives with their tails stuck in holes in the sand. Their heads stick out and wave in the currents like a field of grain.

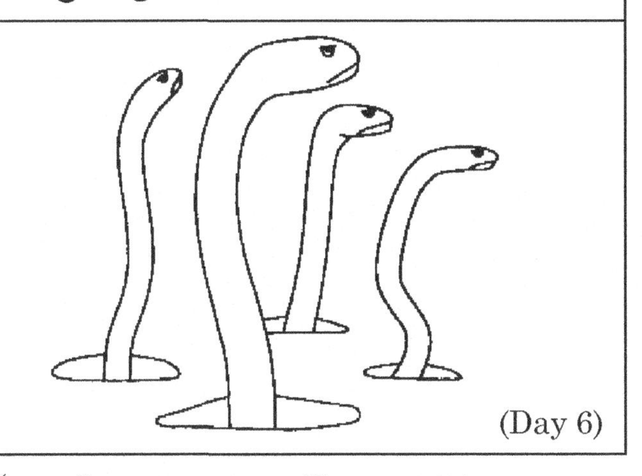

(Day 6)

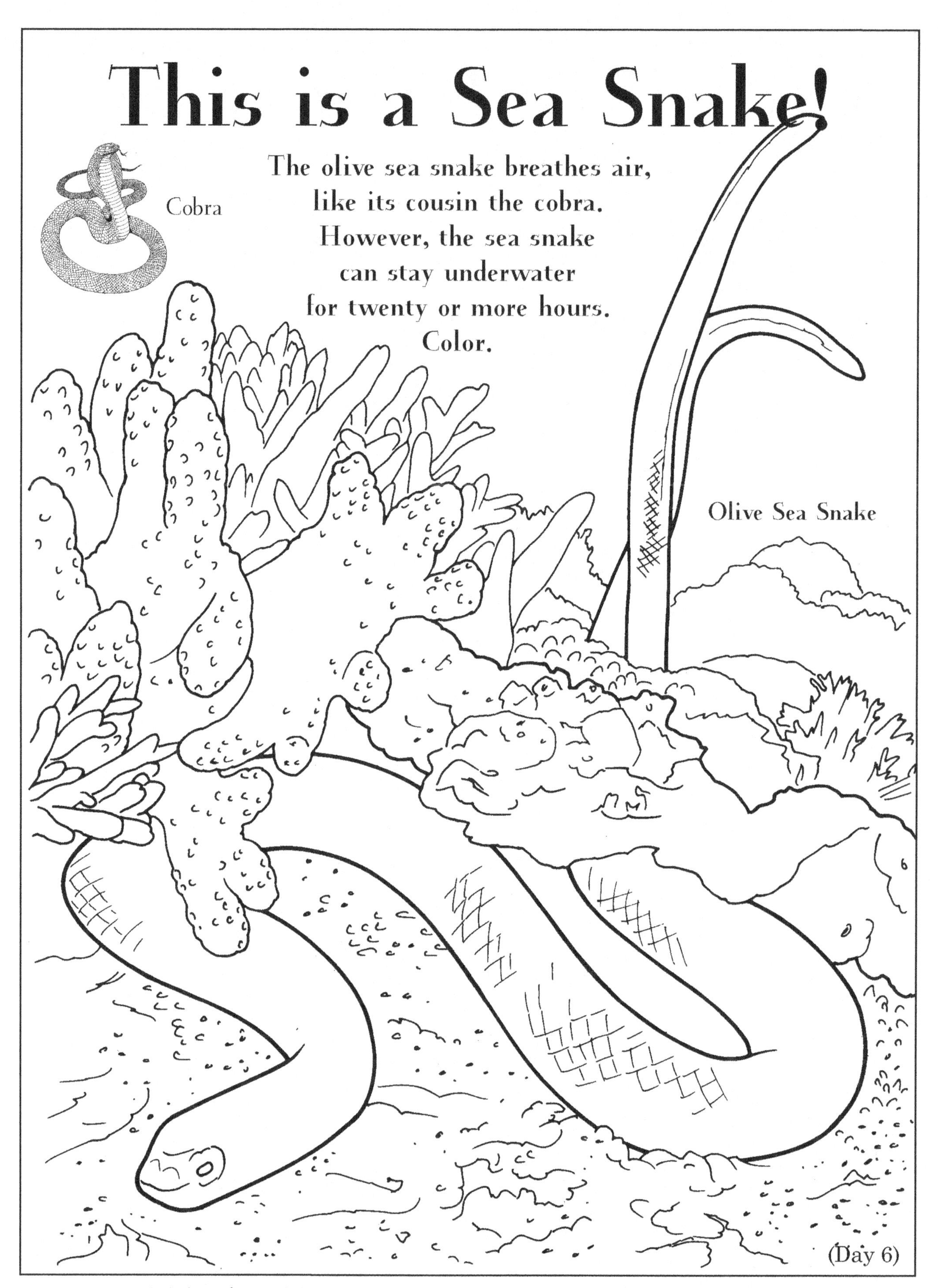

This is a Sea Snake!
The olive sea snake breathes air,
like its cousin the cobra.
However, the sea snake
can stay underwater
for twenty or more hours.
Color.
Cobra
Olive Sea Snake
(Day 6)

Humbleness

"At that time Jesus answered and said, I thank thee, O Father, Lord of heaven and earth, because thou hast hid these things from the wise and prudent, and hast revealed them unto babes."
Matthew 11:25

Because God never gives truth to those who will not accept it, much wisdom is hidden from those who choose not to see. Many who make no pretense of learning show greater wisdom than professed wise men. Even in nature wild animals often outsmart men and trained animals.

Brownie, a hunting dog, found an old fat raccoon in a low, swampy area near a pond. With no tree to climb, the raccoon jumped into the water and started to swim from the dog. Brownie, a faster swimmer, reached the coon just as he climbed onto a log in the middle of the pond. The raccoon turned and faced Brownie. With both front paws he pushed the dog's head under water. Brownie frantically waved his tail and hind feet. Finally he got away and swam to shore.

A week later, while his master fished, Brownie watched by the river bank. The same coon walked right by the dog, which didn't even get up. Unafraid, the raccoon waded into the river and fished for a clam. He found a big one and bit at the closed shell. It wouldn't open, so he laid it on a flat stone. Finding another, he bit it also, to no avail. He kept on fishing, but every clam was closed tight. Finally the flat stone was covered with unopened clamshells. The raccoon walked away with no dinner, leaving all the clams behind on the shore.

Brownie and his master were still fishing when the raccoon returned an hour later. The clams still lay on the rock in the hot sun. He picked up one clam, turned it over, pulled a bit, and the shell opened wide. The orange-colored meat disappeared. Every shell opened easily, and the raccoon had a feast. That wise old fisherman knew that when clams get warm, they get lazy and weak. His God-given wildwood wisdom amazed the man who watched him.

No wonder Jesus thanked His Father for hiding heaven's truths from those who think themselves wise, and revealing it to those who have simple, trusting faith like little children. God is pleased to share His wisdom with those who are **humble** and willing to learn.

In our Bible Lesson, Saul–Paul became one of those **humble** children of God. He then began to learn the wisdom of heaven.

(Day 6)

Learning Humility

What does the Bible say about humbleness?
Read and discuss these verses.

Humbleness vs Pride – Review its meaning!
Humbleness is depending upon God and His will in every decision and letting Him and others take the credit for any successes in your life.

"Likewise, ye younger, submit yourselves unto the elder,
Yea, all of you be subject one to another, and be clothed with **humility**:
for God resisteth the proud, and giveth grace to the **humble**."
I Peter 5:5

"By **humility** and the fear of the LORD are riches, and honor, and life."
Proverbs 22:4

"If my people, which are called by my name, shall **humble** themselves,
and pray, and seek my face, and turn from their wicked ways; then
will I hear from heaven, and will forgive their sin, and will heal their land."
II Chronicles 7:14

"**Humble** yourselves in the sight of the Lord, and he shall lift you up"
James 4:10

"**Humble** yourselves therefore under the mighty hand of God,
that he may exalt you in due time."
I Peter 5:6

"For thus saith the high and lofty One that inhabiteth eternity,
whose name is Holy: I dwell in the high and holy place, with him also
that is of a contrite and **humble** spirit, to revive the spirit of the **humble**,
and to revive the heart of the contrite ones.
Isaiah 57:15

See the Teacher's Key.

(Day 6)

Racoon 1

"Better it is to be of a **humble** spirit with the lowly, than to divide the spoil with the proud."
Proverbs 16:19

A verse to memorize and a picture to color.

(Day 6)

Racoon 2

A man's pride shall bring him low: but honor shall uphold the **humble** in spirit.
Proverbs 29:23

12 – Dorcas

Bible – Acts 9:32-43

Song – "Yield Not to Temptation" (2nd verse)
"None of Self and All of Thee"

Nature – The Food Cycle, and How the Ocean Moves

Character Quality

Thoughtfulness vs Indifference
Thoughtfulness is to consider others and their needs, as Jesus did, instead of yourself.

Memory Verse

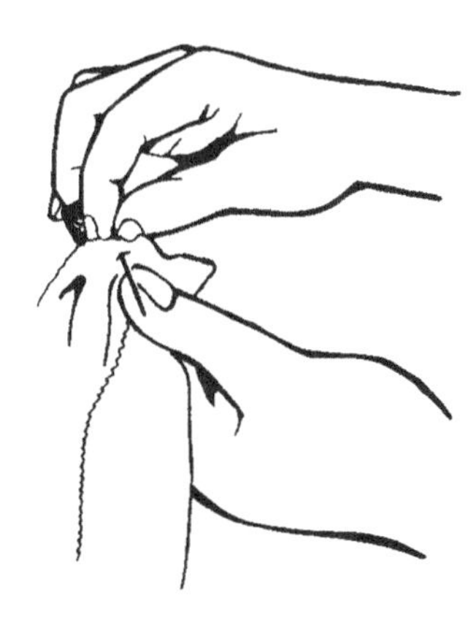

"Let your light so shine before men, that they may see your good works, and glorify your Father, which is in heaven."
Matthew 5:16

The Food Cycle, and How the Ocean Moves

The healing of thoughtful Dorcas
was to be a testimony to Christ and,
like the waves moving,
it would be spread near and far.

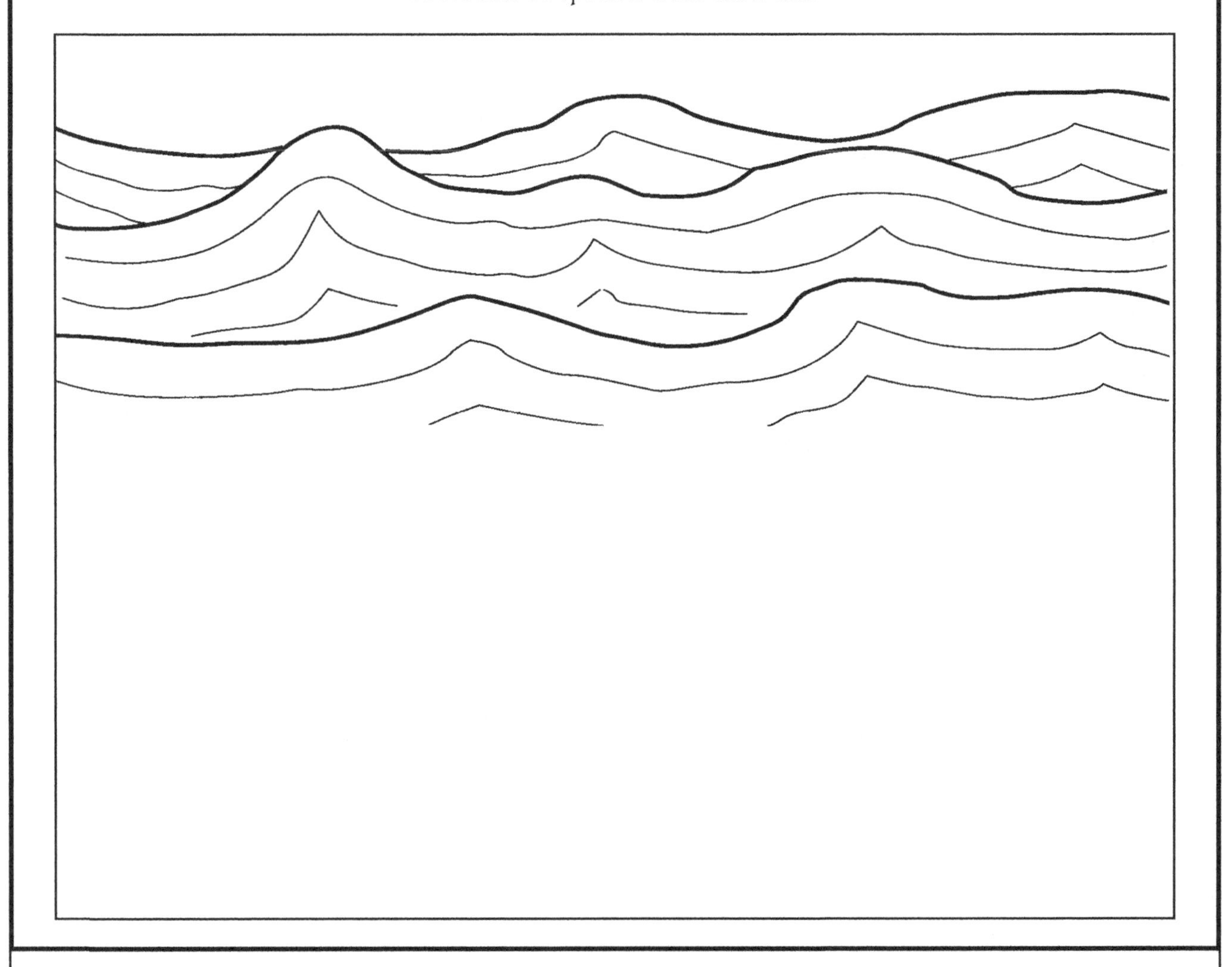

Place sea life stickers in the picture above
for each day this week
you study your lesson, and say your memory verse.

_ _ _ _ _ _ Healed

Begin at the top arrow at "A" and go to the bottom arrow to "D" to see what happened at Lydda. Check Acts 9:34. Fill in all blanks using only 12 of the letters.

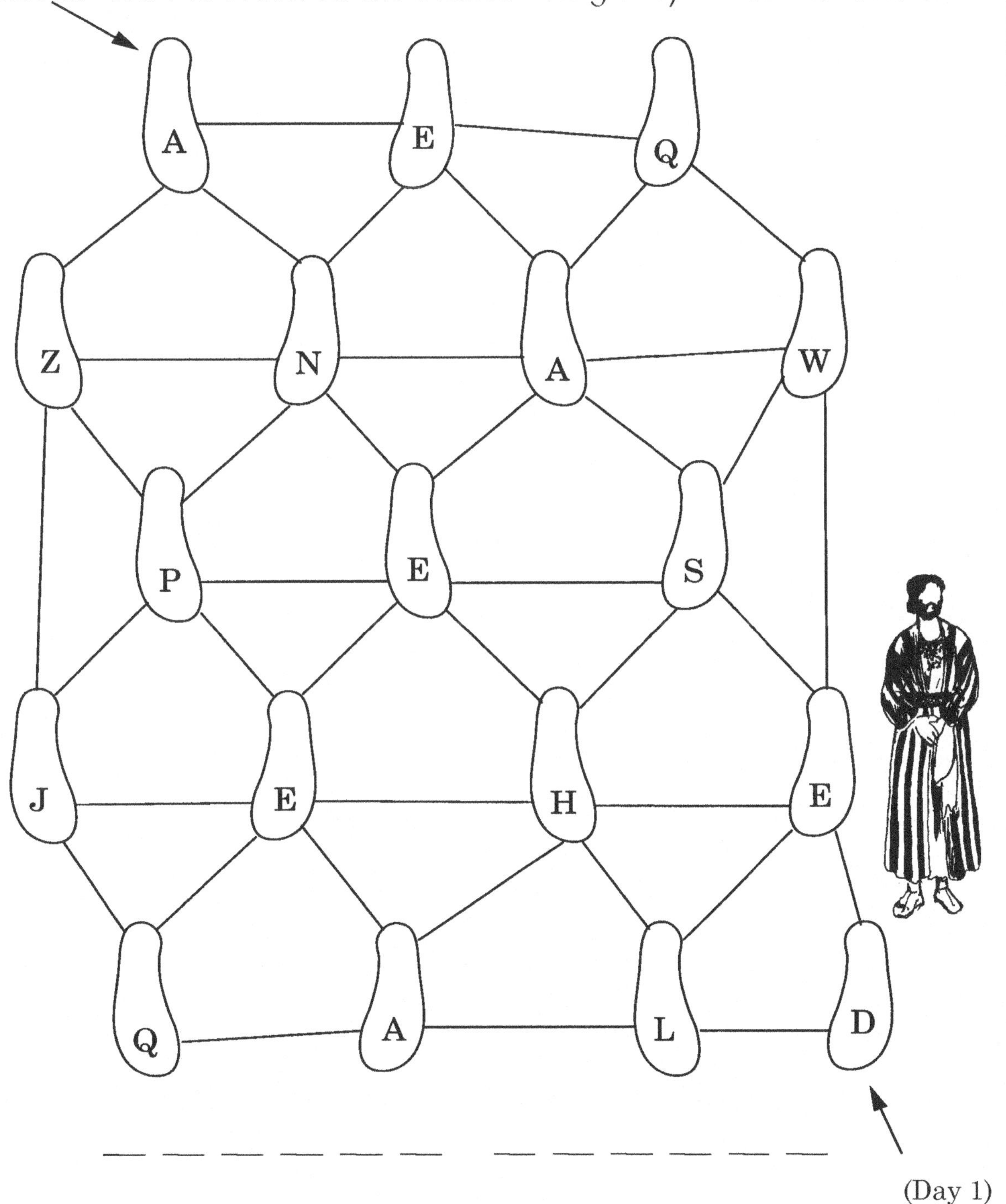

_ _ _ _ _ _ _ _ _ _ _ _

(Day 1)

The Food Cycle

Fill in the blanks to complete the food chain.

One through Four completes the Food Cycle!

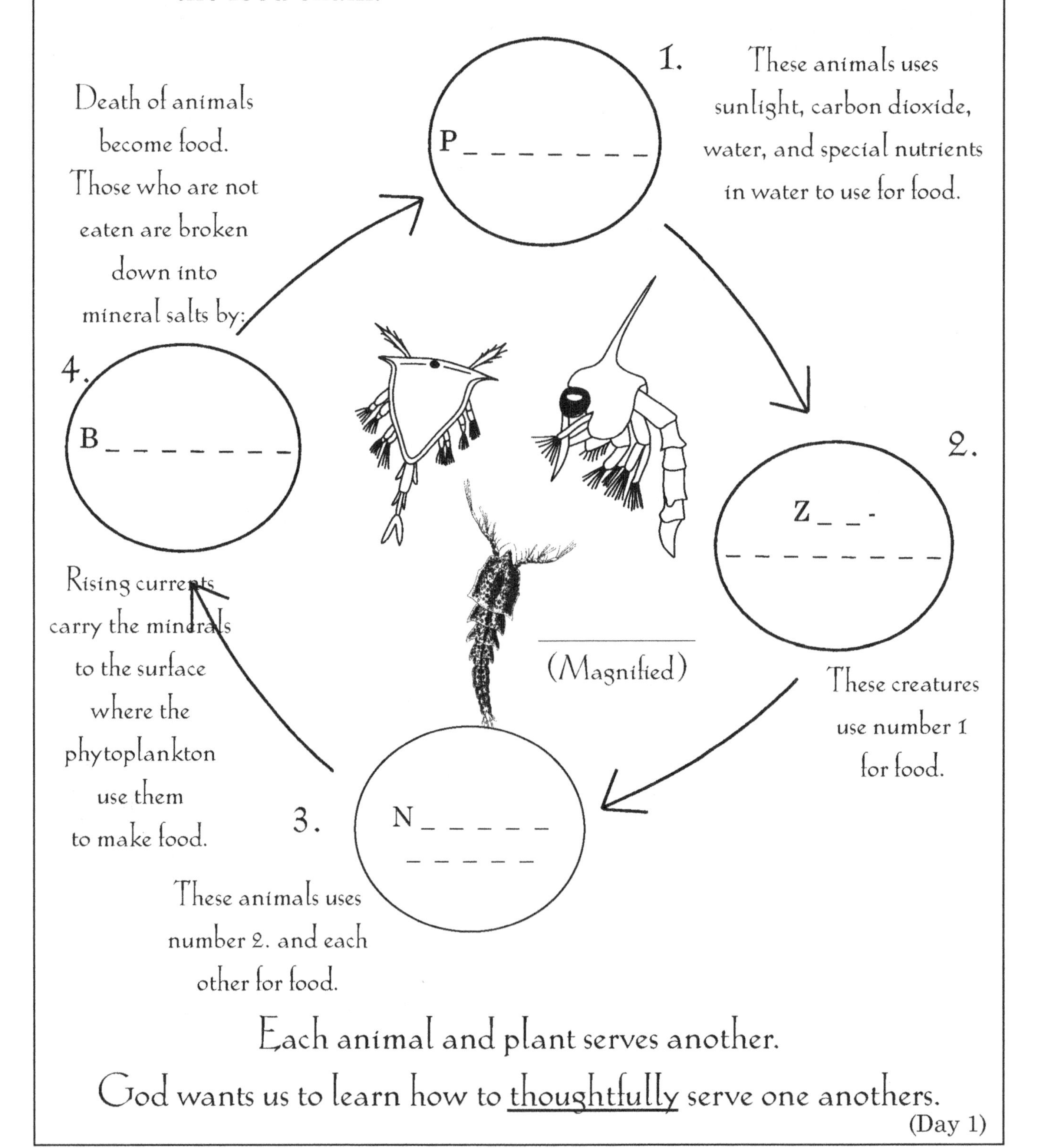

Each animal and plant serves another.

God wants us to learn how to <u>thoughtfully</u> serve one anothers.

(Day 1)

Good Deeds

1. The lady whose skillful fingers were more active than her tongue was called what two names?

2. What did the name which started with the letter "T" mean.

3. Color this picture of this **thoughtful** person.

(Day 2)

"Gazelle"

1. Tabitha means ______________________________.

2. One characteristic of a gazelle is that they ____________________.

3. Dorcas-Tabitha must have been a woman that **thoughtfully** used ____________ ______________________________.

4. Read below about other characteristics of the gazelle. Color this picture. Do any relate to Dorcas? Which ones?

The gazelle is known for its beauty, gracefulness, and gentleness.

Some other facts are: they are vegans. Some are called the dorcas or ariel gazelle, and the word gazelle comes from an Arabic word that means *"to be affectionate."*

The Thomson's gazelle in the picture has a light fawn-colored back that deepens to a wide band of dark brown along the flanks. Its underside is pure white.

(Day 2)

How the Ocean Moves

Review today's Nature Lesson while coloring this picture. Notice the movement of the waters in the sea.

(Day 2)

The Monument of Thoughtful Deeds

Our Lord went about doing good. He did not wait for chances for doing good to come to Him. He sought the chance to do it; went about after it. Certainly there is suggestion of enterprise here for all of us.

Some time since in a New England town there lived and died an old lady. She had worked hard all her life. She had accumulated a little competency. She had earned it honestly. But that was all she had done. Of smiles and kindliness and charities her life was as destitute as is a granite boulder of summer verdure. The kindly people who were her neighbors said she had the reputation of being "a little difficult to get along with." "Yes," said one of them in answer to some inquiry, "Miss Smith is dead, and she left a house and garden and some personal property, and money in the bank, and what do you think she left it all to? To build a monument to herself over in the cemetery." "Well," said the neighbor, reflectively, "I suppose she wanted to be remembered in some way."

Just about this time a young girl died in the same town, whose path had always been a rugged one. Though she had worked hard all her life, she had left no house, or garden, or balance in the bank. But she did leave another sort of monument—a monument of kindly deeds, of pleasant words, of cheerful smiles, that have brightened, and will continue to make bright the lives of all her friends. "Why," said a fellow-worker, "I never could have learned to run my machine if she had not been so kind about showing me." Said a little girl: "She often used to give me a flower when she met me mornings, and if she had no flower she smiled so pleasantly it was just as good." Another young girl exclaimed, "It was a note she wrote me that made me want to be a Christian." And a shy boy said, with tender memories vibrating in his voice, "I came to prayer-meeting first because she asked me to, and she always used to speak to me and say she was glad to see me there." The girls in the Sabbath-school class banded themselves together to try to do some of the kind things that she would do if she were living. Does not the story of this humble, **thoughtful** life make plainly evident to us how even a measurable following of our Lord will set us on enterprises toward beneficence? Better than crafted stone in any cemetery is such an earnest and beautiful example toward seeking opportunities of doing good.

(Day 2)

Doing Thoughtful Things For Others

Doing things to make others happy. Discuss these pictures.

What thoughtful things can you do for your parents and others?

(Day 2)

Upon Life

Rose of Sharron

Lord what is life? 'Tis like a flower,
That blossoms and is gone.
We see it flourish for an hour,
With all its beauty on.
But death come, like a wintry day,
And cuts the pretty flower away.

Lord, what is life? 'Tis like the bow
That glistens in the sky.
We love to see its colors glow;
But while we look they die.
Life fails as soon; today 'tis here!
To night, perhaps, 'twill disappear.

Six thousand years have passed away
Since life began at first,
And millions, once alive and gay,
Are dead, and in the dust.
For life, in all its health and pride,
Has death still waiting at its side.

And yet, this short, uncertain space
So foolishly we prize,
That heaven, that last dwelling place,
Seems nothing in our eyes.
The words of sorrow and of bliss
We disregard, compared with this!

Lord, what is life? If spent with Thee
In duty, praise, and prayer,
However long or short it be,
We need but little care.
Because eternity will last,
When life, and even death, are past.

—*Unknown*

(Day 2)

The Death of Dorcas

What was Dorcas known for?

To answer this question finish the puzzle below.
Use the scrambled words
at the bottom of the puzzle.
The first word
has three letters
and begins with A.
The black squares mean
the end of a word.

Scrambled Word List

Acts 9:39

R	S	D	S	H	H	N	S	D	M	H	M	H	H
O	E	A	A	I	E	A	A	A	A	E	E	I	I
D	H	E	W	N	T	D	T	N	R	L	T	W	W
S		M		S			O		G	I	H	C	T
A				O			C		S	W		H	
C				W					E				
				G					N				
									T				

(Day 3)

Calling To Mind What Others Have Thoughtfully Done For Us.

Call to mind what others have done for you
as you color this picture
of what Dorcas did for the widows in her day.

(Day 3)

Currents 1

Fill in the blanks with words from today's lesson.
What two kinds of circulation is created by the ocean?
Explain.

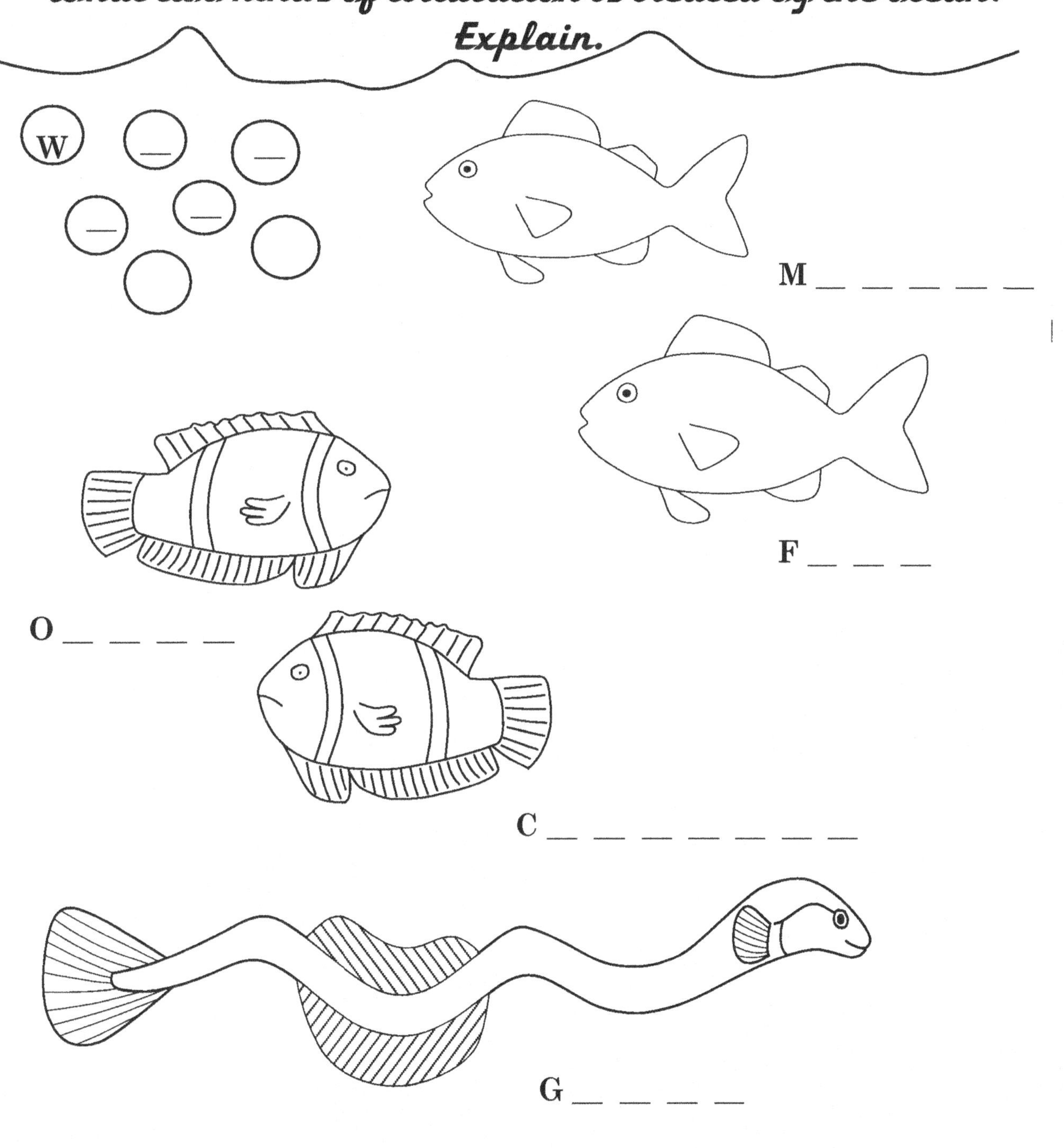

Who in our lesson was busy like the ocean?

____

(Day 3)

The Moving of the Water

The wind blows over the surface of the ocean.
This moves the surface of the water.
The wind moves the currents in a circular pattern called gyres.
(When a person is **thoughtful** toward others
the blessing circles back to themselves. Color and notice the movement.

(Day 3)

"Tabitha, Arise"

"But Peter put them all forth, and kneeled down, and prayed; and turning him to the body said, Tabitha, arise. And she opened her eyes: and when she saw Peter, she sat up.

"And he gave her his hand, and lifted her up...."

Acts 9:40-41

Color this picture.

(Day 4)

Currents 2

Reread today's Nature Lesson.

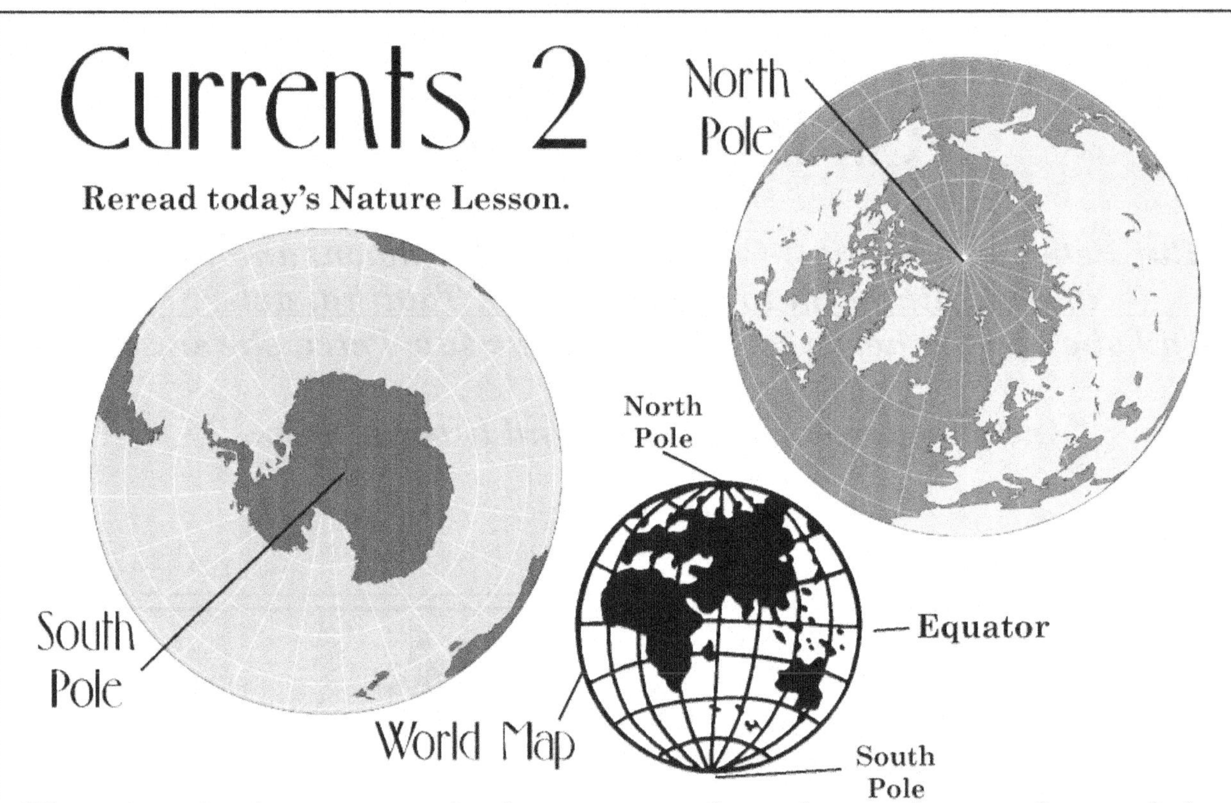

The circulation or vertical currents flow from the surface of the ocean bottom and back again. The currents move slowly along the sea floor in the polar regions and up to the surface. So in the polar regions, the surface water is colder and saltier. This makes the water heavier, and it sinks toward the ocean bottom. Then the cold water spreads out ever so slowly toward the equator. Then water unhurriedly flows back toward the surface to replace the surface waters that sink.

This can remind us about prayer and how the heavenly currents "sink" down to earth, and we, in grateful prayer, let it rise back up. Peter knew he needed God's great current of life to bring Dorcas back to be a living person.

(Day 4)

"Take No Thought"

"The Lord is my shepherd; I shall not want."
Psalm 23:1

Those who are so anxious about the future as to be unhappy in the present, may learn a lesson from a poor black woman. Her name was Nancy, and she earned a moderate living by washing. She was, however, always happy. One day one of those anxious Christians who were constantly "taking thought about the morrow," said to her: "Nancy, it's well enough to be happy now; but I should think your thoughts of the future would sober you. Suppose, for instance, that you should be taken sick and unable to work; or suppose your present employers should move away, and no one else should give you anything to do; or suppose"—"Stop!" cried Nancy. "I never suppose. The Lord is my Shepherd, and I know I shall not want. And," she added to her gloomy friend, "It is all those 'supposes' that are making you so miserable. You ought to give them all up, and just trust in the Lord."

(Day 4)

Glory to Thee

Glory to Thee, my God, this night,
For all the blessings of the light;
Keep me, Oh! Keep me, King of kings,
Beneath the shadow of Thy wings.
Forgive me, Lord, for Thy dear Son,
The ills that I this day have done;
That with the world, myself, and Thee,
I, ere I sleep, at peace may be.
Teach me to live that I may dread
The grave as little as my bed.
Teach me to die, that so I may
Rise glorious in the judgment day.
O, May my soul on thee repose,
And may sweet sleep mine eyelids close;
Sleep that may me more vigorous make,
To serve my God when I awake.
When in the night I sleepless lie,
My soul with heavenly thoughts supply;
Let no ill dreams disturb my rest;
No powers of darkness me molest.
Oh, when shall I, in endless day,
For ever chase dark sleep away
And hymns divine with angels sing,
Glory to thee, eternal King?

—Unknown

Death is like a sleep.

(Day 4)

Alive

"But Peter put them all forth, and kneeled down, and prayed; and turning him to the body said,..."

Finish the above verse by coloring all the spaces with a dot. Fill the blanks below.

Acts 9:40

Then, to make sure God would be honored for this ____________ act he called the

__________ so that Dorcas gave her personal testimony of what God had done for her.

(Day 5)

Thoughtfulness

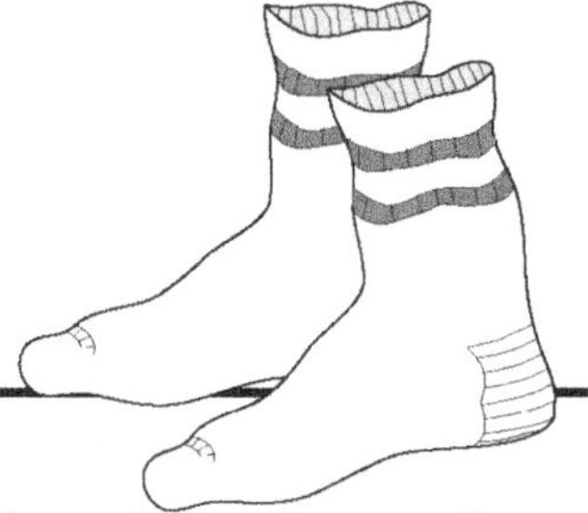

"I must not forget those stockings! There is a box full this week."

Jennie's mother said this in a wearied way. The little girl was playing in her room, and began to think about helping her.

"Where are they?" she asked.

"In the sitting-room," the mother answered, and thought no more about it. An hour later she went downstairs. There sat Jennie in the large arm-chair by the open window, the basket on the table before her, and her little fingers very busy.

"Mother," she said, looking up with a bright smile, "you had twelve pairs of stockings, and I have done six of them."

Jennie had given up a whole hour's play to help and relieve her mother; but she was a very little girl, and she had made a mistake. She sewed the holes over and over. And as she meant to do her best, the stitches were close and tight. Her mother knew that it would be at least half an hour's work to rip them out, but she would not disappoint Jennie's loving and thoughtful heart by letting her know that she had not fully succeeded. She only said, "Well you're a dear, good, little, girl; and now you may run out and play."

Away went Jennie, very happy in the thought that she had helped and pleased her mother. And she had; for the kindness and love she had shown lightened that mother's care, and were more precious to her heart than gold. Pleasant thoughts kept her company, and made her needle move faster.

All of us, little folks and grown folks, are liable to make mistakes, even when we really try to do right. But the love of Christ is only shadowed forth faintly by that mother's love. He, too, takes the will for the deed; counting whatever is done out of love, as done to Him. He sees that no true effort is lost, but makes it to do good, some time, and in some way, whether we see it or not.

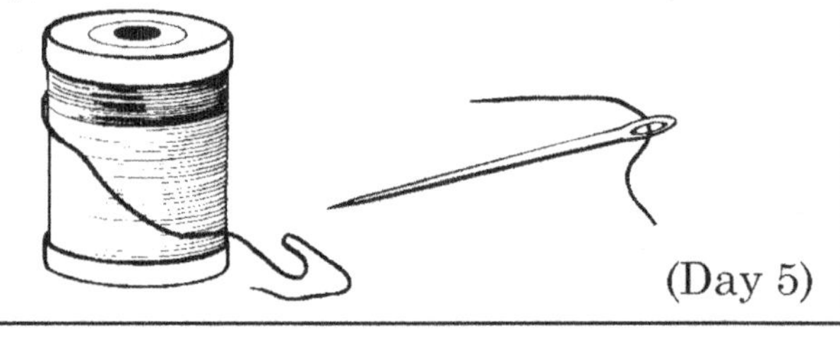

(Day 5)

Waves

Review today's Nature while coloring this picture of the waves.

What is one spiritual lesson for today's Nature Lesson?

(Day 5)

Currents and Waves

What is the difference between a current and a wave?

A Colonial sloop moving
on the waves of the ocean.

(Day 5)

Many Believed

Answer these questions.

1. Why did many believe?

2. Where did Peter tarry?

3. Who did he tarry with?

4. Where was the town located by?

5. Who was Simon a tanner? Read below.

First among the workers in leather is the "tanner" who prepared the leather from the skins of domestic and other animals required for shields, helmets, shoes, girdles, and other articles of leather such as skin-bottles for water, wine, and milk. The tanner is not mentioned in the Old Testament, even though the Israelites depended on his trade for many necessary articles. Possibly it was because the Jews looked upon tanning as an undesirable occupation because dead animals were regarded as unclean and because of its unclean accompaniments such as unpleasant odors and unattractive sights that they looked upon it with much disfavor.

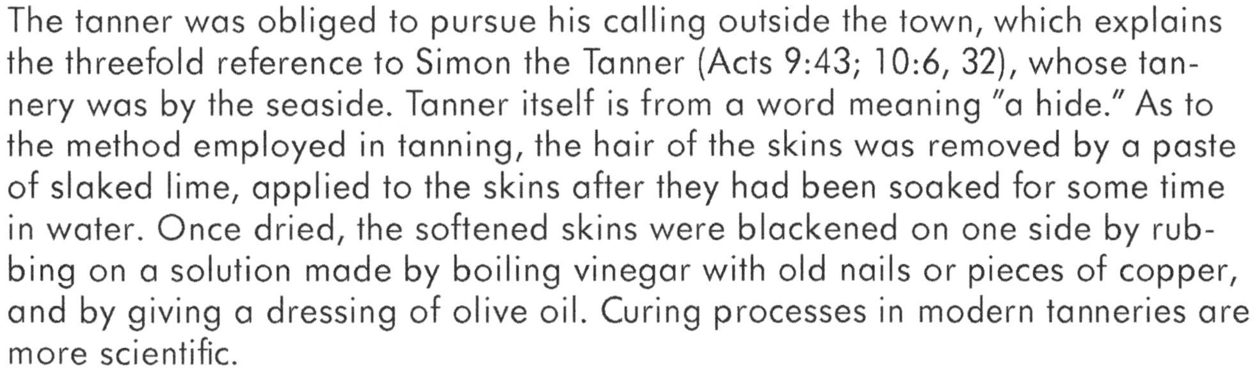

The tanner was obliged to pursue his calling outside the town, which explains the threefold reference to Simon the Tanner (Acts 9:43; 10:6, 32), whose tannery was by the seaside. Tanner itself is from a word meaning "a hide." As to the method employed in tanning, the hair of the skins was removed by a paste of slaked lime, applied to the skins after they had been soaked for some time in water. Once dried, the softened skins were blackened on one side by rubbing on a solution made by boiling vinegar with old nails or pieces of copper, and by giving a dressing of olive oil. Curing processes in modern tanneries are more scientific.

(Day 6)

Tides

"And said, Hitherto shalt thou come, but no further: and here shall thy proud waves be stayed."
Job 38:11

Read this information sheet and fill in the blanks.
Drop a rock to see how gravity works.

The moon's gravity pulls on the earth's oceans and causes tides. When the moon passes above the Earth's oceans, the pull of its gravity makes the water level rise. This is known as high tide. As the earth rotates, high tide travels from east to west. High tide is followed by low tide every six hours. All seashores have two high tides and two low tides every day.

High and Low Tides

A-B = Water Level
A-E = High Tide
E-B = Low Tide

C-D = Water Level
C-E = High Tide
E-D = Low Tide

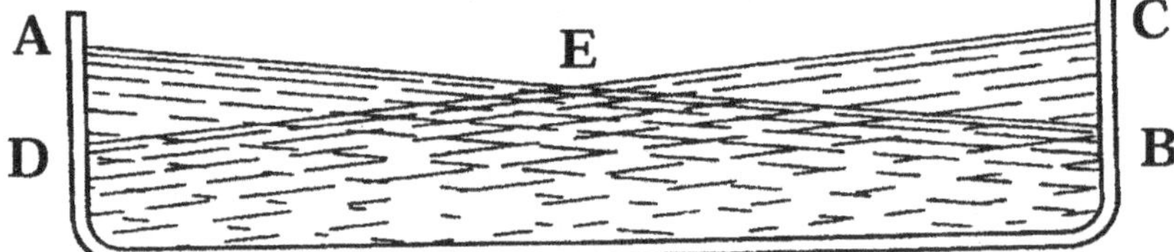

S_ _ O_

R_ _ _ _ _ _ _ _ _ _ _ _ _ _ _

Fill in the blanks telling the spiritual meaning of the sun, moon, and earth. Refer to today's Nature Lesson.

Earth

D_ _ _ _ _ _ _ _ _ _

Moon

S_ _ o_

P_ _ _ _ _ _

(Day 6)

More About Waves

When wind sweeps across the surface of open ocean, the resulting friction generates ripples on the water. Each ripple joins other ripples in rows called swells. Ocean swells, or waves, can travel thousands of miles before they die on a distant shore. Scientists tracked one wave from New Zealand to Alaska! As the swells move toward shore, they pick up speed until they reach shallow coastal water. Then they slow down before breaking against a sandy beach or rocky cliff. When a wave finally reaches the shoreline, it may have only enough strength left to stir up the sandy bottom, or it may have so much power that its spray can break the windows of a lighthouse.

Even though scientists can explain, mathematically, the form of waves, they cannot accurately predict when a really strong wave will hit. Wave watchers, especially surfers, try to guess which wave will be "the big one. "They have contrived superstitious formulas, such as every seventh wave or every ninth wave—but waves just are not predictable. Sometimes huge "killer waves" appear from a relatively calm sea and send unsuspecting swimmers to their deaths against the rocks. Along the coasts of Washington, Oregon, and northern California three or four such deaths will take place each year.

A tsunami (pronounced su-NAH-mee) is the strongest and most dangerous of the killer waves to strike the coast. Often mistakenly called "tidal waves," they have nothing to do with the tides. Whereas the gravitational pulls of the moon and sun control the tides, undersea earthquakes and landslides produce tsunamis, and the waves may travel long distances at speeds of up to 500 miles per hour.

But the amount of death and destruction caused by waves is slight compared to the massive amount of useful power that they generate. Ocean life depends on the movement of waves to provide shellfish with new supplies of microscopic plants and animals and with fresh oxygen.

Just as the largest wave begins as a small ripple, the righteousness of Jesus starts small in our lives and grows to a mighty surge of life-giving power, just as small **thoughtful** deeds.* Read Psalm 89:9 and Psalm 93:4.

(Day 6)

*Adapted from *Nature Quest*

"Mighty Waves"
Ocean swells, or waves, can travel thousands of miles before they die on a distant shore.
Find and read a story about Joseph Bates a sea captain in the 1800 hundreds.
(Day 6)

13 – Peter's Vision

Bible – Acts 10

Song – "Go Preach My Gospel"

Nature – Land at the Bottom of the Sea

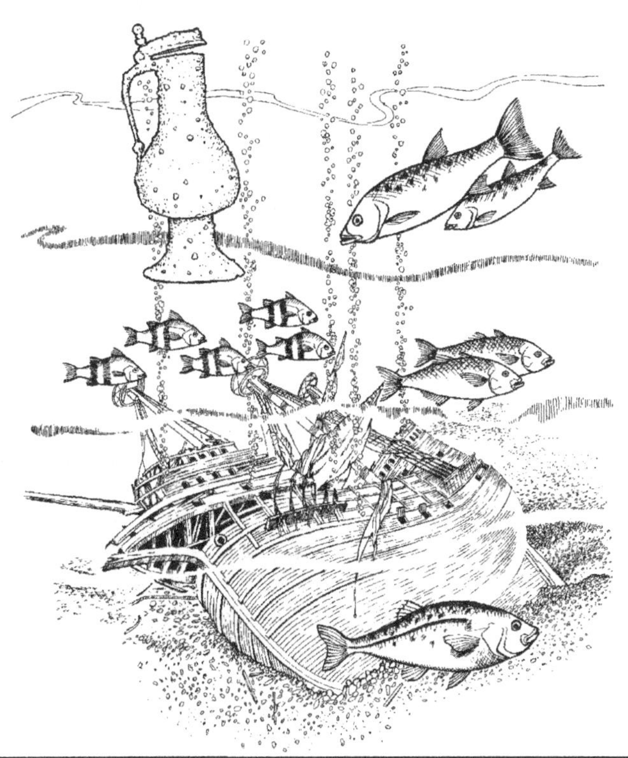

Character Quality

Respectfulness vs Contempt
Respectfulness is the regard and honor in which one holds the distinguished worth or substantial good qualities of others.

Memory Verse

"Then Peter opened his mouth, and said, Of a truth I perceive that God is no respecter of persons."
Acts 10:34

Land at the Bottom of the Sea

**Today, more study is being done on life
and the treasures under the sea.
God wants His people to abandon prejudices,
respect all men, and explore the sea of people of the world
for hidden treasures there.**

**Place sequins, flat gems, pieces of foil, and so forth
by, below, and in the treasure chest
for each day this week you study your lesson,
and say your memory verse.**

Cornelius

Fill in the words to answer the clues.
Then fill in the message below by determining which letter goes with each number.
Not all letters will be in the clues.
If you get stuck see Psalm 25:12.

Clues

1. Cornelius lived in _ _ _ _ _ _ _ _ .
15 14 16 23 14 9 16 14

2. He was a _ _ _ _ _ _ _ _ _ .
15 16 7 10 24 9 18 21 7

3. Cornelius _ _ _ _ _ _ _ _ _ .
3 16 14 9 16 2 17 21 2

4. He gave _ _ _ _ and _ _ _ _ _ _ .
14 6 20 23 8 9 14 26 16 2

Roman Centurion
Roman High Officer

"_ _ _ _ _ _ _ _ _ _ _ _ _ _ _
25 4 14 10 20 14 7 18 23 4 16 10 4 14 10

_ _ _ _ _ _ _ _ _ _ _ _ _ _? _ _ _
3 16 14 9 16 10 4 10 4 16 6 21 9 2 4 18 20

_ _ _ _ _ _ _ _ _ _ _ _ _ _ _ _ _ _
23 4 14 6 6 4 16 10 16 14 15 4 18 7 10 4 16

_ _ _ _ _ _ _ _ _ _ _ _ _ _
25 14 26 10 4 14 10 4 16 23 4 14 6 6

_ _ _ _ _ _ _."
15 4 21 21 23 16

(Day 1)

The Bottom of the Sea

"A devout man, and one that feared God with all his house, which gave much alms to the people, and prayed to God alway."
Acts 10:2

Use these words to point at in the diagram, then color the picture below. (mountains, shelf, plains, slope, mountains & peaks, rise, and valleys)

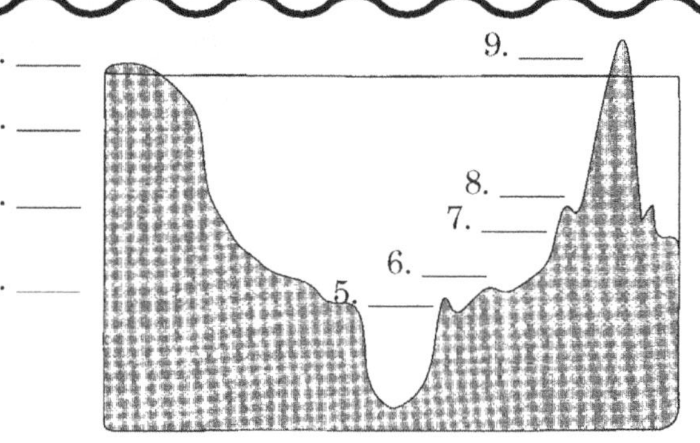

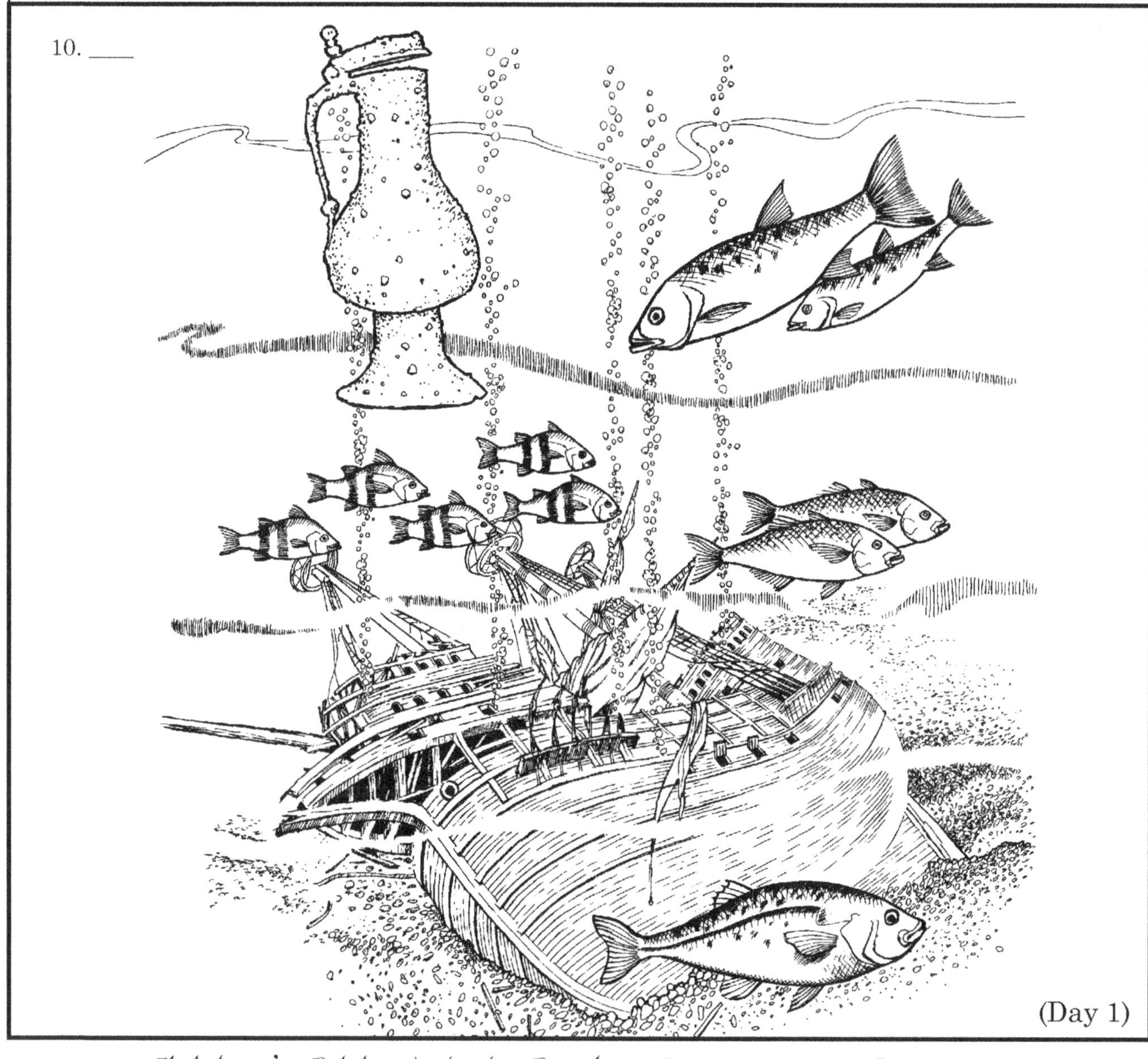

(Day 1)

The Angel's Message

Color and read.

"He [Cornelius] saw in a vision...
an angel of God coming in to him,
and saying unto him, Cornelius.

How many people were sent to Peter from Cornelius?

"And when he looked on him,
he was afraid, and said,
What is it, Lord?
And he said unto him,
Thy prayers and thine alms
are come up for a memorial
before God.

"And now send men to Joppa,
and call for one Simon,
whose surname is Peter."
"...He shall tell thee
what thou oughtest to do."

Acts 10:3-6

Roman man resting at home.

(Day 2)

The Continental Slope and Rise

Read and color.

Remember, the sea bed that borders the continents consists of:

The mountains under the sea look familiar to those we see around us.

1. The continental shelf

2. The continental slope

3. The continental rise.

Mountains

Grand Canyon

The continental shelf slopes gently away from dry land. The slope forms the sides of the continents. In most places there are underwater canyons deeper than the Grand Canyon. The messages to Cornelius would have deep meaning to the early church, deeper than they could imagine.

(Day 2)

A Strange Story

"Call upon me," says God, *"in the day of trouble, and I will deliver thee, and thou shalt glorify me."* This is one of those cheering promises which have been the comfort and safety of God's people in every age. While it gives a condition, it pledges a sure and blessed result, telling us that if in danger, or perplexity, or trouble, we call upon God, He will answer, deliver and save.

Multitudes have tested the promise, and in their own experience have found it to be true. In the hour of perplexity or danger many a child of God has called on Him, when there was no other resource, and has found Him faithful to His promise to deliver, as is shown in the following narrative, which is literally true:

In a large and lone house in the south of England lived a lady of piety and wealth, with only maidservants in the dwelling itself, her menservants being in cottages at a distance from the house. It was her custom to go through the house with one of her servants every evening to see that the windows and doors were properly secured; and one night, after seeing that all was safe, she retired to her room, when, as she entered it, she saw distinctly a man under the bed. What could she do? Her servants were in a distant part of the house, where they could not hear if she cried for help, and even if with her, they were no match for a desperate housebreaker. What, then, did she do? Quietly closing and locking the door, as she was always in the habit of doing, she leisurely brushed her hair, put on her dressing gown, and then, taking her Bible, sat down to read. She read aloud, though in a low and serious tone, choosing a chapter which had special reference to God's watchful care over those who trust Him, whether by day or by night. When it was ended, she knelt and prayed aloud, commending herself and servants to the divine protection, pleading their utter helplessness and their dependence on God to preserve them from danger, and praying for the poor, the sinful, and the tempted, that they might be kept from evil and led to put their trust in God as their Father and Friend. Then, arising from her knees and putting out the candle, she laid herself down in bed, though of course she did not sleep. After a few moments the man came out from his concealment and, standing by her bedside, begged her not to be alarmed.

(Day 2)

"I came here," he said respectfully, "to rob you; but after the words you have read and the prayer you have uttered, no power on earth could induce me to harm you or to touch a thing in your dwelling. But, you must remain perfectly quiet and not make a sound to alarm your servants or to interfere with me. I will give a signal to my companions which will lead them to go away, and you may sleep in peace, for no one shall harm you or disturb the smallest thing in your house." He then went to the window and gave a low whistle, and coming back to the lady's side said: "Now, I am going. Your prayer will be answered and no disaster will befall you."

He left the room and soon, all was quiet; and the lady at last fell asleep, calm in the exercise of her faith and trust in God, her soul filled with thankfulness for His protecting goodness. The man proved true to his word. In the morning it was found that not a thing in the house had been disturbed. And the lady more than once earnestly prayed that the man might be led to forsake his evil course and put his trust in that Saviour who came to seek and save the lost, and who, even on the cross, could accept and save the thief who was penitent.

The deliverance of the lady may seem wonderful, and the story almost too strange for belief. But, sometime after the occurrence, a letter was received by the one who related it, fully corroborating the statement, and adding some facts that enhance both the wonder and the mercy of the escape. The letter says: "In the first place, the robber told her that if she had given the slightest alarm or token of resistance, he was fully determined to murder her, so that it was providential that she took the course she did. Then, before he went away, he said: 'I never heard such words before, and I must have the book out of which you read;' and he carried off her Bible, willingly enough given, you may be sure."

This happened years ago, and only lately did the lady hear any more of the robber. She was attending a religious meeting in Yorkshire, where, after several noted clergymen and others had spoken, a man arose, saying that he was employed as a colporteurs, and told the story of the midnight adventure as a testimony to the wonderful power of the Word of God, concluding with, "I was that man!" The lady rose from her seat in the hall and said, quietly: "It is all true; I was the lady!" and sat down again.

If we had more faith in God's Word and more full and childlike reliance on His promises and his providence, would we not far more frequently find, in our own experience, that He never fails His people in the hour of their need?

Who are invited by God to call upon Him in the day of trouble? Why are you not invited? Why would it be wrong for you to call upon God in your day of trouble? Because you do not repent of your offences against him. Repent now, and then you will have a right to ask Him for help.

The Lord's Prayer

Our Heavenly Father, hear our prayer:
Thy name be hallowed everywhere;
Thy kingdom come; Thy perfect will
In earth, as Heaven, let all fulfill.
Give this day's bread that we may live;
Forgive our sins as we forgive.
Help us temptation to withstand;
From evil shield us by Thy hand.
Now, and forever, unto Thee,
Thy kingdom, power, and glory be.

—*Unknown*

(Day 2)

Peter Praying

**"On the morrow, as they went on their journey,
and drew nigh unto the city,
Peter went up upon the housetop to pray about the sixth hour."**
Acts 10:9

**Find this list of words in the Word Find
that tell how Peter was being led to Cornelius.**

Word List

ANGEL, BEASTS, EAT, FOWLS, HOUSETOP, HUNGRY,
KILL, JOPPA, PETER, SERVANTS, SIMON, TANNER,
TRANCE, THRICE, UNCLEAN, VISION

J	L	I	H	E	C	N	A	R	T
S	L	W	O	F	T	R	I	C	E
P	E	H	U	N	G	R	Y	S	G
K	T	B	S	E	R	A	N	T	L
A	N	G	E	L	L	I	K	N	R
I	O	J	T	A	E	B	E	A	E
N	M	S	O	T	S	E	A	V	N
O	I	F	P	P	E	T	E	R	N
I	S	O	W	L	P	H	S	E	A
S	T	H	R	I	C	A	O	S	T
I	U	S	N	A	E	L	C	N	U
V	T	O	P	E	C	I	R	H	T

What did this vision mean?

**"And the voice spake
unto him again the second time,
What God hath cleansed,
that call not thou common."**

Acts 10:15

(Day 3)

Peter's Vision
Color
this picture
of Peter's
Vision.
(Day 3)

Peaks, Valleys, and Plains

Unscramble these words that describe the shape of the ocean floor.

1. ___ ___ ___ ___ ___

SABNI

2. ___ ___ ___ ___ ___

KASEP

3. ___ ___ ___ ___ ___ ___ ___

LAYVELS

4. ___ ___ ___ ___ ___ ___

NISPAL

5. ___ ___ ___ ___ ___ ___ ___ ___ ___

TONMUSINA

6. ___ ___ ___ ___ ___ ___

DESGIR

The bottom of the ocean
has wide variety and difference in terrain.
God did not want any difference between Jews or Greeks,
but all were to be **respected**.

(Day 3)

Islands

Islands are the peaks of mountains under the ocean.

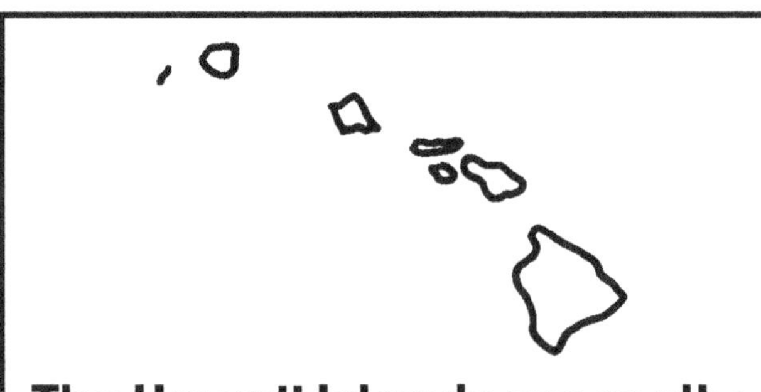

The Hawaii Islands are really just the top of mountains.

(Day 3)

In Cornelius' House

Answer these questions.

1. How did Peter view the command to go to a Roman Soldier's house? How many came to Peter?

2. Who had sent the men to Peter?

3. Who went with Peter? How many were there with him?

4. What did the Centurion do when he met Peter?

5. Who else was there to listen to Peter preach?

6. What was the first thing Peter shared with these people?

7. What does Peter say in Acts 10:34?

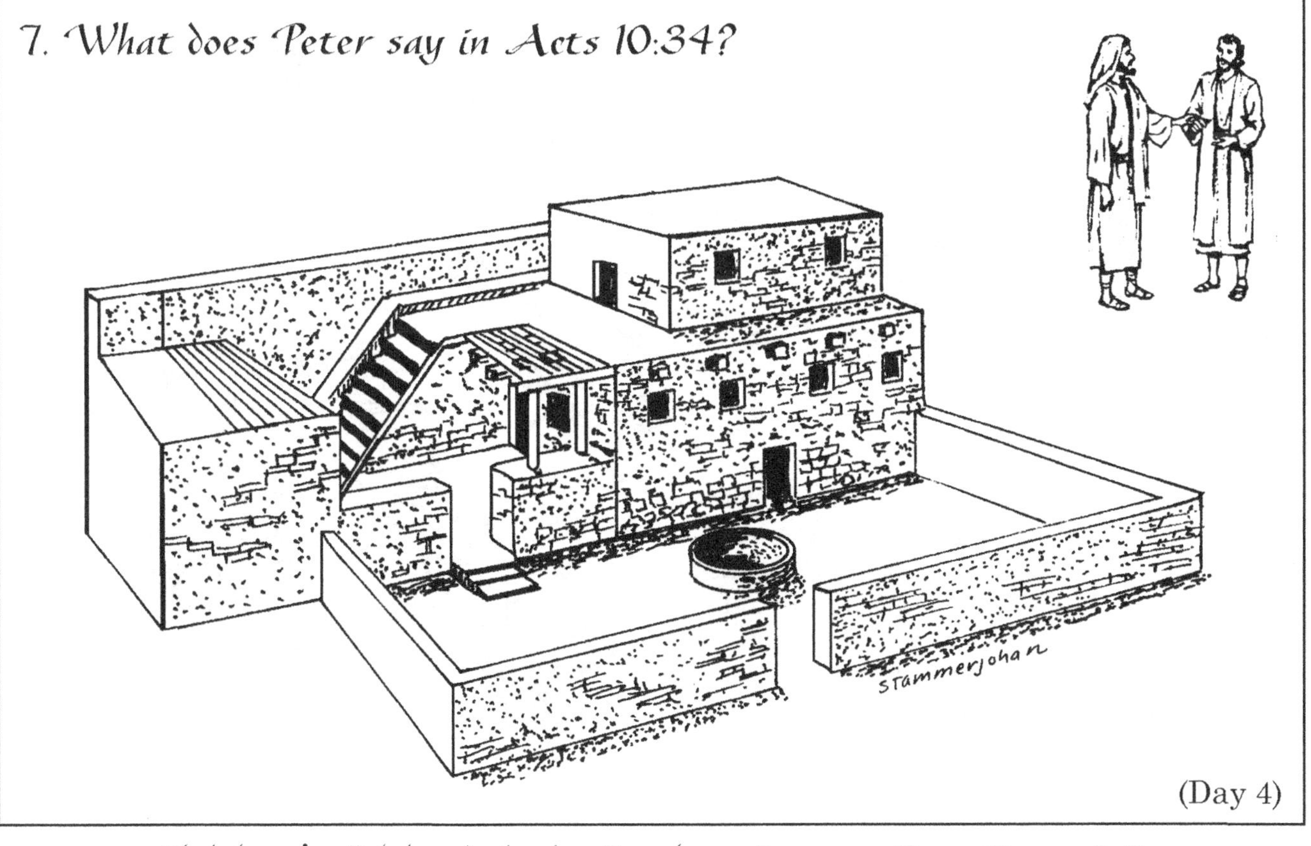

(Day 4)

The Deep Sea

Review today's Nature Lesson and color this picture.

The Flashlight Fish or lantern-eye fish is a strange black foot-long dweller of the waters of the Indo-Pacific.

Review the Deep-Sea Angler. See page 240 of this book.

Its name comes from an unusual organ beneath its eye that glows with a brilliant cream-colored light, flashing at 5-10 second intervals as it rotates up and down. The light is actually produced by a colony of luminous bacteria that live in the fluid within the organ; since the fish cannot turn them off and on, it must rotate the organ to produce the flashing light. It is not known the purpose of the "flashlight."

(Day 4)

Jack's Story

"In as much as ye have done it unto the least of these, ye have done it unto me" (Matthew 15:40).

He had been brought up in the streets; he had been a criminal; he had been in prison; and as his sentence expired and he was going out, the chaplain said; "Jack, you're very young yet, and now is your chance. Try to be an honest man and pray for help. I wish I knew if you will pray."

"You'd make me, if anyone could, but, I am not sure of the use of it yet; I wish I was."

"He just looked at me sorrowful, for I hadn't said even that much before, and I went off."

"And I did mean to keep straight. I'd had enough of prison; but when I went around asking for work, not a soul would have me. A jail-bird!—well; they thought not. I grew angry again, and yet I wouldn't take to the river, for, somehow, I'd lost my courage. Then, I met an old pal, and he took me around to Micky's saloon. The bar-keeper had just been stuck in a fight. It had been a profitable one for Micky, and maybe, he thought, beginning there, I'd go back to the river once more. And there I was three years, and fights night after night of the year. I could stop them when no one else could, for I was always sober."

" 'Why don't you drink?' they'd say; and I'd tell them I did not want to. But I hated it worse and worse. I would have quit the job in a minute if there'd been one to take me by the hand and say, 'Here's honest work.' I looked at ads when I went out, to see if there was one that could be spoken to. And at last I made up my mind for another try. I'd saved some money and could live a while, and one night I just left when Micky paid me. 'Get another man,' I said; 'I'm done,' and I walked out, with him shouting after me."

"Then, I waited three months. I answered advertisements and I put them in. I went here and I went there, and always it was the same story, for I answered everyone square. And at last I was sick of it all; I had nothing to live for. 'I'm tired of living with rascals,' I said, 'and good folks are too good to have anything to do with me. I've had

(Day 4)

all I want. If work don't come in a week I'll get out of this the easiest way.' "

"It didn't come. My money was gone; I'd gone hungry two days; I'd been on half rations before that, till my strength was all gone; I'd pawned my clothes till I wasn't decent. Then, I hadn't a cent even for a place on the floor in a lodging-house, and I sat in the City Hall Park long as they would let me. Then, I got up and walked down Beckman street to the river—slow, for I was too far gone to move fast. But, as I got nearer something seemed to pull me on. I began to run. 'It's the end of all trouble,' I said, and I went across like a shot and down the docks. It was bright moonlight, and I had sense to jump for a dark place, where the light was cut off, and that's all I remember. I must have hit my head against a boat, for when they took me out it was for dead. Two of my old pals hauled me out, and worked there on the dock to bring me to, till the ambulance come and took me to Bellevue."

"I wouldn't have lived, but I didn't know enough not to, being in a fever a month. Then, I come out of it dazed, and it wasn't till I'd been there six weeks that I got my senses fairly and knew I was alive after all."

" 'I'll do it better next time,' I said, being bound to get out of it still; but that night a man in the bed next me began to talk and asked about it. I told him the whole. When I got through, he said, 'I don't know but one man in New York that'll know just what to do, and that's McAuley, of Water street. You go there soon's you can stir and tell him.' "

"I laughed. 'I'm done telling,' I said."

" 'Try him,' he says; and he was that urgent that I promised; I would."

"I went out, trembling and sick, and without a spot to lay my head; and right there I stood by the river and thought it would come easier this time. But, I'd never go back on my word, and so I started down, crawling along, and didn't get there till meeting had begun. I didn't know what sort of a place it was."

"It was new, but the room clean and decent, and just a little sign out, 'Helping Hand for Men.' I sat and listened and wondered till it was over, and then, I tried to go, but first I knew I tumbled in a dead faint and was being taken upstairs.

They made me a bed next to their own room. 'You'd better not,' I said. 'I'm a jailbird and a rascal, and nobody alive wants to have anything to do with me.' "

" 'You be quiet,' says Jerry. 'I'm a jailbird myself, but the Lord Jesus has forgiven me and made me happy, and he'll do the same by you.' "

"They kept me there a week, and you'd think I was their own, the way they treated me. But I stuck it out; 'When I see a man that's always been **respectable** come to me and give me work, and say he's not afraid or ashamed to, then maybe I'll believe in your Jesus Christ you talk about; but how am I going to without it?' "

"And that very night it came. You know him well–the gentleman that looks as if the wind had never blown rough on him, and yet with an eye that can't be fooled."

" 'You don't need to tell me a word,' he says; 'I believe you are honest, and you can begin tomorrow if you're strong enough. It's light work, and it shall be made easier at first.' "

"I looked at him, and it seemed to me something that had frozen me all up inside melted that minute. I burst out crying and couldn't stop. And then, first thing I knew, he was down on his knees praying for me. 'Dear Lord,' he said, 'he is thy child, he has always been thy child. Make him know it tonight; make him know that thy love has always followed him and will hold him up, so that his feet will never slip again.' "

"These words stayed by me. I couldn't speak, and he went away. He knew what he'd done."

"That's all. Some of the men shake their heads; they say it wasn't regular conversion. All I know is, the sense of God come into me then, and it's never left me. It keeps me on the watch for every soul in trouble. I'm down on the docks on nights. I know the signs, and now and then I can help one that' not to far gone. I'm going myself, you see. There isn't much left of me but a cough and some bones, but I shall be helping men to the last. God is that good to me that I'll go quick when I do go; but, quick or slow, I bless Him every hour of the day for the old mission and my chance."

Have respect for those that are in trouble, and help them.

Respectfulness

Judge not another—keep in mind
The golden rule for all mankind;
Whenever tempted to expose
Another's follies, think of those
That lurk within; the wish repress
Your scorn of others to express
Whenever to ridicule inclined,
Ah! think how sensitive your mind
Perhaps that very moment, too,
Someone may be displeasing you.
Ah! look within, thou need not roam,
For **respectfulness** begins at home.

—*Unknown*

(Day 4)

Peter and Cornelius

Choose from these Bible verses (6-8 or more) to mark your Bible in a chain reference fashion.

Deuteronomy 10:17

Deuteronomy 16:19

II Chronicles 19:7

Job 34:19

Psalm 82:1-2

Matthew 22:16
(Mark 12:14, Luke 20:21)

Romans 2:10-11

Galatians 2:6

Ephesians 6:9

Colossians 3:11, 25

James 2:4, 9

I Peter 1:17

"Then Peter opened his mouth, and said, Of a truth I perceive that God is no respecter of persons."
Acts 10:34

(Day 5)

Exploring

Which fishes below would you say are unusual?
Color them black, brown, or dark purple.
Color the other fish bright colors.
Review today's Nature Lesson.

The world
is spiritually blind
and needs
the "Light of Life."

(Day 5)

Scuba Diver

The scuba system incorporates a tank of compressed air
worn by the diver, with rubber hoses that carry air from the tank to a
mouthpiece held in the diver's mouth.
Study done by scuba divers help expand our information
about the interesting life in the ocean.
Peter's sermon was to expand the knowledge
of Cornelius, his household, and friends.

Color this picture.

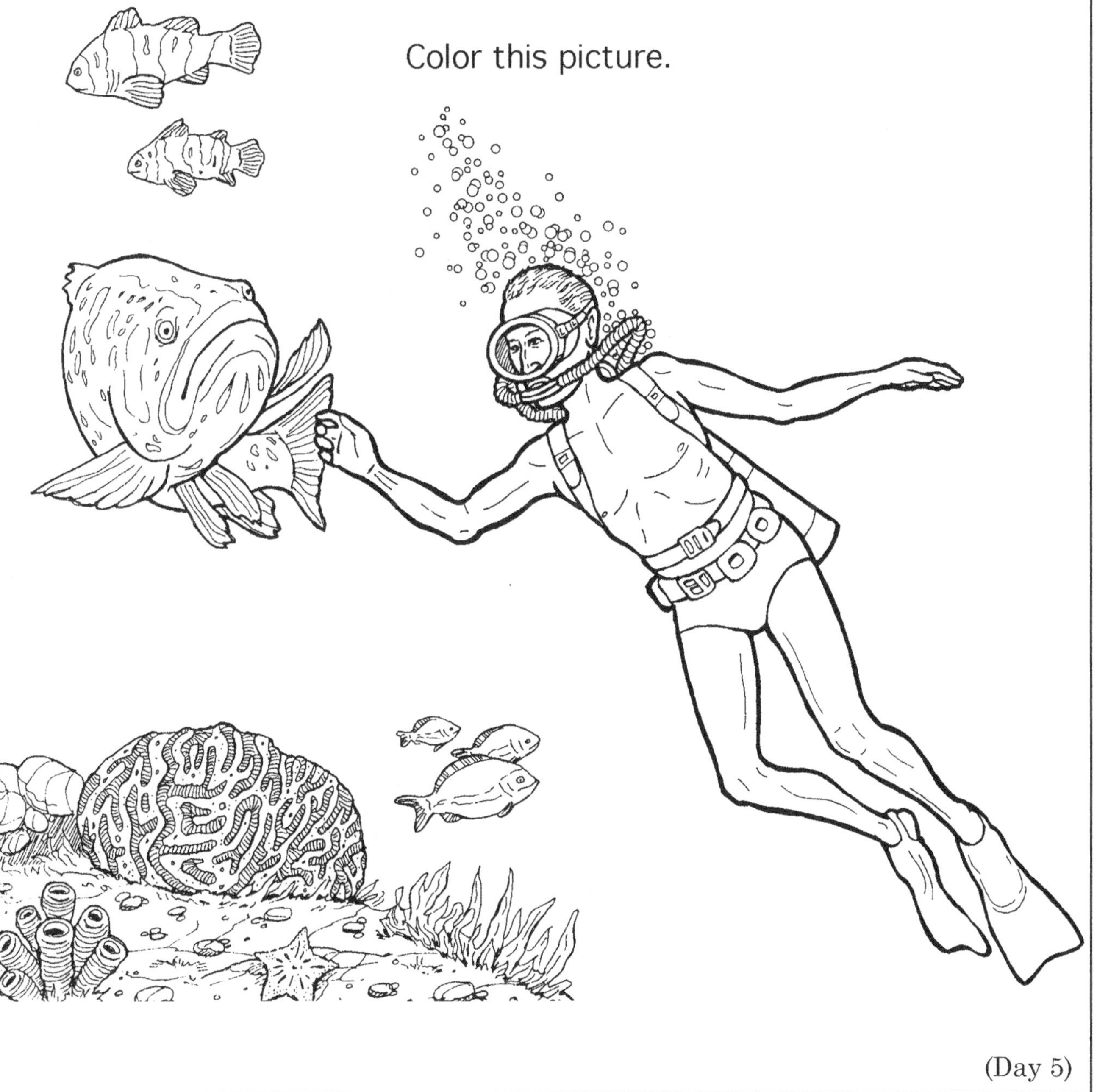

(Day 5)

"Hard Hat" Divers

This equipment is designed to protect the diver from the crushing water pressure encountered while working at depths of 500 to 3,000 feet.

A picture to color.

circa 1950

circa 1990

(Day 5)

Submersible "Nautile"

One of the current class of underwater research vessels
is the bright yellow submersible, Nautile,
one of the deep-diving submersibles used to explore the ocean floor.

A picture to color.

The Nautile's titanium pressure sphere can carry three passengers:
a pilot, a co-pilot, and an observer—usually a marine scientist
or underwater archaeologist.
The submersible has an air supply sufficient
for eight hours of deep-sea exploration.

Think of a parallel to the Bible Lesson for this week.

(Day 5)

Gulper

A true unusual eel that lives in the cold waters 5,000–9,000 feet deep throughout the world. It is 2 feet long. Because it is difficult to find food at this depths, the gulper has a huge mouth, with needle-sharp teeth, which can swallow fish larger than itself.

Though no one has ever seen a gulper hunting, it is thought that it waits suspended in the water, perhaps luring its prey with the luminous red tip of its tail. Its victims may simply swim into its maw (mouth) without realizing it, or the gulper may entwine its long tail around its meal before opening its mouth at all four corners and swallowing it down.

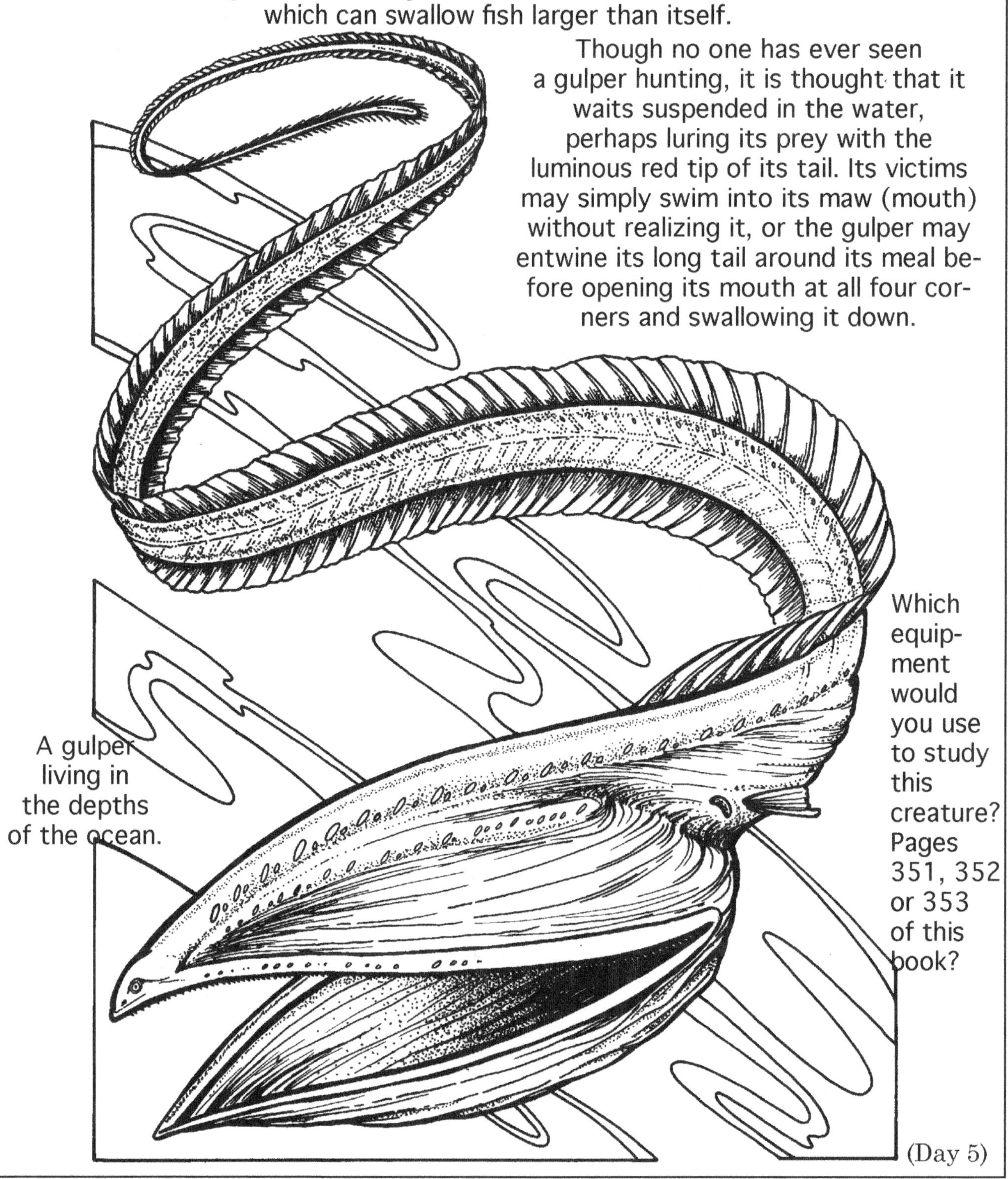

A gulper living in the depths of the ocean.

Which equipment would you use to study this creature? Pages 351, 352 or 353 of this book?

(Day 5)

The Gentiles

Fill in the missing words above.

"While Peter yet _ _ _ _ _ _ these _ _ _ _ _ _.

the _ _ _ _   _ _ _ _ _ _   _ _ _ _ _ on _ _ _

them which _ _ _ _ _ _ the _ _ _ _ _."

Acts 10:44

"Can any _ _ _   _ _ _ _ _ _ _ _   _ _ _ _ _ _ _,

that these should not be _ _ _ _ _ _ _ _ _ _,

which have _ _ _ _ _ _ _ _ _ _ _ the

_ _ _ _ _   _ _ _ _ _ _ _ as well as we?

"And he commanded them to be _ _ _ _ _ _ _ _ _ _

in the _ _ _ _ _ of the _ _ _ _ _.

Then prayed they him
to tarry certain days."

Acts 10:47-48

(Day 6)

Divers in the Sea

Draw a diver with what he needs to go to the depths of the sea. Color the picture.

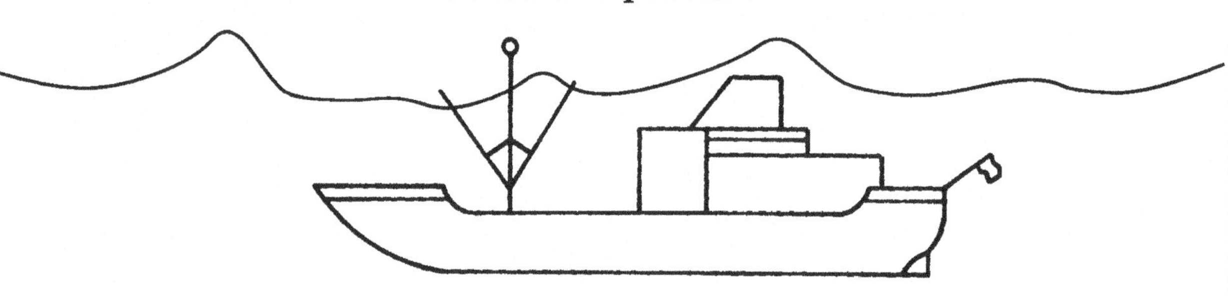

To find the treasures in the world we need the:

H __ __ __   __ __ __ __ __ __ __

H __ __ __   __ __ __ __ __ __

(Day 6)

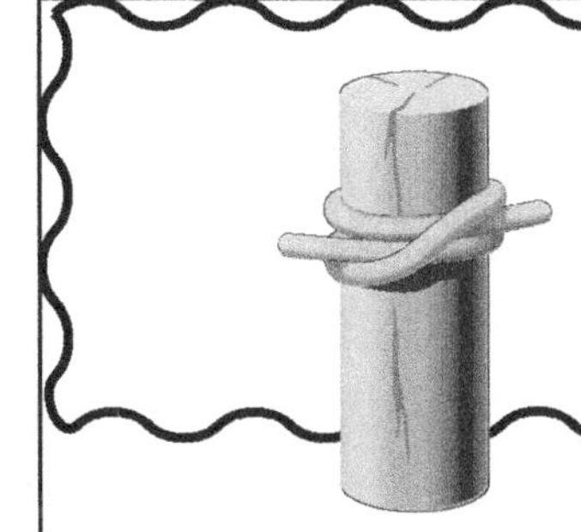

Sea Stories

By Joseph Bates

Sailing

When I was a youth I had a strong desire to be a sailor. After repeated entreaties with my parents, they at last complied with my wishes. A new ship, lying at the wharf near my father's, was about to sail and the Captain agreed with my father to take me with him for his cabin-boy.

We sailed from Fairhaven, Massachusetts, to take our cargo on board at New York City for London, England. On our passage to N.Y. City we sailed by the way of Long Island Sound. In this route, several miles from the city is a very narrow and dangerous passage bounded with rocks on the right, and a bound shore on the left, called "Hurl Gate." What makes it so dangerous is the great rush of water that passes through this narrow channel. As the tide ebbs and flows each way, it rushes with such impulsiveness that few dare venture to sail through against it without a strong steady wind in their favor. For want of watchfulness and care, many vessels have been whisked from their course by this rushing foam and hurled against the rocks, wrecked and lost in a few moments of time. Sailors call it "Hell Gate."

As our gallant ship was bringing us in sight of the dreadful place, the pilot took the helm and requested the captain and officers to call all hands on deck. He then stationed us in various parts of the ship for the purpose of managing the sails in case of an emergency, according to his judgment. He then requested us to remain silent while passing this dangerous gate-way, that we might the better understand his orders. In this way every man and boy at their post, with their eyes silently fixed on the pilot waiting his orders, our good ship winged her way through the hurling foam and passed on safely to her anchorage before the city.

This little incident taught me the necessity of knowing my position at all times, that I may act promptly and decidedly under all circumstances. I thought the foregoing fact might in some way illustrate the present position of the children and youth that have and are becoming interested in the doctrines

(Day 6)

of the Bible. We see that those who take hold of these divine truths are taking the most important position that was ever occupied by mortal man. Your zeal to do what you can and your love and consideration in this blessed cause of God is all called for now. Therefore, be earnest in prayer and ever at your post and on your watch.

Mark, the thorough knowledge and experience of our pilot as he guided our good ship through the hurling dangerous gateway. But we see how much depended on not only every man's having a special appointed station in the ship, but also the knowledge of his duty in his station that no confusion might arise when the pilot's orders were given, even to the cabin boy. So is the end of the gospel dispensation you have come to the "*perilous times*" and the strait and narrow gateway (Matthew 7:14; Luke 13:24) that leads to the glorious city of our God. Your Commander and Pilot of the glorious gospel ship is thoroughly qualified and competent to put her through this narrow way; and He tells us plainly if we fail in getting through this narrow way, we shall be found passing through the broad way and wide gate that leads to destruction (Matthew 7:13), and consequently will never reach the heavenly City.

Then, as so much depends on your occupying the place marked out by one of the leading officers of the gospel ship (I Corinthians 12; Ephesians 4:4-7; 5:29, 27), strive earnestly dear children, stand in your place, and be ready at your post, and have your eye fixed on the Helmsman–hearken to His voice, promptly obey, and He will carry you safely through the narrow way.

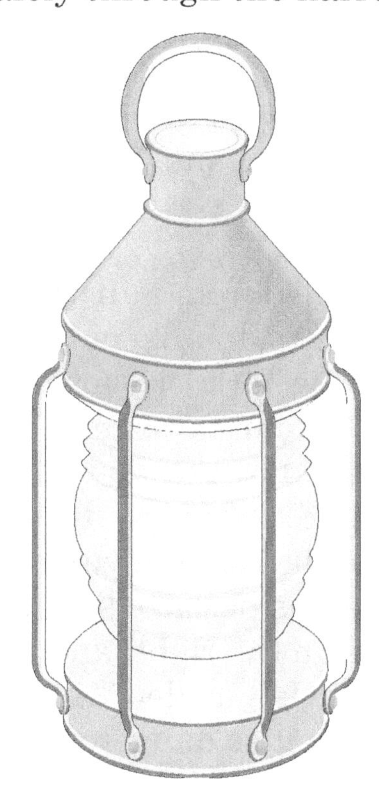

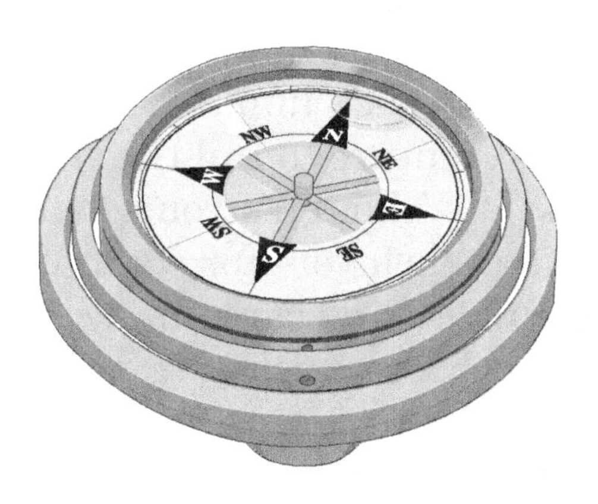

The Cabin Boy and The Shark

My first European voyage from New York to London and back, opened new scenes before me, not uncommon to a seafaring life.

One circumstance occurred on our homeward voyage some eighteen days after departing from Land's End, England, which I will here relate.

In the Sunday morning, a large shark was following us. A large piece of meat was fastened to a rope and thrown over the stern to tempt him to come up a little nearer, that we might fasten to him with a barbed iron made for such purposes; but no inducement of ours seemed to affect him. He maintained his position where he could grasp whatever fell from either side of the ship. A shark is a voracious sea-fish.

On such occasions the old stories about sharks are revived. How they swallow them at two mouthfuls. They hear so much about them that they attribute more to their wisdom than what really belongs to them. It is said that sharks have followed vessels on the ocean for many days when there were any sick on board, that they may satiate their voracious appetites on the dead bodies that are cast into the sea. Sailors brave and fearless men; they dare meet their fellows in almost any conflict, and brave the raging storms of the sea; but the idea of being swallowed alive, or even when dead by these voracious creatures, often causes their stout hearts to tremble. Still they are often credulous and superstitious.

Towards the evening, when we had ceased our fruitless labors to draw the shark away from his determined position astern of the ship, I ascended to the main -top-gallant masthead to ascertain if there was any vessel in sight, or anything to be seen but sky and water. On my way down, having reached about fifty feet from the deck, and sixty from the water, I missed reaching the place which I designed grasping with my hand, and fell backwards, striking a rope in my fall which prevented my being dashed upon the deck, but it whirled me into the sea. As I came up on the top of the waves, struggling and panting for breath, I saw at a glance the ship–my only hope–was passing onward beyond my reach. With the encumbrance of my thick heavy clothing, I exerted all my strength to follow. I saw the captain, officers, and crew

(Day 6)

had rushed towards the ship's stern. The first officer hurled a coil of rope with all his strength, the end of which I caught with my hand. He cried out, "Hold on!" I did so until they hauled me through the sea to the ship, and set my feet upon the deck.

To the question of if I was hurt, I answered, "No."

Said another, "Where is the shark?" I began to tremble even as they had done, while they were in anxious suspense fearing he would grasp me every moment. The thought of the shark had never entered my mind while I was in the water. I then crossed over to the other side of the ship, and behold he was quietly gliding his way along with us, not far from the side of the vessel, seemingly unconscious of our gaze. And we did not disturb him in any way. For sailors and passengers were all so glad that the cabin boy was rescued, not only from a watery grave but from his ferocious jaws, that they had no disposition to trouble him. He was soon missing and we saw him no more. But the wonder to all was, how he came to change his position to a place where he could neither see nor hear what was transpiring on the other side and stern of the ship. Surely Noah's and Daniel's God was there! The very same God that so recently commissioned the Advent Angel (Revelation 10) to proclaim to all on land and sea that Jesus the Messiah is coming. A second, and then a third following them, saying, "*Here are they that keep the Commandments of God, and the faith of Jesus.*"

Dear children, if you have a desire to join this highly honored, home-bound company, and be forever saved in the kingdom of God, lay fast hold of the rope, and hold on!

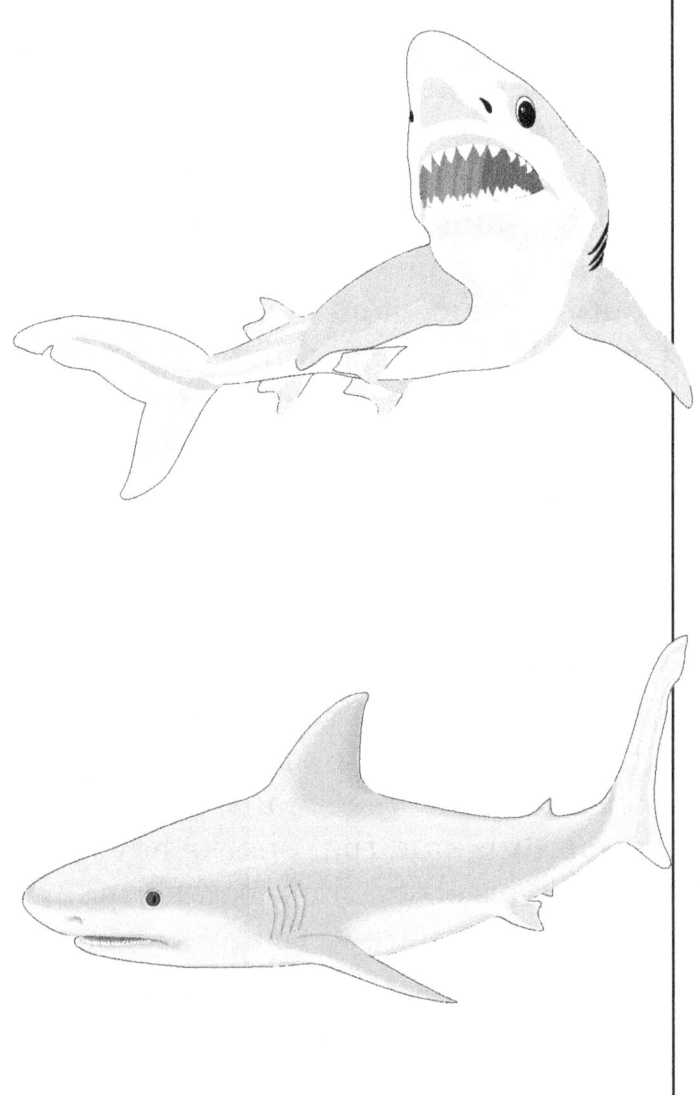

Breaking the Cable, Captured, and Condemned

After repairing damages to our ship in Ireland, we sailed again on our Russian voyage, and in a few days we fell in with and joined an English convoy of two or three hundred merchant vessels bound into the Baltic Sea, convoyed by British ships of war to protect them from their enemies. On reaching a difficult place called the "Mooner Passage" a violent gale overtook us which in spite of our efforts was driving us onto a dismal, shelterless shore.

With the increasing fury of the gale and darkness of the night, our condition became more and more alarming until finally our Commodore hoisted the "lighted lantern," a signal for all the fleet to anchor without delay. The long wished for morning at length came which revealed to us our alarming position. All that were provided with cables were contending with the boisterous seas driven against us by the furious gale. It seemed almost a miracle to us that our cables and anchors still held. While watching one after another as they broke their cables and were drifting toward the rocks to be dashed in pieces, our own cable broke! With all haste we crowded what sail we dared onto the ship, and she, being a fast sailor, we found by the next day that we had gained some distance in the meanwhile. Here a council was called which decided that we should make sail from the convoy and take a lone chance through the sound, by the coast of Denmark.

Not many hours from this, while we were congratulating ourselves respecting our narrow escape from shipwreck, and out of reach of the Commodore's guns, two suspicious looking vessels were endeavoring to cut us off from the shore. Their cannon balls soon began to fall around us, and it became advisable for us to stop and let them come aboard. They proved to be two Danish privateers, who captured and took us to Copenhagen, where ship and cargo were finally condemned, in accordance with Bonaparte's decrees, because of our connections with the English.

In the course of a few weeks we were all called to the courthouse to give testimony respecting our voyage. Previous to this, our supercargo and part owner had promised us a handsome reward if we would

(Day 6)

testify that our voyage was direct from New York to Copenhagen, and that we had no connections with the English. To this proposition we were not all agreed. We were finally examined separately, my turn coming first. I suppose they first called me into court because I was the only youth among the sailors. One of the three judges asked me in English if I understood the nature of an oath. After answering in the affirmative, he bid me look at a box near by , (about 15 inches long and 8 high), and said, "That box contains a machine to cut off the two forefingers and thumb of everyone who swears falsely here." "Now," said he, "hold up your two forefingers and thumb on your right hand." In this manner I was sworn to tell the truth, and, regardless of any consideration [of losing a reward], I testified to the facts concerning our voyage. Afterwards, when we were permitted to go aboard, it was clear enough that the little box had brought out the truthful testimony from all–that we had been wrecked by running against an island of ice fourteen days from New York; refitted in Ireland; after which we joined the British convoy, and were captured by the privateers. After this, some of our crew, as they were returning from a walk where they had been viewing the prison, said that some of the prisoners thrust their hands through the gratings to show them that they had lost the two forefingers and thumb of their right hand. They were a crew of Dutchmen that were likewise taken and had sworn falsely. We now felt thankful for another narrow escape by telling the truth.

"We want the truth on
every point,
We want it too, to
practice by."

With the condemnation of our ship and cargo, and loss of our wages, in company with a strange people who had stripped us of all but our clothing, our Russian voyage ended. But before winter set in, I obtained a berth on board a Danish brig bound to Pillau, in Prussia, where we arrived after a tedious passage, our vessel leaking so badly that it was with difficulty that we kept her from sinking until we reached the wharf. In this extremity I obtained a berth on an American brig from Russia, bound to Belfast, Ireland. But I must close now.

Dear Youth: By reading the foregoing sketch you will at once see how soon troubles came after our cable broke from the anchor. This will illustrate the perilous condition of those who while on the voyage of life to the port of eternal rest, allow their cable to break away from the heavenly anchor. This cable is faith and the anchor to which it is secured is hope. As the strength of the mariner's cable is tried by storms and tempests, so the Christian's cable (faith) is proved by the various trials and commotions of life. Therefore, we should watch and pray and be sure that our cable is firmly fastened to the blessed hope, which we have as an *"anchor of the soul both sure and steadfast."*

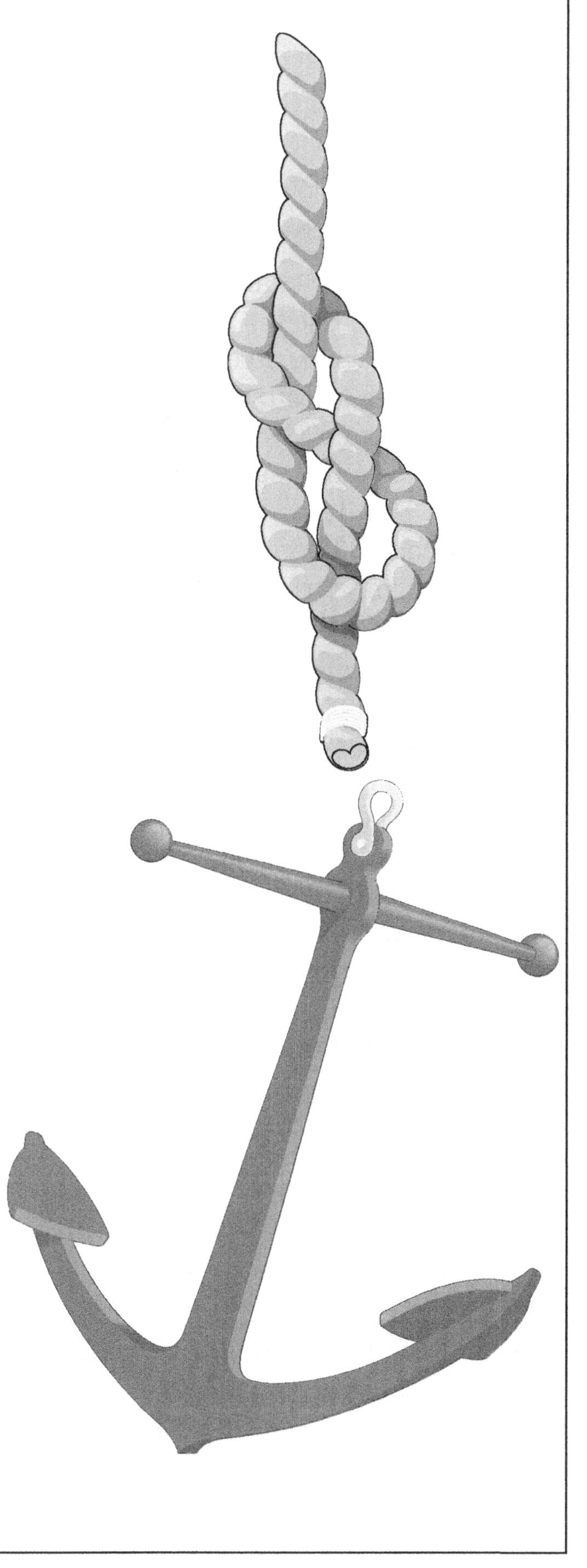

Anchors have sharp points called flukes. The rope attached to the anchor is a cable. Sailors could not go to sea without an anchor. Every ship carries several, and when they are likely to be dashed on the rocks, they quickly drop their big anchors and then are safe.

But sailors are not the only ones who use anchors. Every Christian has one. His anchor is Hope. This the Apostle calls *"the anchor of the soul."* When storms arise and we are like to be overwhelmed in despair, our Hope-anchor is worth having, and such an anchor the heavenly Captain will give all who are sailing under His orders. Praise the Lord for the blessed hope!

Sing the hymn,
"We Have an Anchor."

The Anchor

A Sermon for Children by J. N. Loughborough

An anchor is an instrument which sailors use for fastening their ships, when no other means can be had for securing them. This way of securing vessels is of most importance when storms arise and the ship has drifted into some dangerous coast. Then, as the massive anchor, firmly attached to the ship by the great cable, is thrown out and buries itself in the ground, the weary mariner feels that he is safe. It is not my intention however to talk to you at this time about sailing on the ocean, or casting anchor on her coasts; but to speak of the Christian's anchor. Christian voyagers on board Zion's ship, are poorly fitted out for their trip unless they have an anchor, which may be cast into good anchor ground when storms arise and threaten to dash their bark in pieces on the perilous coast.

That the Christian has an anchor is clearly set forth by Paul. *"Which hope we have as an anchor of the soul, both sure and steadfast, and which entereth into that within the veil"* (Hebrews 6:19). Thus, we learn the true Christian has an anchor fastened in firm anchor-ground that will hold, for it centers in Christ. It is an anchor too that will never fail. It is made of two immutable things (Hebrews 6:17) These things are:

First, God's Word of promise to Abraham; and Second, His oath which was given to confirm that promise.

We shall readily see by looking at this matter a little what the promise to Abraham is. Paul tells us (Romans 4:13) that this promise was that he should be *"heir of the world,"* and that God made it sure to Abraham by an oath. He was not to have it in this life, but was *"after"* to receive it for an inheritance. While he was a sojourner here, as we are now, he *"...looked for a city which hath foundations, whose builder and maker is God"* (Hebrews 11:10). But Peter tells us (II Peter 3:13) that it is the New Earth which is to be the inheritance of the saints; and John shows us (Revelation 21:2) that when the earth is renewed and the saints live there, the Holy City, the New Jerusalem will be located in it.

(Day 6)

If this inheritance spoken of in the promise had been given to Abraham, God's better plan could not have taken effect: that they without us should not be made perfect (Hebrews 7:19). Neither could Paul stand and be "*...judged for the hope of the promise...*" (Acts 26:6). But he did thus stand, and considered that the promise he was contemplating involved the resurrection of the dead. (See Acts 26:7-8.) We learn then from this short investigation that the Christian's anchor is the hope of a future inheritance, which the Lord has promised to all that obey him.

This hope holds God's people in their dangers as an anchor holds the ship in the storm. When the attractions and pleasures of the world would draw us away from the Lord, the glories of the better land eclipse them all, and serve as an anchor to keep us from making shipwreck of our faith.

It was this anchor that kept Moses in Pharaoh's palace. He chose rather to suffer affliction with the people of God, than to enjoy the pleasures of sin for a season. He might have had a bountiful share in the treasures of Egypt—been called the son of Pharaoh's daughter, and lived deliciously in king's courts. But he chose rather to forego the present enjoyments of this world, and enjoy the kingdom which would a thousandfold eclipse the splendor of earth's most glorious kingdoms.

Paul also, while suffering with the people of God, *"thrice beaten with rods," "five times receiving forty stripes save one,"* and in all manner of perils, could say, *"...Our light affliction which is but for a moment worketh for us a far more exceeding and eternal weight of glory"* (II Corinthians 11:25, 24; 4:17). His anchor held him.

Cannot we, dear young friends, lay aside every desire for worldly pleasure, although it may be grievous, and in the language of the poet, say:

Come joy or come sorrow,
  Whatever may befall,
An hour with my God
  Will make up for them all.

Jewfish

The jewfish, the largest member of the grouper or sea-bass family, has olive-green skin covered with dark spots. Some of these creatures can weigh over 650 pounds. They live in large holes or dens relatively close to shore, and may pounce on passing fish to vary their usual diet of lobsters and other crustaceans. Although normally sluggish, they can become aggressive; there have been reports of attacks on divers, and some have disappeared in South Pacific areas where jewfish live. But although there is speculation that these fish devour humans, no actual evidence of it has ever been found.

A picture to color.

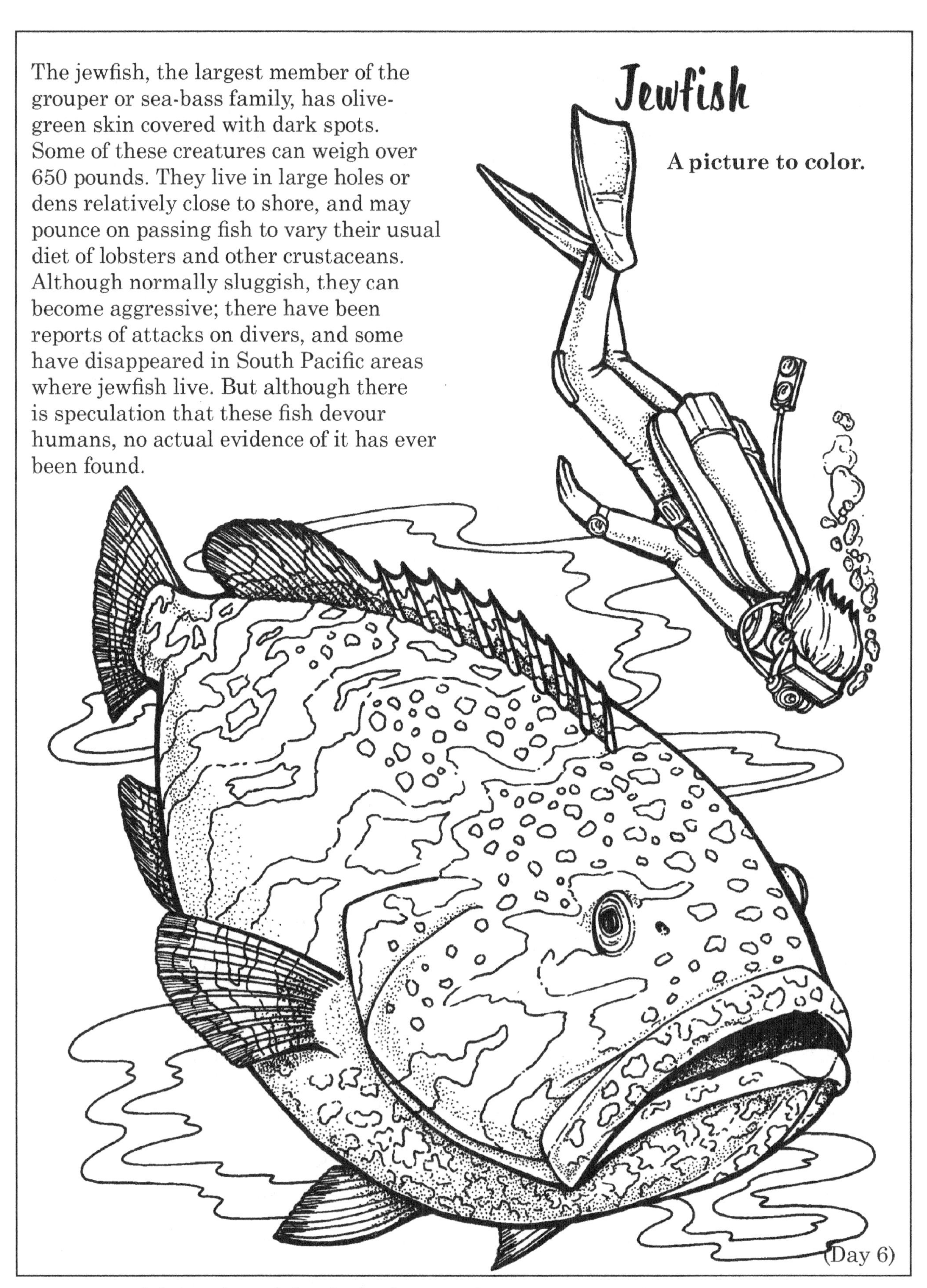

(Day 6)

Children's

Bible Activities, Stories, and Poems

From "Why Did Jesus Choose to Die" to "Pete's Vision"

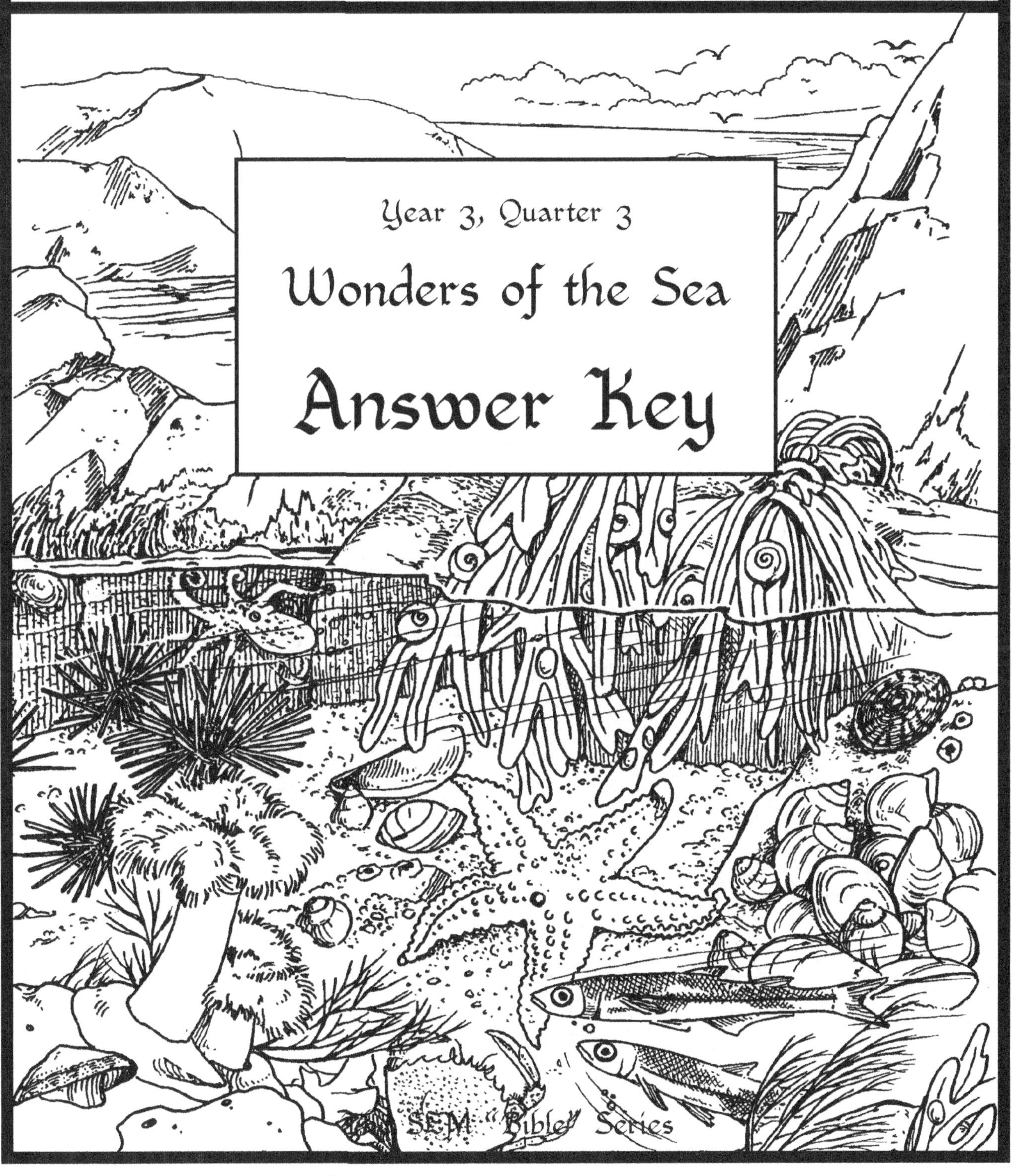

Oceans or Seas

Answer Key

LESSON 1

Page 3

Immanuel

Page 11

"Then said I, Lo, I come (in the volume of the book it is written of me,) to do thy will O God" (Hebrews 10:7).

Page 12

1. Atlantic Ocean (second largest)
2. Pacific Ocean (largest)
3. Indian Ocean (third largest)

Review about the 4 and 5th oceans with the student.

4. Arctic Ocean
5. Antarctic Ocean

Page 13

1. Jesus

2. Selfishness
   Law of **love**

3. Jesus took upon Himself our nature, and passed through our experiences.

4. *"Wherefore in all things it behooved him to be made like unto his brethren, that he might be a merciful and faithful high priest in things pertaining to God, to make reconciliation for the sins of the people."*

Page 13 continued

5. "He endured every trial to which we are subject. And He exercised in His own behalf no power that is not freely offered to us. As man, He met temptation, and overcame in the strength given Him from God...His life testifies that it is possible for us also to obey the law of God."

6. *"I delight to do thy will, O my God: yea, thy law is within my heart."*

Page 14

1. 70% (Draw a circle for the student and color off 70%, by cutting the circle into 10 equal pieces, so the child can visualize 70%.)

2. "*He gathereth the waters of the sea together as an heap: he layeth up the depth in storehouses.*" (Psalm 33:7)

3. The law was made for the benefit of His created beings.

4. The ocean shows us the great power of God.

"Fear ye not me? saith the LORD: will ye not tremble at my presence, which have placed the sand for the bound of the sea by a perpetual decree, that it cannot pass it: and though the waves thereof toss themselves, yet can they not prevail; though they roar, yet can they not pass over it?" (Jeremiah 5:22)

5. If the world's highest mountain (Mount Everest) was placed in the deepest spot there would still be more than 1 mile (1.6

Page 14 continued

kilometers) of water covering the mountain top.

6. The law of God

7. Mountain tops

Page 17

1. "It was Satan's purpose to bring about an eternal separation between God and man; but in Christ we become more closely united to God than if we had never fallen. In taking our nature, the Saviour has bound Himself to humanity by a tie that is never to be broken."

2. Christ is forever linked with the saved.

3. "*...And his name shall be called Wonderful Counselor, The Mighty God, The Everlasting Father, The Prince of Peace.*"

4. "He who is *'holy, harmless, undefiled, separate from sinners,' 'is not ashamed to call us brethren.'* "

5. "In Christ the family of earth and the family of heaven are bound together."

6. "Christ glorified is our brother."

Page 18

Christ – **love**, giving, humbleness, joy, obedience, **unselfishness**

Satan – pride, taking, hate, discord, disobedience, selfishness

Page 22

1. 70
2. South
3. Psalm 33:7
4. Pacific Ocean

Page 22 continued

5. One half
6. 12,200 feet (3,730 meters)
7. Equator
8. Poles
9. 34° – 39° F. (1° – 4° C.)
10. Depths

Page 24

Love's self-sacrifice
earth and heaven
bound bonds
union

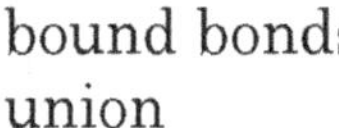

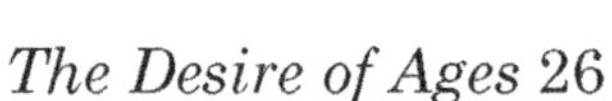

The Desire of Ages 26

Page 27

1.
   1. Chloride
   2. Sodium
   3. Sulfur
   4. Magnesium
   5. Calcium
   6. Potassium

2.
   1. Sodium
   2. Chloride

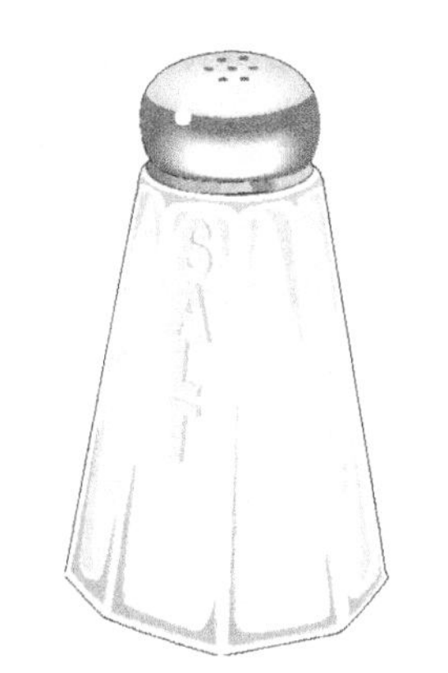

3.
   1. **Unselfish**
   2. **Love**

4. Its salt

LESSON 2

Page 33

1. "Seven of the disciples were in company. They were clad in the humble garb of fishermen; they were poor in worldly goods, but rich in the knowledge and practice of the truth, which in the sight of heaven gave them the highest rank as teachers. They had not been students in the schools of the prophets, but for three years they had been taught by the greatest Educator the world has ever known. Under His instruction they had become elevated, intelligent, and refined, agents through whom men might be led to a knowledge of the truth."

2. "Much of the time of Christ's ministry had been passed near the Sea of Galilee. As the disciples gathered in a place where they were not likely to be disturbed, they found themselves surrounded by reminders of Jesus and His mighty works...."

3. "...On this sea, when their hearts were filled with terror, and the fierce storm was hurrying them to destruction, Jesus had walked upon the billows to their rescue. Here the tempest had been hushed by His word. Within sight was the beach where above ten thousand persons had been fed from a few small loaves and fishes. Not far distant was Capernaum, the scene of so many miracles. As the disciples looked upon the scene, their minds were full of the words and deeds of the Saviour." (*The Desire of Ages* 809-310)

Page 34

1. The ocean provides food,

2. Energy,

3. Minerals,

4. Influences the climate,

5. And is a great highway.

Page 36

Petroleum
Natural Gas
Power Plants that generate Electricity

God (Father, Son, Holy Spirit)

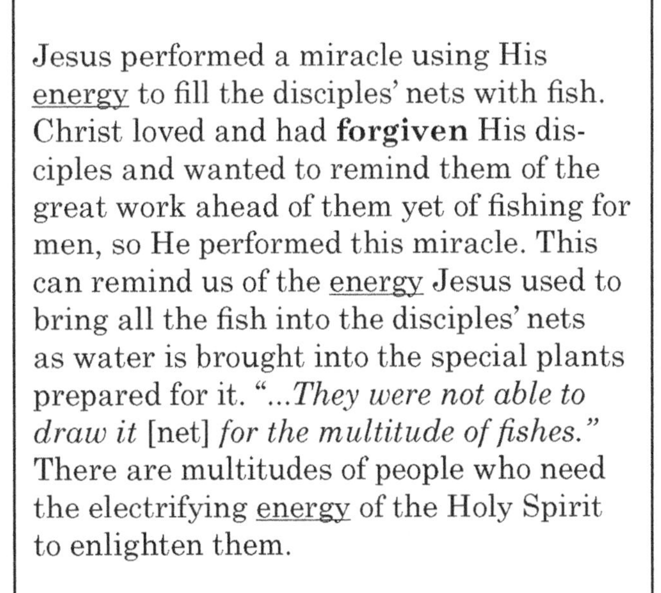

Jesus performed a miracle using His energy to fill the disciples' nets with fish. Christ loved and had **forgiven** His disciples and wanted to remind them of the great work ahead of them yet of fishing for men, so He performed this miracle. This can remind us of the energy Jesus used to bring all the fish into the disciples' nets as water is brought into the special plants prepared for it. "*...They were not able to draw it* [net] *for the multitude of fishes.*" There are multitudes of people who need the electrifying energy of the Holy Spirit to enlighten them.

All true spiritual energy comes from God.
Jesus' Energy

Page 42

Sand and gravel are mined from the sea floor and contain valuable minerals. **Forgiveness** is a valuable character quality.

Page 42 continued

"Jesus teaches that we can receive **forgiveness** from God only as we **forgive** others. It is the love of God that draws us unto Him and that love cannot touch others' hearts without creating love for our brethren."

Page 43

1. Matthew 14:14-21

2. Matthew 4:18-22

3. Luke 5:4-7

Review The Desire of Ages 810-811.

4. "To send"

"And he said unto them, Go ye into all the world, and preach the gospel to every creature" (Mark 16:15).

Page 44

1.-2. Coral, pearls, shells, sponges, and fresh water

3. Pearls can remind us of **forgiveness**. They are the clam's beautiful response to an irritating grain of sand. Sponges from the ocean bottom are found in many stores. Sponges can also make us remember to be **forgiving**. When others are clumsy and spill something we often use a sponge to help clean up the mess. When others lose self-control, and spill out angry words we can act like a sponge and take it all in without reacting poorly. After all, that is the way Jesus acted when Peter cursed and denied Him. In some dry areas near the ocean, the salt is removed from the ocean to produce fresh water.

Page 47

"So when they had dined, Jesus saith to Simon Peter, (S +eye=i) (mom –m +n) Simon, (opposite of daughter) son of Jonas, (love +test –te) lovest (th +ou) thou (m +see –se) me (core –c +m) more (th +an) than (the +see –e) these? He saith unto him, Yea, Lord; thou knowest that I love thee. He saith unto him, Feed (m +eye –ee) my (lambs) lambs" (John 21: 15)

Three times

Page 49

The ocean is the source of most of the rain, (precipitation) that falls to the earth. The sun's heat evaporates water from the ocean's surface and other bodies of water. The water rises as vapor and is carried inland as clouds. It then falls back to the earth as rain, sleet, snow, or in some other form.

God's **forgiveness** draws us to Him. Jesus was drawing Peter closer to Himself, like water is drawn up into the air to form clouds. He had forgiven him. *"I have blotted out as a thick cloud, thy transgressions, and, as a cloud, thy sins..."* (Isaiah 44:22).

Page 51

"Jesus thus made known to Peter the very manner of his death; He even foretold the stretching forth of his hands upon the cross. Again He bade His disciple, *'Follow me.'* Peter was not disheartened by the revelation. He felt willing to suffer any death for his Lord."

Page 52

1. Cruise Ship
2. Ferry
3. Coast Guard
4. Sail Boat
5. Motor Boat

LESSON 3

Page 57

Matthew 28:19-20 (all except last word)
Read Psalm 4:7 about **gladness**. Find other verses in the Bible about **gladness**.

All once except <u>go</u> (2), <u>teach</u> (2), Son (2) and <u>end</u> (3).

Read with the children other verses in the Bible that talk about the gospel to the world. (Mark 16:15; Isaiah 52:10; Luke 24:47; Acts 2:38-39; Romans 10:18; Colossians 1:23)

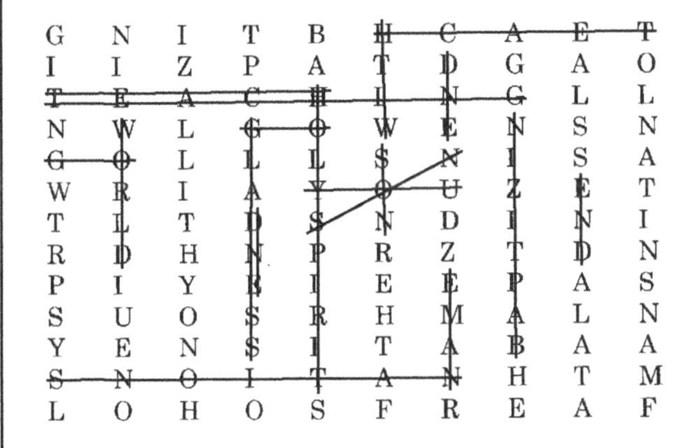

G	N	I	T	B	H	C	A	E	T
I	I	Z	P	A	T	D	G	A	O
T	E	A	C	H	I	N	G	L	L
N	W	L	G	O	W	E	N	S	N
G	O	L	L	L	S	N	I	S	A
W	R	I	A	Y	O	U	Z	E	T
T	L	T	D	S	N	D	I	N	I
R	D	H	N	P	R	Z	T	D	N
P	I	Y	R	I	E	E	P	A	S
S	U	O	S	R	H	M	A	L	N
Y	E	N	S	I	T	A	B	A	A
S	N	O	I	T	A	N	H	T	M
L	O	H	O	S	F	R	E	A	F

Page 58

Whale, Fish
Jellyfish, Starfish, Sea Cucumber
Sea Anemone, Plankton, Eels

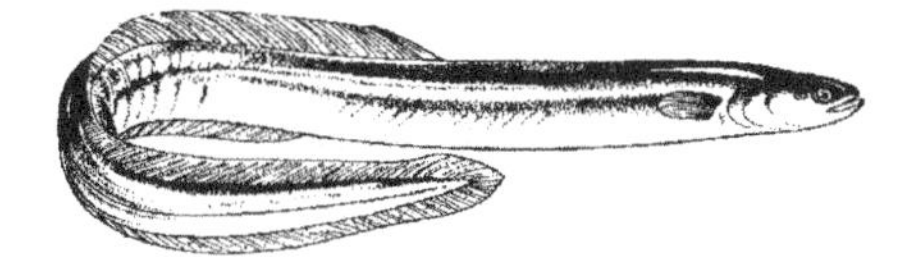

Page 59

"At the same time there floated down to them the sweetest and most joyous [**glad**] music from the angel choir."

Page 60

1. One

2. Plankton float in the water where they get sunlight and nutrients.

3. Usually they just drift but some kinds of plankton have long, whip-like parts that help them to swim.

4. Remember, the plankton <u>serve</u> as food for other sea creatures. Jesus' loving words <u>served</u> as spiritual food. How **glad** the disciples were that the tender Saviour did not speak harshly to them on account of their faults and failures. Jesus had spent His life on earth <u>serving</u> people.

5. Diatom cells contain both green and yellow-orange pigments that help them to capture the <u>sun's energy</u>. They have a golden-brown color. The disciples were capturing the love-energy that beamed from the face of the *"<u>Sun of righteousness</u>"* as He talked with them. He would provide the disciples with strength and <u>energy</u> for their great work of carrying the gospel to every creature. "The work committed to the disciples would require great efficiency; for the <u>tide</u> of evil ran deep and strong against them." (*The Acts of the Apostles* 31)

6. A diatom is one cell living in a glass-like shell made of opal. The shell consists of two parts that fit, one inside the other, like a box with its lid. Most diatoms are oblong or circular in shape. Others resem-

Page 60 continued

ble tinkertoys, hats, pocketbooks, and stick men. They usually multiply by a cell dividing into two cells. After each diatom cell divides, each new cell retains part of the parent shell and builds a new part to fit into it. Some diatoms stay linked together after dividing to make a chain, or ribbon-shaped colonies. Jesus would stay linked with the disciples through the Holy Spirit.

7. Diatoms have inner growth clocks that are set by the sun. When the sun shines more directly into the ocean waters after the winter is over it stimulates the diatoms who have been resting like wheat seed in a field. The diatoms then use the sea minerals that flow inside their cell to form a great wall that divides it in two. Then they split apart into two glassy plants. So many diatoms multiply in the spring season that it causes the ocean to change color. It is no longer the blue-green of winter but has changed into the warm golden-brown of spring. And just as when land meadows flower. The animals of the sea come to graze.

8. The diatoms going from their resting (seed-like) stage to their "blooming" stage reminds us how many of the seeds Jesus had planted in the hearts of the people in Jerusalem would bloom and multiply. The disciples were to go back and harvest them and plant more seeds of truth.

9. Some scientists say there may be more than 12,000 species of diatoms. They are identified by their shells.

10. When diatoms die their shells sink to the bottom of the sea.

Page 60 continued

11. The accumulations of diatom shells are used in many ways, like in polishing powder. They look like tiny jewels of the most interesting shapes. The disciples would be like jewels scattered through the sea of people.

12. Diatoms usually live in colder areas of the ocean. The disciples would continue to live and work in the spiritually cold area of the world. Some diatoms even live in the sea ice.

13. Most dinoflagellates also are one-celled. They are any one of an order of tiny marine flagellates, They usually live in more tropical areas. A dinoflagellate has two flagella (whiplike parts) it can use to move in a swirling motion. Some dinoflagellates make very powerful poisons. When they over-populate the water they discolor it, causing a red tide that kills sea animals.

Page 65

1. Two angels

2. Like men

3. "To look long and steadily at"

4. "*...This same Jesus, which is taken up from you into heaven, shall so come in like manner as ye have seen him go into heaven*" (Acts 1:11).

Page 66

1. Diatoms or phytoplankton

2. Jellyfish or Zooplankton

3. Plankton

4. Plankton

5. All in nature serves one another. The angels came to serve the disciples with the **glad** news of Jesus' return in the future.

Page 68

See page 51 in the Family Bible Lesson.

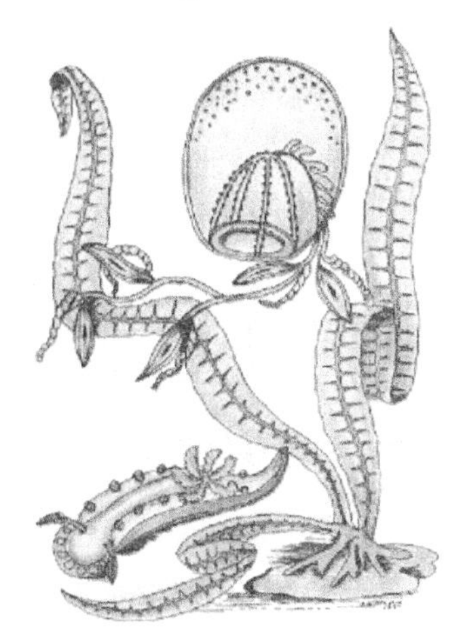

Page 75

"Gift of Yahweh"

"And they gave forth their lots; and the lot fell upon Matthias; and he was numbered with the eleven apostles." Acts 1:26

Page 77

Corals, sea anemones, and hydras

See the *Family Bible Lessons* pages 53-54.

Page 79

There are many paths that can be taken.

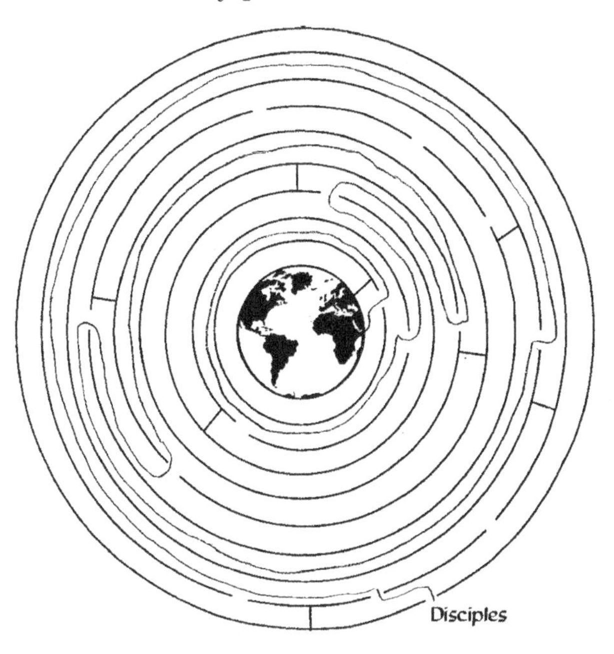

Page 80

1. Jelly-like
2. Pea
3. Tentacles
4. Umbrella
5. Polyps
6. Fish
7. Stings
8. Sea Wasps
9. Hydras

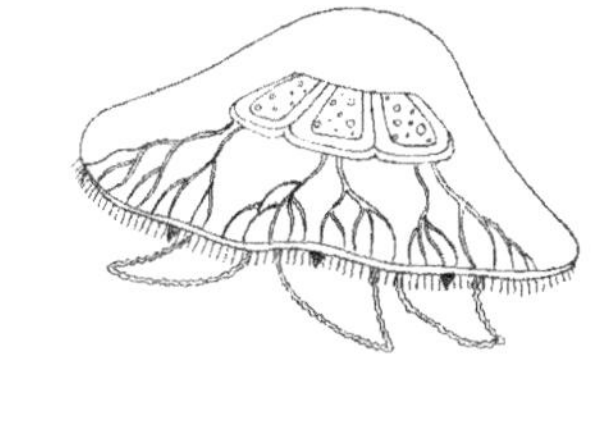

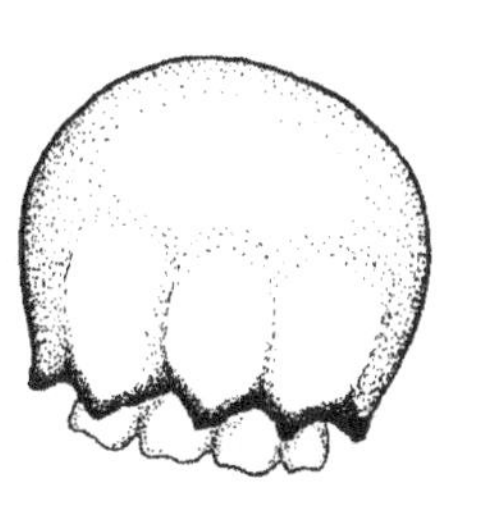

LESSON 4

Page 85

1. Holy Spirit
2. Fire
3. **Purity**
4. Praising
5. Command
6. Wait

"And when the day of Pentecost was fully come, they were all with one accord in one place" (Acts 2:1).

Page 86

Nektons are sea creatures that can swim freely in the water.

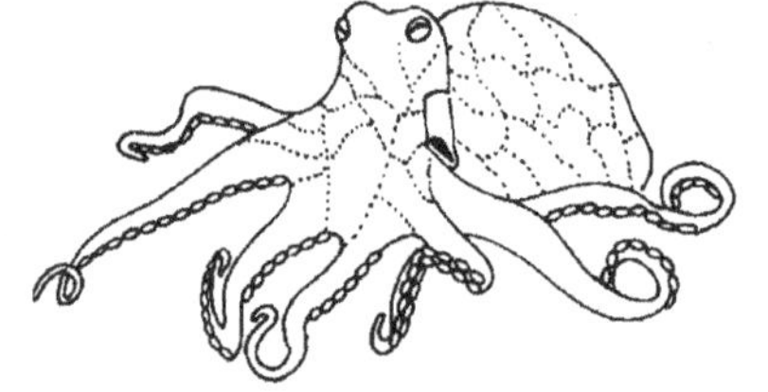

1. No
2. Yes
3. Yes
4. No
5. Yes
6. Yes

Page 95

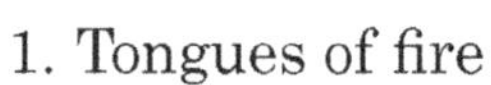

1. Tongues of fire
2. **Purity**
4. Prayer
5. Scroll—Study

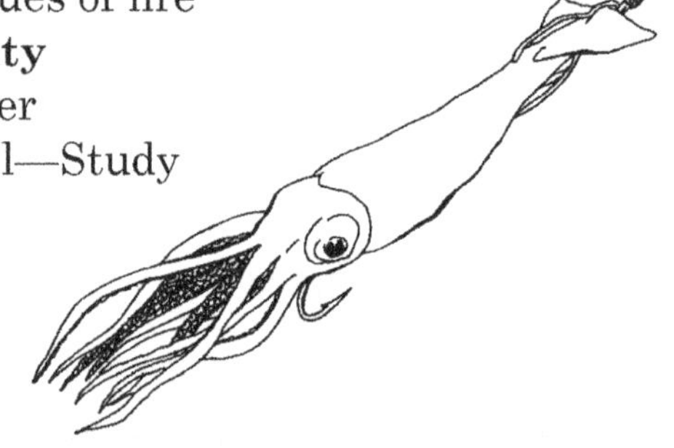

Page 97

A squid can move backward through the water with tremendous speed by forcing water through a tube that lies beneath its head. They are often called "Sea Arrows" because of this.

Page 100

1. Sea Cow, water plants, about 100 pounds (45 kilograms) a day

2. 3 kinds

Caribbean Manatee
Amazon Manatee
African Manatee

3. The manatee has light to dark gray skin, with bristly hairs scattered over its body. The front legs are shaped like paddles, and its tail is rounded. It has no hind legs.

One kind of manatee may grow to 13 feet (4 meters) long and weigh up to 300–500 pounds (1,600 kilograms).

Page 103

O
On
"One"

F
Fill
"Filled"

T
Ton
"Tongue"

H
Hear
"Heart" or *"Heard"*

R
Pent
"Repent"

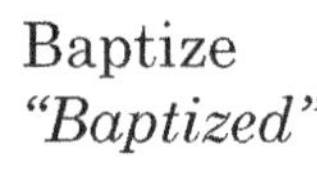

B
Baptize
"Baptized"

Page 105

Purity

Page 106

A few answers but think of more:

Signs or miracles

Sold personal things and gave away to those in need

Spoke in foreign languages

Cast out demons

Went to far corners of the earth with the message

LESSON 5

Page 113

List of letters in each word:
1 <u>a</u>
2 at, of, is, to
3 and, <u>man</u>, <u>his</u>, <u>was</u>, the, <u>ask</u>
4 lame, from, womb, <u>whom</u>, <u>they</u>, laid, gate, alms, them, that, into
5 daily, <u>which</u>
6 temple, called
7 certain, carried, entered
8 mother's
9 beautiful

Teacher might like to have extra copies of the puzzle.

Across & Down
1A Womb
2D Mother's
3A Beautiful
4D Entered
5D Laid
6D From
7A Certain
8D Temple
9A Carried
9D Called

Page 113 continued

10A Lame
11A Is
12A The
12D To
13A Gate
14D Alms
15A Daily
16D Into
17A Them
17D That
18A At
19A Of
20A Ask

Page 114

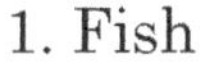

1. Fish
2. Lobster
3. Jellyfish
4. Barnacles
5. Starfish
6. Octopus

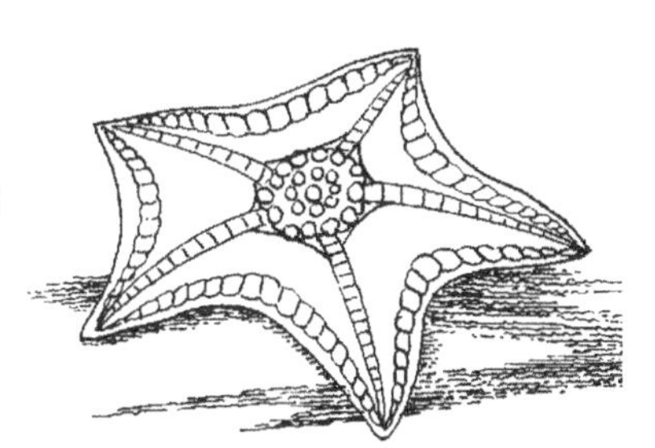

Page 116

"And he leaping up stood, and walked, and entered with them into the temple, walking, and leaping, and praising God."

"And all the people saw him walking and praising God:

"And they knew that it was he which sat for alms at the Beautiful gate of the temple: and they were filled with wonder and amazement at that which had happened unto him."

Page 118

Seaweed

Kelp differs in size and form. One kind of kelp, called giant kelp, has hundreds of branches with even more leaves. It can be as long as 200 feet (61 meters). <u>In areas where it is found, it forms underwater forests</u>. Other kelp is smaller with only a single branch less than 3 feet (1 meter) long.

Many marine animals, like snails and sea urchins, feed on kelp. Other creatures, like lobsters and many fish, use kelp for shelter. The temple was to be like kelp, where many people could come to worship and to find shelter and be fed spiritually. Peter and John went up to pray and there they saw the crippled man.

Page 123

1. Astonished

2. 40 years

3. He was "now rejoicing in the full use of his limbs, free from pain, and happy in believing in Jesus."

4. The "Beautiful gate" today is the church who are to help the poor and maimed that are placed there by God for His true servants to minister to.

5. "The great work of the gospel is not to close with less manifestation of the power of God than marked its opening. The prophecies opening of the gospel are again to be fulfilled in the latter rain at its close. Here are *'the times of refreshing'* to which the apostle Peter looked forward....Servants of God, with their faces lighted up

Page 123 continued

and shining with holy consecration, will hasten from place to place to proclaim the message from heaven....Miracles will be wrought, the sick will be healed, and signs and wonders will follow the believers." (*The Great Controversy* 611-612)

6. Student, answer.

Page 126

Snail, Swan, Sea Urchin,*
Snowdrops, Starfish,* Sea Horse,* Sloth, Spider, Sea Lion,* Sperm Whale,* Sunflower,
Spruce, Skunk, and Strawberry

*Other animals that live in the sea.

Page 129

"Repentance includes <u>sorrow</u> for sin and a <u>turning</u> away from it. We shall not <u>renounce</u> sin unless we see its <u>sinfulness</u>; until we turn away from it in <u>heart</u>, there will be no real <u>change</u> in the life.

"Every act of <u>transgression</u>, every neglect or rejection of the <u>grace</u> of Christ, is reacting upon yourself; it is <u>hardening</u> the heart, <u>depraving</u> the will, <u>benumbing</u> the understanding, and not only making you less inclined to yield, but less capable of yielding, to the <u>tender</u> <u>pleading</u> of God's Holy Spirit."

Page 130

"The seed that the Saviour had sown sprang up and bore fruit."
The Acts of the Apostles 60

Page 132

1. "Thus the disciples preached the resurrection of Christ."

2.-3. "Many among those who listened were waiting for this testimony, and when they heard it they believed."

4. It brought to their minds the words that Christ had spoken, and they took their stand in the ranks of those who accepted the gospel.

5. In **giving** to others the precious words about Christ we become stronger ourselves and grow in Him.

Page 133

Starfish <u>reproduce</u> by releasing eggs into the sea from special organs located in the arms. The eggs form into tiny young (larvae). After a time, each larva settles down on the sea bottom and develops into a starfish.

Disciples <u>reproduce</u> "new creatures" in Christ by scattering the seed of the Word among the sea of people.

Page 134

Starfish, tiny crabs, young octopi, anchovies, purple sea urchins, pale-golden sea anemones, limpets, blue mussels, pinkish bloodworms, an assortment of snails, seaweed such as the dark brownish-green fucus, and the purple or yellow-ochre Irish moss.

LESSON 6

Page 139

Influence

Page 140

1. Tiny Animals
2. Starfish, Fish, Sea Anemones
3. South Pacific

Page 141

1. "Annas and Caiaphas, with the other dignitaries of the temple"

2. "In that very room and before some of those very men, Peter had shamefully denied his Lord."

3. "Those present who remembered the part that Peter had acted at the trial of his Master, flattered themselves that he could now be intimidated by the threat of imprisonment and death."

4. "He was filled with the Holy Spirit, and by the help of this power he was resolved to remove the stain of his apostasy by honoring the name he had once disowned."

5. "With holy **boldness** and in the power of the Spirit Peter fearlessly declared: *'Be it known unto you all, and to all the people of Israel, that by the name of Jesus Christ of Nazareth, whom ye crucified, whom God raised from the dead, even by him doth this man stand here before you whole. This is the stone which was set at nought of you builders, which is become the head of the corner. Neither is there salvation in any other: for there is none other name under heaven given among men, Whereby we must be saved.'* "

Page 141 continued

6. Peter's weak point had become his strong point through the Spirit's grace. What an encouragement to us who have character weaknesses to overcome.

Page 142

1. **Coral reefs** are the result of the untiring industry of its members, the little coral animals. Every day they did their little part faithfully in building the great structure they were a part of.

2. **Coral reefs** can remind us that each of us has an important role to play in the body of the church. We build it up or tear it down by the little actions we perform each day. *"Now ye are the body of Christ, and members in particular. And God hath set some in the church, first apostles..."* (like Peter and John). They had a special job to do in building the foundation of the church, and so do you.

3. **Fringing reefs** are platforms of living coral under the sea that extend out from the shore.

Barrier reefs follow along the shoreline, but are separated from it by water. They form a barrier between the water near the shore and the open sea. A barrier reef may be a long series of reefs separated by channels of open water. Usually barrier reefs surround volcanic islands of the South Pacific. Barrier reefs of coral stand up **boldly** to the sea as the disciples did to the sea of people.

An atoll is a ring-shaped coral island in the open sea. It is formed when coral builds up on a mud bank or on the rim of a volcano's crater. The atoll surrounds

Page 142 continued

a body of water called a lagoon. One or more channels connect the lagoon to the open seas.

Page 145

Feared
Threats

Page 146

1. Fringing Reef
2. Barrier Reef
3. Atoll

Page 149

1. Eggs or by budding

2. Witnessing

3. Small, knob-like growths called buds appear on the body of an adult polyp. These buds grow larger and larger and finally separate from the parent, then they begin to deposit their own limestone, forming a colony.

4. Budding helps the main colony increase in size.

5. **Boldness**, faith, courage, truth

Page 150

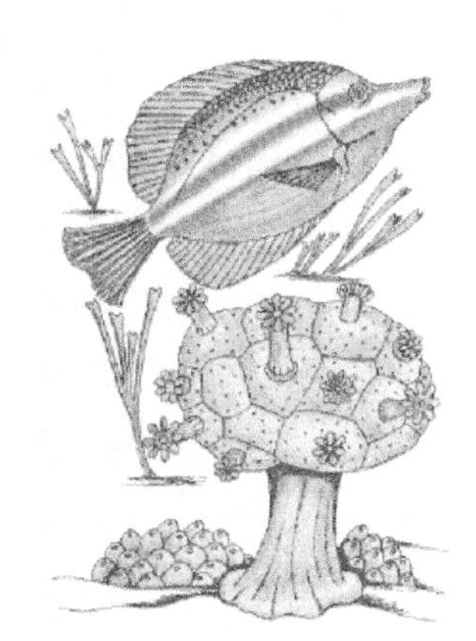

Page 154

1. New colonies of coral polyps form when the adult polyps of an old colony produce eggs. The eggs grow into tiny forms that swim away. Then the creatures settle down on the sea bottom and begins to form new colonies by budding.

2. Soon the disciples would be scattered from Jerusalem to form new groups of believers throughout the world.

3. Different marine animals eat living coral that are forming. Usually the loss of coral to such animals is offset by the development of new coral colonies and the growth of old ones.

4. In one area large numbers of crown-of-thorns starfish destroyed stony coral colonies on many reefs of the southwest Pacific Oceans. Find a picture.

5. Scientists do not know why the starfish have become so numerous. This can remind us of the Jewish leaders trying to stop the **bold** witness of the disciples who brought many to Christ even though they were persecuted.

Page 155

1. Yes
2. No
3. Yes
4. Yes
5. Yes
6. Yes
7. Yes

Page 157

1. Spotted Snail

2. Brain Coral

3. Burrowing Shrimp

Page 158

1. Staghorn Coral

2. Stony Mushroom Coral

3. Use an encyclopedia to gain more information about Astrangia Coral.

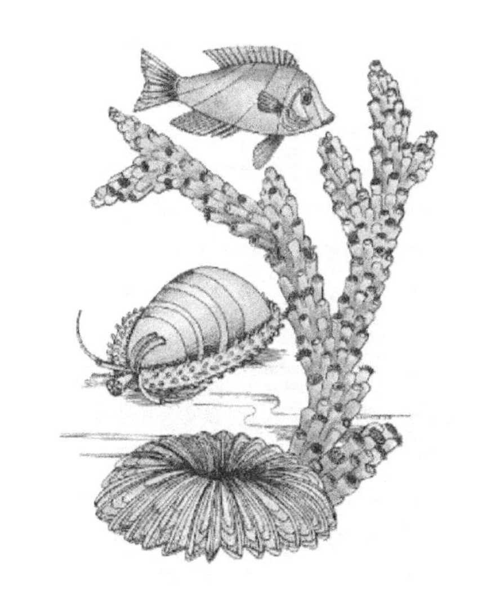

LESSON 7

Page 163

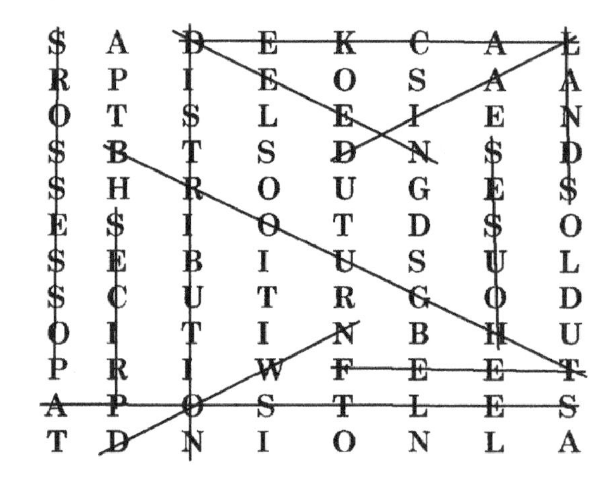

Page 171

1. Sold (4 letters)
2. Named (5 letters) (D)
3. Brought (7 letters) (O)
4. Apostles (8 letters) (O S L)
5. Possession (10 letters) (O S)

Page 172

One suggestion: Green reminds us of faith and the people who were carefully giving trusted in God to fulfill their personal needs.

Page 173

"Lying lips are abomination to the Lord: but they that deal truly are his delight." (Proverbs 12:22)

Page 174

Page 179

Giving
Carefulness
Unselfishness

Page 182

Page 183

A few ideas

Carefulness	**Truthful**
care	truth
careful	truthful
fare	ruthful
are	

Covetousness	**Falsehood**
covetous	false
cove	hood
us	sea
no	as
son	so

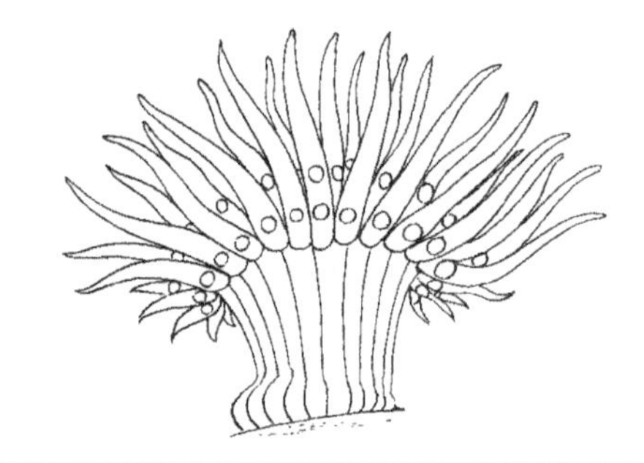

LESSON 8

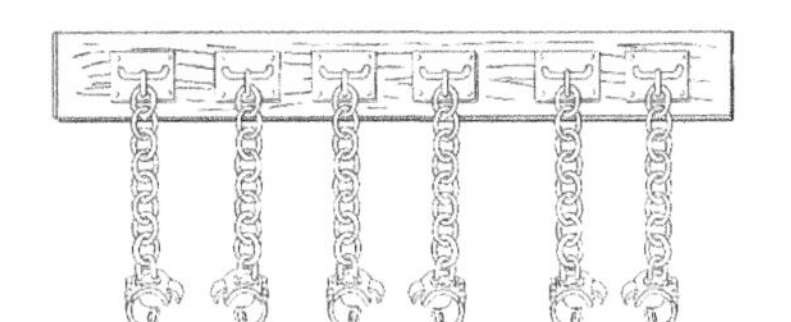

Page 189

12. Signs, wonders
14. Believers, added, multitudes, men, women
15. Brought, forth, sick, shadow, overshadow
16. unclean, spirits, healed

Page 191

1. "The priests and rulers saw that Christ was extolled above them. As the Sadducees, who did not believe in a resurrection, heard the apostles declaring that Christ had risen from the dead, they were enraged, realizing that if the apostles were allowed to preach a risen Saviour, and to work miracles in His name, the doctrine that there would be no resurrection would be rejected by all, and the sect of the Sadducees would soon become extinct. The Pharisees were angry as they perceived that the tendency of the disciples' teaching was to undermine the Jewish ceremonies, and make the sacrificial offerings to no effect."

2. "Hitherto all the efforts made to suppress this new teaching had been in vain; but now both Sadducees and Pharisees determined that the work of the disciples should be stopped, for it was proving them guilty of the death of Jesus."

The leaders had the Sanctuary service to tell them of the Messiah to come, die, and then live again for the sins of man, which was before them daily but they did not truly understand these services.

3. "Filled with indignation, the priest laid violent hands on Peter and John, and put

Page 191 continued

them in the common prison."
(*The Acts of the Apostles* 78)

4. The Jewish rulers were sinning by not advancing with the light of truth. They were not seeking further truth but were content with the truth as they already had it.

5. When we **obey** the Holy Spirit's leading, sometimes it can bring trials to our life, but God has a way of escape. As we advance in the light of the truth we enjoy more of the Spirit's presence.

Page 192

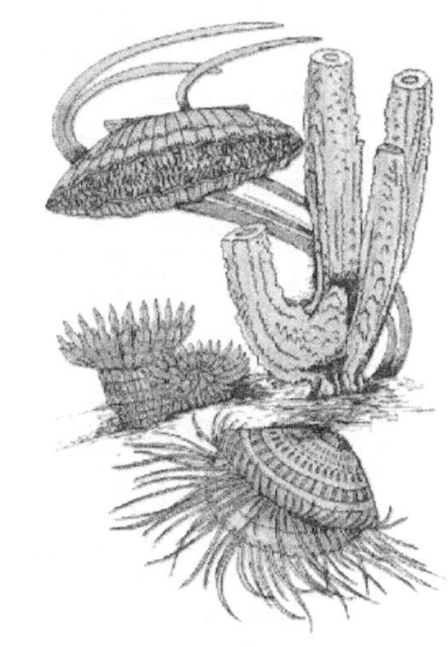

Page 197

"But the angel of the Lord by night opened the prison doors, and brought them forth and said,

"Go, stand and speak in the temple to the people all the words of this life."

Acts 5:19-20

Page 199

The sponge has two kinds of openings on its body surface. The first are small pores called ostia, and the second is a large osculum. The ostia allows water to enter the body and the osculum lets water leave the body. The water brings tiny plants and animals into the sponge which becomes the sponge's food. Waste products and water leave the sponge through the osculum.

Page 200

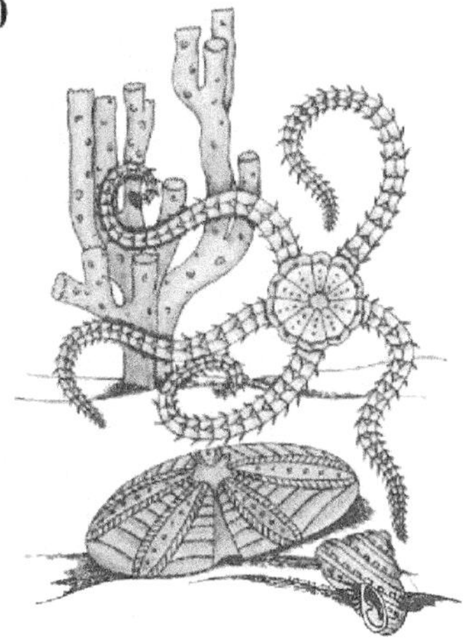

Page 201

"But when the officers came, and found them not in the prison, they returned and told,

"Saying, the prison truly found we shut with all safety, and the keepers standing, without before the doors: but when we had opened, we found no man within."

Acts 5:22-23

"...Behold, the men whom ye put in prison are standing in the temple, and teaching the people.

"Then went the captain with the officers, and brought them without violence: for they feared the people, lest they should have been stoned." Acts 5:25-26 (Angel)

Page 202

Page 207

1. Nothing

2. Disciples

3. Without violence

4. **Obey**

5. Gamaliel

Page 208

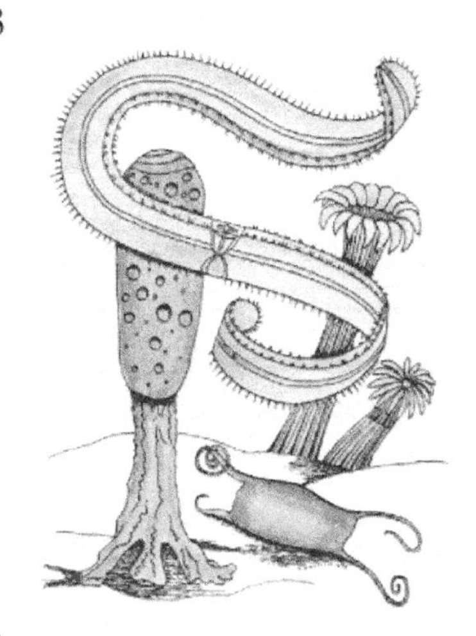

Page 210

1. Calcaria

2. Hexactinellicla

Page 210 continued

3. Sclerospongiae

4. Demospongiae

5. Righteous

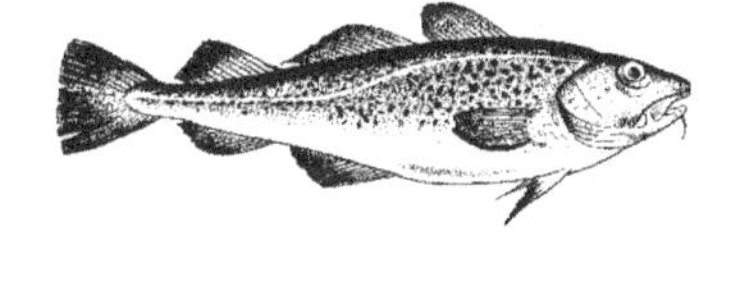

6. Wicked

LESSON 9

Page 215

1. fish, tuna, shark, tail, surgeon fish, sunfish, clown trigger fish, scales, trunk fish, angel fish, fins, spotted goatfish, trumpet fish, butterfly fish, hogfish, damsel fish, flame fish, scrawledfile fish, hatchet fish, oarfish, eel, puffer, bass, perch, trout, catfish, sturgeon, paddle fish salmon, silver hatchet fish

2. Grumble, complain, fault finding, whine

3. Water, wave, lakes, ocean, river, stream, creek, rain

4. School, assistance, helping, aiding, aid, helped, helpfulness, help, usefulness

5. *"Let brotherly love continue."*

Page 223

Stephen
Philip
Prochorus
Nicanor
Timon
Parmenas
Nicolas

Page 223 continued

1. Stephen

2. He "...was a man of deep piety and broad faith."

3. Saul of Tarsus

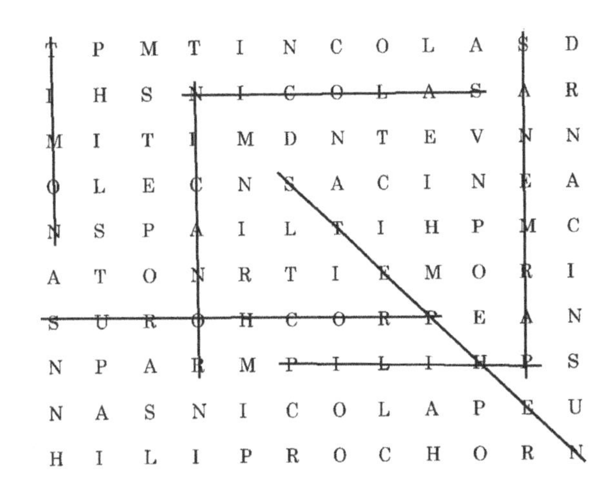

Page 224

1. Backbone
2. Gills
3. Cold-blooded
4. Fins and scales
5. 21,700
6. Named
7. Ichthyologists
8. Two
9. Jawed and jawless

Fish

Eel (fish)

Fish

He who does the will of God.

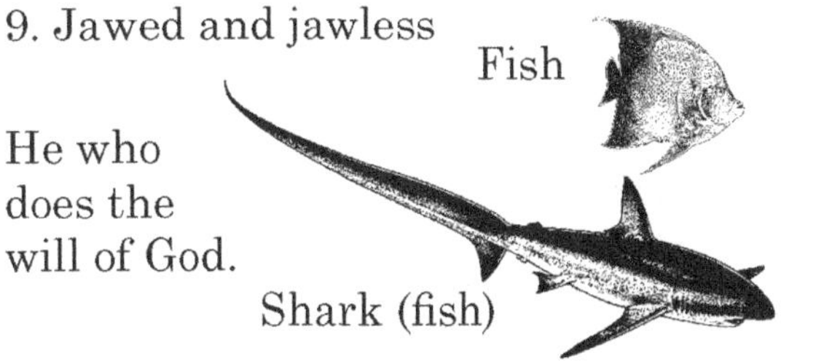

Shark (fish)

Shark (fish)

Stingray (fish)

Page 225

1. "Because the priests and rulers could not prevail against the clear, calm wisdom of Stephen...."

2. "...They determined to make an example of him; and while thus satisfying their revengeful hatred, they would prevent others, through fear, from adopting his belief."

3. "Witnesses were hired to bear false testimony that they had heard him speak blasphemous words against the temple and the law. *'We have heard him say,'* these witnesses declared, *'that this Jesus of Nazareth shall destroy this place, and shall change the customs which Moses delivered us.'* "

4. "As Stephen stood face to face with his judges to answer to the charge of blasphemy, a holy radiance shone upon his countenance, and *'all that sat in the council, looking steadfastly on him, saw his face as it had been the face of an angel.'* Many who beheld this light trembled and veiled their faces, but the stubborn unbelief and prejudice of the rulers did not waver."

5. "When Stephen was questioned as to the truth of the charges against him, he began his defense in a clear, thrilling voice, which rang through the council hall. In words that held the assembly spellbound, he proceeded to rehearse the history of the chosen people of God. He showed a thorough knowledge of the Jewish economy and the spiritual interpretation of it now made manifest through Christ. He repeated the words of Moses that foretold of the Messiah: *'A Prophet shall the Lord your God raise up unto you of your brethren, like unto me; him shall ye hear.'* He

Page 225 continued

made plain his own loyalty to God and to the Jewish faith, while he showed that the law in which the Jews trusted for salvation had not been able to save Israel from idolatry. He connected Jesus Christ with all the Jewish history. He referred to the building of the temple by Solomon, and to the words of both Solomon and Isaiah: *'Howbeit the Most High dwelleth not in temples made with hands; as saith the prophet, Heaven is my throne, and earth is my footstool: what house will ye build me? saith the Lord: or what is the place of my rest? Hath not my hand made all these things?'* "

6. "When Stephen reached this point, there was a tumult among the people. When he connected Christ with the prophecies and spoke as he did of the temple, the priest, pretending to be horror-stricken, rent his robe. To Stephen this act was a signal that his voice would soon be silenced forever. He saw the resistance that met his words and knew that he was giving his last testimony. Although in the midst of his sermon, he abruptly concluded it." (*The Acts of the Apostles* 98-100)

7. – 8. Stephen was trying to **help** these men understand the work of Christ. But, unfortunately, they did not want his **help**. (No)

9. Pray for God's **help** when you are in difficulties to give a right answer for your faith.

Page 226

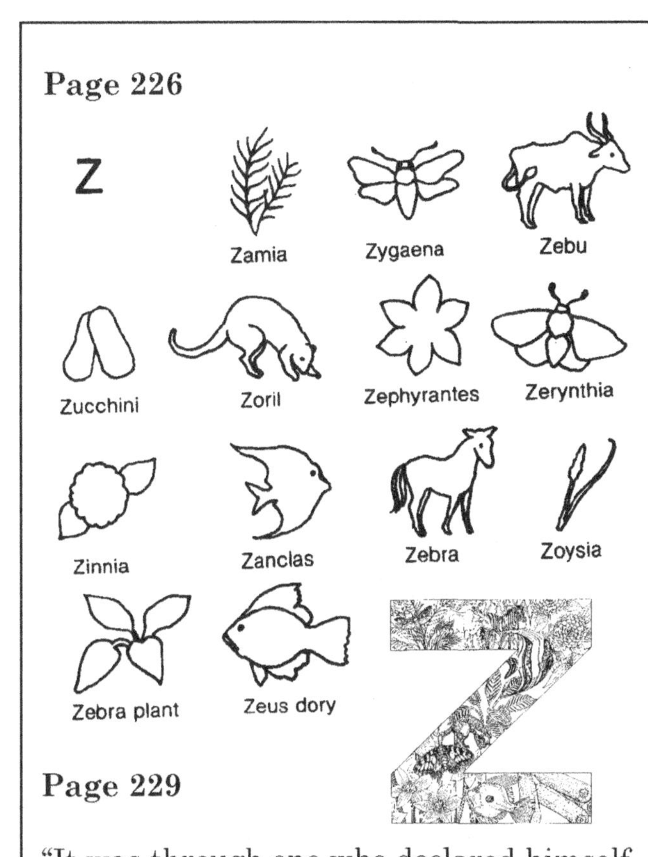

Page 229

"It was through one who declared himself to be a *'brother, and companion in tribulation'* (Revelation 1:9), that Christ revealed to His church the things that they must suffer for His sake. Looking down through long centuries of darkness and superstition, the aged exile saw multitudes suffering martyrdom because of their love for the truth. But he saw also that He who sustained His early witnesses would not forsake His faithful followers during the centuries of persecution that they must pass through before the close of time. *'Fear none of those things which thou shalt suffer,'* the Lord declared; *'behold, the devil shall cast some of you into prison, that ye may be tried; and ye shall have tribulation:..be thou faithful unto death, and I will give thee a crown of life.'* (Revelation 2:10)." *The Acts of the Apostles* 588

Page 233

3A martyrdom
3D memory
1D proclaimed
2D countenance
7A witnessed
6D beholders
4D Stephen
5D death
8A face
9A church
10A Saul
11A touched
11D testified
12A minds
13A sore
14A truth
15D trial
16D glory
17A faith
18A words

Page 234

1. Smell
2. See
3. Taste
4. Feel
5. Hear

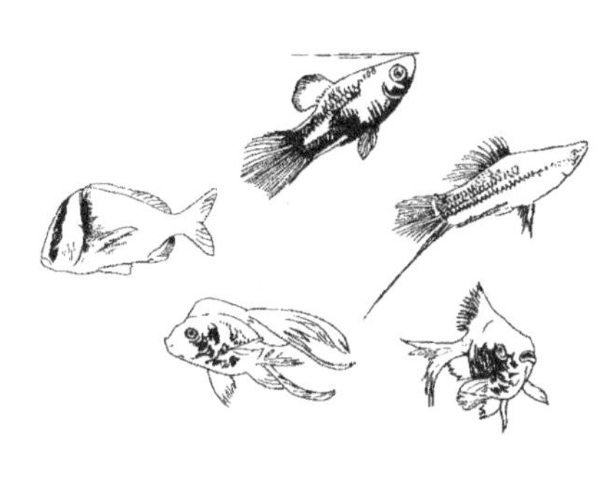

LESSON 10

Page 240

1. Scattered abroad
2. Haling to prison
3. JudeA and Samaria
4. Persecution
5. entEring every house
6. Angler fish and stonefish
7. Herring, freshwater sunfish, and rays
8. Variety
9. Tuna
10. Perfect
11. Pipefish

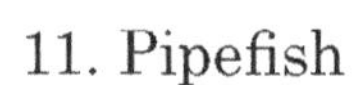

Page 241

One suggested answer:
The Ethiopian basked in the knowledge of Christ the Saviour.

Page 243

1. "Philip, one of the seven deacons, was among those driven from Jerusalem."

2. He *'went down to the city of Samaria, and preached Christ unto them. And the people with one accord gave heed unto those things which Philip spake, hearing and seeing the miracles which he did. For unclean spirits...came out of many that were possessed with them: and many taken with palsies, and that were lame,*

Page 243 continued

were healed. And there was great joy in that city.'" (*The Acts of the Apostles* 106)

3. "Philip's work in Samaria was marked with great success...."

4. "And, thus encouraged, he sent to Jerusalem for help."

5. "The apostles now perceived more fully the meaning of the words of Christ, *'Ye shall be witnesses unto me both in Jerusalem, and in all Judea, and in Samaria, and unto the uttermost part of the earth'* (Acts 1:8)." (*The Acts of the Apostles* 107) (Taking the gospel to the world.)

With the power of the Holy Spirit they were to witness to the world about Christ.

Page 246

It is found back by the tail of the butterfly fish.

Page 253

1. Heavenly messenger or angel

2. Deacon, Gaza

3. *"And he arose and went: and, behold, a man of Ethiopia, a eunuch of great authority under Candace queen of the Ethiopians, who had the charge of all her treasure, and had come to Jerusalem for to worship"* (Acts 8:27).

4. Jerusalem

5. Worshiping

Page 253 continued

6. He had read from Isaiah and had questions. See Acts 8:28.

7. "God saw that when converted he would give others the light he had received and would exert a strong influence in favor of the gospel."

Page 257

1. "Angels of God were attending this seeker for light, and he was being drawn to the Saviour."

2. "By the ministration of the Holy Spirit the Lord brought him into touch with one who could lead him to the light."

3. Philip was directed to go to the Ethiopian and explain to him the prophecy that he was reading."

Page 258

1. These may float in the sea, stick to plants or rocks.

2. Fish eggs contain a lot of yolk. The baby develops by feeding on the yolk. When the baby fish hatches it still lives on the yolk of the egg. The yolk lasts until the fins of the young fish are fully grown. Then they are ready to swim about looking for food. Philip helped the Ethiopian to develop in understanding about Christ. He was then baptized. Then Philip left him.

3. Some fish only lay a few large eggs. A dogfish will lay its egg inside of a case. This case hardens and is a protection to the developing egg.

Page 258 continued

4. A female guppy keeps her eggs inside her body. The young hatch and then they are born.

5. Some sharks give birth to live young, called pups, while others lay an egg in an egg case. See page 254 of this book.

6. Male tilapias carry eggs in their mouth and even shelter the young in their mouth after they hatch.

Page 259

7. The way the tilapia cares for its eggs and young can remind us how the Holy Spirit cared for the Ethiopian's spiritual needs. He also cares for us.

8. The male stickleback shows his red belly to the female to **encourage** her to lay her eggs in the nest he has built. He drives other males away. The male bitterling catches the female's attention and leads her to a mussel where she may lay her eggs. She lays them through a special egg-laying tube. The male dragonet is brightly colored. He has a very big pointed fin on his back that he lifts to attract a mate. The Ethiopian was attracted to the book of Isaiah by the Holy Spirit.

9. The male Siamese fighting fish makes a nest of bubbles at the surface of the water. The female then lays her eggs in the bubble nest. The male stays by to guard it. California grunion come ashore by the high tide. They make places in the sand to bury their eggs. A female salmon makes a nest in the river gravel. The African lyretail bury their eggs in the mud. The babies do not hatch until the rains come again. **Find pictures of these fish.**

Page 259 continued

10. As the males and females come together to lay eggs, so Philip was sent by the angel to come together with the Ethiopian to help him understand the seeds (eggs) of truth in the book of Isaiah.

Page 260

Gar and Goldfish

Gooseberry, gull, giraffe, gnu, grebe, grapes, goose, ginkgo, gorilla, goldenrod, geranium, grasshopper

Page 261

"...See, here is Water; what doth hinder me to be baptized?" Acts 8:36

Page 262

The seahorse is a fish so circle it and the colt–head, kangaroo–pouch, monkey–tail, and the chameleon–changes color.

When the seahorse reproduces the female lays dozens to hundreds of eggs in the male's special pouch. They are covered with blood-filled tissue that forms a separate chamber for each egg. They mature in the pouch during the next month (about 30 to 50 days) and finally are released as a tiny "herd" of live young about the size of a comma. They have transparent bodies which become colored gray, black, yellow, green, pink, brown, red, or orange a they grow older depending on the variety. When it is time to release the young, the father seahorse anchors himself to a seaweed stem and rocks back and forth to help the babies out of the pouch. The young seahorses are experiencing "new birth." The Ethiopian

Page 262 continued

experienced a "new birth" and was **encouraged** to be baptized.

Before the yolk-laden babies assume the standard upright swimming posture, they spend the first few days swimming horizontally like fish. Immediately after they are born, the young seahorses latch onto the nearest vegetation.

LESSON 11

Page 269

"Deliver me not over unto the will of mine enemies: for false witnesses are risen up against me, and such as breathe out cruelty."

Psalm 27:12

Page 270

Most fish eat shellfish, worms, and other water creatures, but most of all they eat other fish. Some fish eat plants like algae, and other water plants. Other fish such as, flying fish, herring, the whale shark, giant mantaray, and basking shark, live mainly on plankton. Some fish are scavengers and feed mainly on waste products and on the dead bodies that sink to the ocean floor. Fish killing and eating one another reminds us how Saul was threatening and killing the disciples of Christ.

Fish do not have regular meals but eat what they can when they can. Sometimes fish may go days without finding food while others catch food all the time. By looking at the shape of a fish's mouth you can get a good idea of how it catches its food.

Page 273

1. "On the last day of the journey, *'at midday,'* as the weary travelers neared Damascus, they came within full view of broad stretches of fertile lands, beautiful gardens, and fruitful orchards, watered by cool streams from the surrounding mountains."

2. "After the long journey over desolate wastes such scenes were refreshing indeed."

3.-4. "While Saul, with his companions, gazed with admiration on the fruitful plain and the fair city below, *'suddenly,'* as he afterward declared, there shone *'round about me and them which journeyed with me' 'a light from heaven, above the brightness of the sun'* (Acts 26:13), too glorious for mortal eyes to bear."

5. "Blinded and bewildered, Saul fell prostrate to the ground." (*The Acts of the Apostles* 114)

6. The light was brighter than the sun.

7. Falling down helps **humble** us. That is why we kneel to pray.

Page 282

1. Saul	10. Test
2. Light	11. Eyes
3. Shined	12. Saw
4. Down	13. Opened
5. Own	14. Pen
6. Voice	15. Damascus
7. Ice	16. Dam
8. Persecute	17. Led
9. Persecutest	18. Hand

Page 285

1.-2. "But how unlike his anticipations was his entrance into the city? Stricken with blindness, helpless, tortured by remorse, knowing not what further judgment might be in store for him, he sought out the home of the disciple Judas, where, in solitude, he had ample opportunity for reflection and prayer." (*The Acts of the Apostles* 118)
(Straight Street)

3.-4. "While Saul in solitude at the house of Judas continued in prayer and supplication, the Lord appeared in vision to *'a certain disciple at Damascus, named Ananias,'* telling him that Saul of Tarsus was praying and in need of help. *'Arise, and go into the street which is called Straight,'* the heavenly messenger said, *'and inquire in the house of Judas for one called Saul, of Tarsus: for, behold, he prayeth, and hath seen in a vision a man named Ananias coming in, and putting his hand on him, that he might receive his sight.'*" [God loves to answer prayer. While Saul was in the very act of praying, God was arranging the answer.]

5. "Ananias could scarcely credit the words of the angel; for the reports of Saul's bitter persecution of the saints at Jerusalem had spread far and wide. He presumed to expostulate: *'Lord, I have heard by many of this man, how much evil he hath done to thy saints at Jerusalem: and here he hath authority from the chief priests to bind all that call on thy name.'* But the command was imperative: *'Go thy way: for he is a chosen vessel unto me, to bear my name before the Gentiles, and kings, and the children of Israel.'*"

Page 285 continued

6. "Obedient to the direction of the angel, Ananias sought out the man who had but recently breathed out threatenings against all who believed on the name of Jesus; and putting his hands on the head of the penitent sufferer, he said, *'Brother Saul, the Lord, even Jesus, that appeared unto thee in the way as thou camest, hath sent me, that thou mightiest receive thy sight, and be filled with the Holy Ghost.'* "

7. (Since Jesus had adopted Saul into the heavenly family Ananias called him "Brother.") " *'And immediately there fell from his eyes as it had been scales: and he received sight forthwith, and arose, and was baptized.'* " (*The Acts of the Apostles* 121-122)

8, The Lord allowed Saul to lose his sight that he might **humbly** wait upon Him.

Page 291

"...That ye should shew forth the praises of him who hath called you out of darkness into his marvelous light."

I Peter 2:9

Page 292

1. Eggs

2. Elver

3. Glass Eel

4. Yellow Eel

5. Silver Eel

Page 295

disciples, night
basket

Lord
Jesus
slay
Caesarea, Tarsus

Page 300

Review its meaning!
Pride is putting ourselves on an equal level with God–given authority. **Humility** is abasing ourselves and submitting to the righteous rule of God and His authorities.

I Peter 5:5
Submission and **humility** go together. Clothed with **humility** means it comes from within and shines out for others to see. The reward is God gives us power or grace to be **humble**.

Proverbs 22:4
Success in life only comes by **humility** and the honoring of God.

II Chronicles 7:14
If we are **humble** and pray and study and obey the instructions of what we learn there will be rewards from God in our daily life and the hereafter.

James 4:10 and I Peter 5:6
We first and foremost **humble** ourselves in the eyes of the Lord, not necessarily in the eyes of others.

Isaiah 57:15
God **humbles** us here that we might dwell in heaven.

Page 300 continued

More Bible Texts if Needed
Proverbs 16:19; Proverbs 29:23; II Chronicles 26:16; Daniel 5:20; Ezekiel 28:5; Colossians 3:12; James 4:6-10; I Kings 21:29; II Chronicles 34:19, 21, 27; Philippians 2:7.

LESSON 12

Page 305

Title: Aeneas

Aeneas Healed

Page 306

1. Plankton

2. Zooplankton

3. Nekton Group

4. Bacteria

Center of circle
Plankton (Magnified)

Page 307

1. Dorcas and Tabitha

2. Gazelle

3. Student color the picture.

Page 308

1. Gazelle

2. Move very quickly

Page 308 continued

3. ...each moment wisely.

4. Beauty, gracefulness, and gentleness, they are vegans, some are called the dorcas or ariel gazelle, the word gazelle comes from an Arabic word that means *"to be affectionate,"*

Page 311

Some Ideas:
Picking up toys for Mother.
Helping little brother fly a kite.
Helping parents paint a fence.
Helping mother in the kitchen.
Raking leaves for Father.
Bring in the groceries for Mother.

Page 313

"...And showing the coats and garments which Dorcas made while she was with them." (Act 9:39)

Page 315

Horizontally and Vertically

One is by the wind horizontally and the other is the vertical flow in the ocean itself. The Holy Spirit moves people to be **thoughtful** toward each other (horizontally) and this can turn them toward God (vertically). (**Be sure to include this spiritual lesson.**)

Winds
Moving
Flow
Ocean
Currents
Gyres

Dorcas

Page 321
"...Tabitha, arise. And she opened her eyes: and when she saw Peter, she sat up."

Thoughtful
"Saints"

Page 323

Waves move up and down in water. The down wave reminds us how Dorcas was dead and the rising of the wave reminds us of how Dorcas was raised to life.

Page 324

Currents
The circulation or vertical movements of currents flow from the surface of the ocean bottom and back again. The currents move slowly along the sea floor in the polar regions and up to the surface.

Waves
The waves move up and down on the surface of the water. The wind causes these ocean waves, from small ripples to great hurricane waves larger than 100 feet (30 meters) high. The size of such a wave is determined by the speed of the wind, how long the wind blows, and how far it blows over the ocean. The wind continues to blow out at sea and waves grow to a great size then break. The breaking is called a white-cap. Even after the wind calms or stops, the waves continue to move over the ocean surface and travel great distances from where they began. It is like throwing a pebble into a pool of water and watching the ripples move away from the place the stone struck. The healing of **thoughtful** Dorcas was to be a testimony to Christ and, like the waves moving, it would be spread near and far.

Page 325

1. The miracle of Dorcas raised from the dead.

2. Joppa

3. Simon a tanner

4. *"He lodgeth with one Simon a tanner, whose house is by the sea side...."* (Acts 10:6)

5. Read the information about Simon the tanner on this page 325 in the Activity Book.

Page 326

Son of Righteous
Disciples
Sea of People

(The moon reflects the light of the sun to earth, as the disciples were to relect light from Jesus to the sea of people!)

LESSON 13

Page 231

1. Caesarea (Use this word to find letters in other words.)

2. Centurion

3. Feared God

4. Alms and prayed

"What man is he that feareth the LORD? him shall he teach in the way that he shall choose."
Psalm 25:12

Page 332

Diagram
1. Mountain
2. Shelf

Page 332 continue

3. Slope
4. Rise
5. Valley
6. Rise
7. Slope
8. Shelf
9. Peaks & mountains

Picture
10. plains

Page 333

2 Servants and
1 Soldier were sent
3 total

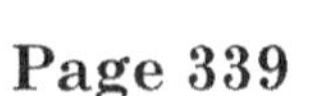

Page 339

"...God is no ***respecter*** *of persons."*

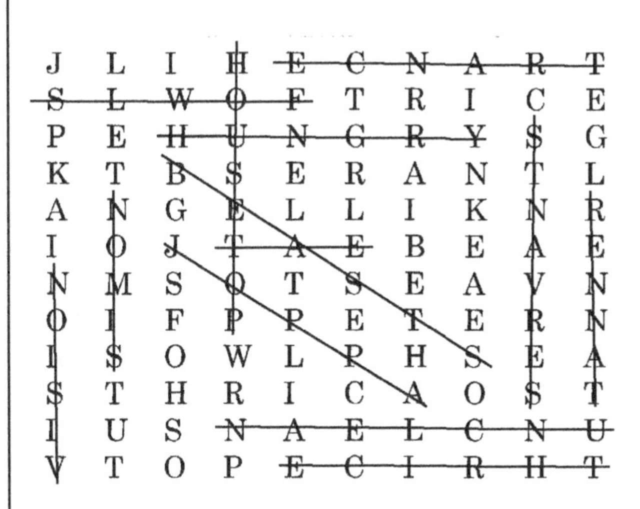

J	L	I	H	E	C	N	A	R	T
S	L	W	O	F	T	R	I	C	E
P	E	H	U	N	G	R	Y	S	G
K	T	B	S	E	R	A	N	T	L
A	N	G	E	L	L	I	K	N	R
I	O	J	T	A	E	B	E	A	E
N	M	S	O	T	S	E	A	V	N
O	I	F	P	P	E	T	E	R	N
I	S	O	W	L	P	H	S	E	A
S	T	H	R	I	C	A	O	S	T
I	U	S	N	A	E	L	C	N	U
V	T	O	P	E	C	I	R	H	T

Page 341

1. Basin
2. Peaks
3. Valleys
4. Plains
5. Mountains
6. Ridges

Page 343

1. "To Peter this was a trying command, and it was with reluctance at every step that he undertook the duty laid upon him; but he dared not disobey." 3 came for Cornelius.

2. "He *'went down to the men which were sent unto him from Cornelius; and said, Behold, I am he whom ye seek: what is the cause wherefore ye are come?'* They told him of their singular errand, saying, *'Cornelius the centurion, a just man, and one that feareth God, and of good report among all the nation of the Jews, was warned from God by a holy angel to send for thee into his house, and to hear words of thee.'* "

3. Brethren, six

4. "As Peter entered the house of the Gentile, Cornelius did not salute him as an ordinary visitor, but as one honored of heaven and sent to him by God. It is an Eastern custom to bow before a prince before their parents; but Cornelius, overwhelmed with **reverence** for the one sent by God to teach him, fell at the apostle's feet and worshiped him. Peter was horror stricken, and he lifted the centurion up, saying, *'Stand up; I myself also am a man.'* "

5. "While the messengers of Cornelius had been gone upon their errand, the centurion *'had called together his kinsmen and near friends,'* that they as well as he might hear the preaching of the gospel. When Peter arrived, he found a large company eagerly waiting to listen to his words."

Page 343 continued

6. "To those assembled, Peter spoke first of the custom of the Jews, saying that it was looked upon as unlawful for Jews to mingle socially with the Gentiles, that to do this involved ceremonial defilement. '*Ye know,*' he said, '*how that it is an unlawful thing for a man that is a Jew to keep company, or come unto one of another nation; but God hath showed me that I should not call any man common or unclean. Therefore came I unto you without gainsaying, as soon as I was sent for: I ask therefore for what intent ye have sent for me?*'

"Cornelius then related his experience and the words of the angel, saying in conclusion, '*Immediately therefore I sent to thee; and thou hast well done that thou art come. Now therefore are we all here present before God, to hear all things that are commanded thee of God.*'"

7. "Peter said, '*Of a truth I perceive that God is no* **respecter** *of persons: but in every nation he that feareth him, and worketh righteousness is accepted with him.*'" (*The Acts of the Apostles* 137-138)

Page 350

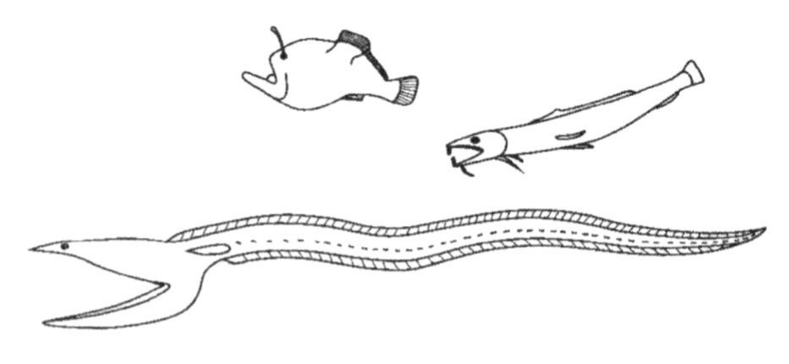

Page 354

See page 353.

Page 355

"*While Peter yet spake these words, the Holy Ghost fell on all them which heard the word.*" Acts 10:44

"*Can any man forbid water, that these should not be baptized, which have received the Holy Ghost as well as we?*"

"*And he commanded them to be baptized in the name of the Lord. Then prayed they him to tarry certain days.*" Acts 10:47-48

Page 356

Holy Spirit
Holy Bible

All Things Bright and Beautiful

All things bright and beautiful, All creatures great and small,
All things wise and wonderful, the Lord God made them all.

Each little flower that opens, Each little bird that sings;
He made their glowing colors, He made their tiny wings.

The purple headed mountains, The river running by,
The sunset, and the morning That brightens up the sky,

The cold wind in the winter, The pleasant summer sun,
The ripe fruits in the garden, He made them every one.

He gave us eyes to see them, and lips that we might tell
How great is God Almighty, Who has made all things well.

—Cecil F. Alexander

Mark 4:29

Made in the USA
Monee, IL
19 July 2022